生態保育系列（三）

台灣保育動物新傳

A New Age for Wildlife Conservation in Taiwan

張靜茹等　著

序【一】
Preface (1)

多年來，台灣街道上不時遊走一些遭遺棄的流浪狗，飢餓困乏、肌膚潰爛，最近的調查更顯示，原本應該是小朋友最愛的寵物小狗，已經成為孩童出門時的最怕；同時，美國許多州政府也在為灰狗賭博賽跑頭痛，當這些賽狗精力被刮用殆盡、失去比賽價值，往往只能被賽狗場無情射殺、甚至被活埋。……

僅看看小狗這一被人類譽為最好的朋友在世界各地的命運；今天人們還要浪費時間去爭辯那一個國家、哪一種文化比較尊重生命、愛護動物、關心生態嗎？

光華雜誌繼《台灣特稀有生物》、《中國人與動物》後，出版了第三本生態保育書籍。表面上看，這本書討論的是過去幾年發生在華人社會裡，牽涉到不同文化衝突的生態保育議題；但對這些議題的來龍去脈加以檢視後，看來紛繁的現象卻展現清楚面貌。

原來，人類對動物的看法，其間容或有長遠來文化發展呈現的差異；但面對真實的生命，一條蛇、一隻蟲、一隻大象、老虎，近代人類卻同樣有著驕傲、隨意役使、忽視其他生命也有生之渴望的事實。

在一切以商業利益思考、物質主義高漲、都市擴張、人們只見短利下，亙古來人類摸索出的資源永續利用、為後代子孫謀福利、保存人類長遠生活環境等生存原則，都已成為奢談。特別是富裕國家的人民，在奢華口腹之慾、刺激的消費下，很難面對地球上還有許許多多挨餓人口的事實，也無法警覺到自己的消費，是如何糟蹋著地球上的生命、生態，如何傷害著自己所居住的土地。

因此今天國際間的生態保育工作，不需要浪費時間在互相攻擊；不同地區的人們應該做的，是更積極實際地為關心生態、尊重生命而付出。

對像台灣這樣生活無虞的國度，人們更需要想想選擇過什麼樣的日子？我們選擇少用一張紙、少吃一餐魚翅、少用一枚象牙印章，就會有更多生命不至滅絕，有一些人不須為貢獻市場機制而犧牲原有最基本的生活，人類所建立的文明，也才有遠景可言。

事實上，撇開所有生態保育的論調，人們只要想想，地球上各種生命型態或許不同，生命處境或許不一；生命的有限性卻是相同，最終的去處也如一，面對在同樣路上的其他生命，人們能不生一絲同情，讓自己與其他生命的互動更充滿善念嗎？　□

發行人

程建人

4

For many years now, the sight of stray dogs abandoned by their owners has been a common one on Taiwan's streets. A recent survey indicates that these starving, mangy beasts, which should be the most beloved pets of children, are in fact that which they fear most when they venture out. In the US, various state governments are facing a different sort of dog problem, one related to the greyhounds which compete at dog-tracks. Once these dogs have been "used up" and can no longer race, they are often shot or even buried alive.

When even "man's best friend" is subject to such fates all over the world, why are people wasting time arguing about which countries and cultures are more respectful of life and better protect animals?

Following in the tradition of *Taiwan's Extraordinary Plants and Animals* and *Animals and the Chinese*, *Sinorama* magazine is now publishing a third book on wildlife conservation. On the surface, the book discusses issues involving conflicts between Chinese attitudes about conservation and those of other cultures. However, when one examines the origins of these complex issues, the nature of the problems becomes clearer.

While people's attitudes towards animals may differ depending on their culture, modern people have one thing in common: regardless of their cultural background, when faced with another living being, whether it be in the form of a snake, an insect, a tiger or an elephant, they tend to have an arrogant, at-my-pleasure attitude which ignores that other living being's desire to live.

The world has changed. It has become more urban, and modern people are more materialistic. They tend to look at issues in commercial terms and to focus on short-term gain. The old principles of managing the use of resources, leaving enough for future generations and protecting the environment in which we live have been abandoned. This is particularly true of the people of the world's wealthy nations for whom rampant consumption and the gratification of every appetite are a way of life. Such people seem unaware that there are many people in the world who do not have enough to eat. They also seem unaware of the living beings that are sacrificed to their appetites and the damage that they cause to their own lands.

The conservation movement needn't waste its time in international sparring matches. What everyone should be doing, regardless of their nationality, is actively respecting and caring for life. In wealthy nations such as Taiwan, people must give thought to what kind of life they wish to lead. If we choose to use one less piece of paper, eat one less bowl of shark's fin soup, buy one less ivory chop, we can save species from extinction. Perhaps if we were to do so, indigenous peoples would not need to change their traditional ways of life just to gratify the insatiable appetites of the modern world. In fact, it is only by wasting less that human civilization will have a future.

Cutting through the conservationist rhetoric, all people need to do is realize that although life on earth comes in many forms, ultimately, all of us come to the same end—we die. Therefore, in encountering other living beings traveling this same path, can't we extend a little sympathy and understanding? Can't we share a little kindness with our fellow creatures?

(tr. by Scott Williams)

Publisher

序【二】

Preface (2)

臺灣是受到菲律賓海洋板塊及歐亞大陸板塊擠壓，而在東亞大陸邊緣所隆起的島嶼。當全球氣候受到第四紀冰河時期氣溫降低的影響，她因位處北半球南方以及北迴歸線經過而溫暖潮濕的氣候，自然成為亞洲大陸生物遷徙的避難所。冰河退卻氣候回暖後，生物便以二條路線開始遷徙，一條往北遷移，另一條往高海拔遷移，造成了臺灣的高山植群與北方植群相近似，而於中海拔偏高的冷溫帶針葉林區，與冰河時期當時氣候型態相近似，因此該區內有許多當時的物種得以存活下來，這正是此一林帶內古老孑遺生物特別多的原因。以全世界同緯度各地區的生物相看來，臺灣的植物資源是得天獨厚。從古植物演化史及地質史上的探討，可以瞭解為什麼在這個蕞爾小島上，竟薈萃了源自各方豐富的生物種類；而以植物研究的角度來看，臺灣也是世界上第三紀地質年代古植物群保存最好的天然植物園。

全世界維管束植物種類約有三十萬種，臺灣地區維管束植物種類有四千零二十一種，其中特有種約為一千餘種，如臺灣穗花杉、臺灣粗榧、臺灣油杉、清水圓柏、臺東蘇鐵等；動物資源方面，陸地哺乳動物六十四種、鳥類約四百五十種、爬蟲類九十四種、兩棲類三十三種、淡水魚近一百五十種、昆蟲已定名的約一萬七千六百種；海域動植物方面，約有四千至四千五百種，約佔全球百分之十。臺灣全島面積雖僅三萬五千七百八十平方公里，但在這一片土地上卻孕育著這麼多的自然景觀資源，值得我們珍惜自然資源能永續利用，以為後代子孫留下一片樂土，是為我國生態保育的政策目標。

野生動物為重要之生態資源，不僅具有維持生態平衡之功能，自古在人類生活及發展上扮演極重要角色。目前世界各國均體認到，保育野生動物為維持人類永續發展及生存不可忽視之任務。

光華雜誌多年來對於野生動物保育相關報導，著墨頗多，其目的希望喚醒國人重視國內動物保育問題，並藉此提昇全民保育觀念。今將發行《台灣保育動物新傳》專書，詳實紀錄國內所發生野生動物保育問題及其演進過程，頗具歷史及教育意義，值得國人重新回顧並檢討過去對於動物保育問題的認知。

多年以來，政府執行野生動物保育工作已略具成效，除國人已普遍具有保育共識及觀念外，部分野生動物族群亦有明顯之增長，此一成果深受國內外人士之肯定。基於野生動物保育為當前之世界潮流，我國今後將本著善盡國際保育責任之決心，加強推展野生動物保育工作，使野生動物族群穩定繁衍，達到永續利用之目的。□

行政院農委會主任委員
Chairman
Council of Agriculture, Executive Yuan

The island of Taiwan, at the edge of East Asia, was pushed up out of the sea by the pressure of the Philippine Sea plate against the Eurasian continental plate. As global temperatures fell during the Quaternary Ice Age, the warm, damp climate given to Taiwan by its location in the southern part of the northern hemisphere, straddling the Tropic of Cancer, made it a natural refuge for species from the Asian continent. When the glaciers retreated and temperatures rose again, these species began to migrate along two routes: one northward, and the other upward toward higher altitudes. This has given Taiwan's high mountain areas plant populations similar to those in more northerly regions. Climatic conditions in the cool-temperate coniferous forests at medium to high elevations are similar to those which prevailed at sea level in the ice age. For this reason many species from that period have been able to survive, which is why there are so many relic species in these forests. Compared with other regions at the same latitude around the world, Taiwan is blessed with a uniquely rich flora. The study of plant evolution and our little island's geological history reveal why it is endowed with such a diversity of species of so many different geographical origins. From the point of view of botanical research, Taiwan is a natural botanic garden in which ancient plant populations dating from the Tertiary geological period are preserved better than anywhere else in the world.

In the world today there are some 300,000 species of vascular plants. In Taiwan, 4002 vascular plant species have been recorded, of which around 1000 are endemic. Examples include the Formosan amentotaxus (*Amentotaxus formosana*), the Taiwan cowtail pine (*Cephalotaxus wilsoniana*), the Taiwan keteleeria (*Keteleeria davidiana* var. *formosana*), the Chinese juniper variety *Juniperus chinensis* var. *tsukusiensis* and the Taiwan cycas (*Cycas taiwaniana*). The island's fauna include 64 terrestrial mammal species, some 450 species of birds, 94 reptiles, 33 amphibians, almost 150 freshwater fish, and some 17,600 named species of insects. The waters around Taiwan are also home to some 4–5000 marine plant and animal species, or some 10% of the world's total. Although Taiwan is only 35,780 square kilometers in area, this little patch of the earth's surface teems with life, and the abundance and beauty of its natural resources are worthy of being cherished. Sustainable use of natural resources, and bequeathing a pristine environment to later generations, are the goals of the ROC's conservation policies.

Wildlife is a major ecological resource which not only has a function in maintaining ecological balance, but has also played an important role in human life and development since ancient times. Today, nations around the world are coming to recognize that protecting wild animals is an essential task in maintaining the sustainable development and survival of the human race.

Over many years *Sinorama* magazine has published numerous articles on wildlife conservation, in order to encourage our fellow citizens to attach greater importance to wildlife conservation within Taiwan, and thereby raise the environmental consciousness of the whole nation. *A New Age for Wildlife Conservation in Taiwan* presents a detailed record of the problems and progress of wildlife conservation in the ROC, and as such is of considerable historical and educational value. It is well worth reading to recall and reconsider our past attitudes toward wildlife conservation issues.

The government's many years of work in the area of wildlife conservation has begun to show results. Not only have people in Taiwan now generally gained an appreciation for the environment and a consensus on conservation issues, but some wildlife populations have grown markedly, and this success has attracted considerable praise from both within and without the ROC. Wildlife conservation has become a worldwide trend, and the ROC will continue to redouble its efforts in pursuing conservation work, with the determination to fulfill our international obligations and allow wildlife populations to propagate themselves stably, to achieve the goal of sustainable use. □

(tr. by Robert Taylor)

序【三】
Preface (3)

隨著人類對生物多元性與影響生物多元性的種種力量了解益增，野生動物的保育運動也如大自然一般生生不息地演化進步，在國際社會如此，在台灣亦然。回顧國際保育運動的發展，聯合國於一九七二年舉行的斯德哥爾摩人類環境會議可說具有決定性的影響，該會議引發了之後諸多以野生動物為關懷主題的會議，其中包括一九七三年的華盛頓公約組織(CITES)，以及一九九二年生物多樣性會議。

台灣由於無法加入諸如華盛頓公約組織等由聯合國主辦的計劃，多年來埋首於經濟發展，常為國際社會所忽視。然而隨著經濟力量的提升，台灣成為各類消費產品的重要市場，其中野生動物也是在台灣進行交易的消費產品之一。一九八〇年代，台灣人對野生動物的嗜愛震驚了許多國際保育人士。這所謂的嗜愛，有時意味著將本地不產的珍禽異獸變作盤中美味，將野生動物用於裝飾、醫療、當作寵物豢養等其他用途也十分常見。八〇年代後期，由於証據顯示人猿、老虎、豹、長臂猿、珍奇鳥類及其他不產於台灣的動物在台灣可以輕易取得作為寵物，野生動物的裝飾、醫療及寵物豢養用途遂引起了保育界的注意。最後，將野生動物運用於醫療上的交易行為引發了國際社會的強烈關切，也造就了台灣本身在保育工作上的重大轉折。

一九八九年，在台灣保育人士的努力之下，通過了野生動物保育法，在保育工作上有了重大的進展。然而該法並不完備，加上有証據顯示瀕臨絕種的犀牛角在台灣仍有大量的交易，許多民間組織開始強烈要求華盛頓公約組織及其會員國對台灣採取制裁行動，這樣的要求在一九九四年美國政府引用培利修正案對台灣採取經濟制裁時達到高峰，在此之前美國從未引用培利修正案對他國政府採取制裁行動。針對此一制裁行動，各界反應不一，有譽之為全球保育領袖模範者，亦有嘲謔其為心胸狹隘的文化霸權者，然而無論個人觀點為何，培利修正案（後於一九九五年取消制裁）引發台灣對野生動物保育前所未有的重視，這是無可否認的事實。然而培利修正案的長期效果為何？

一九九四年野生動物保育法的快速通過是培利修正案的具體成果之一。台灣的野生動物保育法係亞洲地區同類型法條中最嚴厲者，其制定確實大幅減少了保育類動物的交易，然而，當人們認為限制野生動物交易的法條與人類福祉有所抵觸時，法條便難以服人。文化與習俗中根深蒂固的行為無法以一個新制定的法條輕易拔除，同時限制交易也可能使某些經濟來源原本貧乏的人民喪失一項重要的收入，此外也有些人相信限制野生動物在醫療用途上的交易危害了人類接受適當醫療的基本人權。因此，若要全民接受對野生動物的交易加以限制，大眾不僅要了解野生動物保育法的執行機制，更重要的是必須了解其背後的原理。

就台灣來說，媒體對培利修正案事件的大幅報導以及政府對違反野生動物法者的嚴苛處罰，無疑有效減少了非法的野生動

Like Nature itself, the wildlife conservation movement continues to evolve with time as our understanding of biological diversity and the forces affecting it grows. This is as true for the international community as it is for Taiwan. In tracing the development of the international conservation movement, the United Nation's 1972 Stockholm Conference on the Human Environment (UNCHE) was in many ways a watershed conference which triggered the development of numerous wildlife conventions including the 1973 Convention on Trade in Endangered Species of Wild Fauna and Flora or CITES and, most recently, the 1992 Convention on Biological Diversity.

Unable to participate in UN-sponsored initiatives like CITES, Taiwan, for many years, concentrated on its economic development and was often overlooked by the rest of the world. However, as Taiwan's economic power increased, the island became a major market for all types of consumer goods, including wildlife. During the 1980s, many international conservationists were alarmed by stories of Taiwan's appetite for wildlife. In some cases, this was quite literally an appetite for wildlife with some exotic species ending up on someone's dinner plate. Other uses for wildlife, decorative, medicinal, and as pets were also common. It was the latter which caught the attention of the conservation community in the late 1980s as evidence emerged of orangutans, tigers, leopards, gibbons, rare birds and other exotic pets being readily available in Taiwan. Ultimately though, it was trade in wildlife for medicinal purposes that propelled Taiwan into the international spotlight and brought about Taiwan's own watershed in wildlife conservation.

In 1989, after years of effort by local conservationists, Taiwan made a significant step forward with the introduction of its Wildlife Conservation Law (WCL). However, shortcomings in the law and evidence of significant trade in horns from highly endangered rhinoceros species prompted a number of non-governmental organizations (NGOs) to aggressively campaign for action by CITES and its member states. This culminated in 1994 in a decision by the US government to impose limited trade sanctions against Taiwan under the terms of a piece of domestic legislation known as the Pelly Amendment. This was the first time that the USA had used the Pelly Amendment to impose sanctions against another government and the decision received a variety of reactions, ranging from praise as an example of global conservation leadership to derision as narrow-minded cultural imperialism. Whatever one's viewpoint, one has to accept that the Pelly sanctions (later lifted in 1995) highlighted wildlife conservation in Taiwan in a way that had never been achieved before. But what were its lasting effects?

One of the most concrete results was the rapid revision of the WCL in 1994 which resulted in one of the most stringent laws in the Asian region and greatly curtailed trade in protected animal species. However, when wildlife trade control legislation and human welfare are seen to conflict, laws may be seen as having little legitimacy. Newly introduced regulations are unlikely to change behavior that is entrenched in culture and custom. Trade controls may deprive people already with few economic alternatives of an important source of income. In the case of wildlife used for medicinal purposes, these controls may be viewed by some as eroding a basic human right—access to proper medical treatment. It is crucial that the public understand both the mechanics of wildlife trade controls and, more importantly, the rationale behind them if people are to accept controls as valid.

In Taiwan's case, extensive media coverage of the Pelly issue and, no doubt, the severe punishments for non-compliance with the WCL appear to have resulted in a major reduction in illegal wildlife trade.

However, there is also a strong sense of conservation having been imposed from outside by foreign NGOs and governments. Such a view is unfortunate for a myriad of reasons, not least of which being that it ignores the efforts of dedicated local conservationists who were responsible for

物交易行為，然而一般民眾強烈認為保育意識是國外民間團體及他國政府強行灌輸給台灣的，這樣的看法十分不智，不智的原因眾多，最起碼的是，國內保育人士曾兢兢業業推動保育工作的發展，這看法卻將他們的貢獻一筆抹煞，不能不說是項謬誤。同時，國人也錯以為達成永續發展勢必全面禁絕特定動物的交易，普遍將野生動物保育與動物保護混為一談，並且誤認所謂「野生動物」必指體型碩大、外型令人驚奇的動物，生活在不知名的地方，與人類日常生活鮮少關連。

在這樣的情況下，保育議題與文化政治層面的牽扯將愈來愈複雜，生態的考量反將退居次要。幸而隨著時間推移，這些觀點也有了改變。這樣的改變從本書報導重點的轉變中可看出。早期保育議題的報導重點在於如何避免台灣成為國際保育界的眾矢之的，以及台灣未來可能遭受的制裁行動，而今議題重點已轉為台灣如何在國際間發揮其保育力量。此外，這些報導也使民眾了解「野生動物」不只是指生活在野外的動物，我們在日常生活中、在宴席桌上、在高價位的精品服飾店裡、在家附近的公園裡，也時常可見。本書收集的報導也呈現了中國人對野生動物入藥或其他用途的不同觀點，以及這些觀點長期以來

的發展及轉變，這也是相當重要的一點。

由此我們可以知道像光華這樣一本刊物在野生動物保育議題上的重要性。這樣的刊物不僅協助民眾建立對野生動物保育的認識，也帶領民眾了解影響保育政策的因素。國際保育界既龐大又多元，儘管訂有長期目標，然而長期目標要如何達成，目前爭議仍多，相左的意見也紛然雜存，隨著人們逐漸了解貧困對野生動物及其棲地的影響，也逐漸明白文化多元的重要，如何將經濟及文化因素納入保育政策的考量也成為備受討論的議題。光華雜誌具有多種語文版本，能夠觸及國內外廣大的讀者群，使讀者能同步了解台灣及其他各地的保育工作發展狀況。

能夠了解各種不同的觀點並參與保育政策的辯論對於保育工作的成敗有著關鍵性的影響。儘管保育工作永無結束的一天，台灣近十年來的確有長足進步，未來也將對國際保育界有良多的貢獻。光華雜誌出版的《中國人與動物》以及《台灣保育動物新傳》對台灣從惡名昭彰的「野生動物終結者」到成為國際保育工作的實際參與者間的發展過程有詳實的介紹，對於有興趣了解台灣保育工作歷史及未來發展方向的人們，這套叢書也提供了十分寶貴的資訊。　□

野生物貿易調查委員會　在台代表

斐馬克

many of the positive developments made. There is also a sense that the usual response to any hint of unsustainable use is a demand for a complete ban on trade in the species of concern. There is a tendency to confuse wildlife conservation with animal protection when the two are, in fact, quite different. Finally, "wildlife" is often viewed as large, impressive creatures, living somewhere "out there," with little connection to our daily lives.

Under these circumstances, conservation issues can become increasingly entangled in cultural and political debates with ecological considerations taking second place. Fortunately, with time, these views seem to be changing. The changes are reflected in many of the articles presented in this collection as the focus shifts from how Taiwan can avoid international criticism and the possibility of future sanctions to how Taiwan can play its part in international conservation efforts. The articles also bring home that "wildlife" is not only something we encounter only in remote wilderness areas, but also may run into during our daily lives, at the banquet table, in upmarket boutiques, in our neighborhood parks. Equally important, the collection expresses the diversity of views within Chinese culture toward the utilization of wildlife for medicinal or other purposes and how these views have developed and changed over time.

This highlights the important role that a publication like *Sinorama* can play in building not just awareness of wildlife conservation as an issue, but also understanding of the many factors influenc-ing conservation decisions. The international conservation community is large and diverse. Although agreement over long-term objectives does exist, just how we should work toward achieving those objectives often is hotly debated and opposing points of view are common. The need to incorporate economic and cultural concerns into effective conservation strategies is one example of the ongoing debate with increasing awareness of the impact that poverty has on wildlife and habitat as well as increasing awareness of the value of cultural diversity. With its multi-lingual editions, Sinorama reaches a broad domestic and international audience and can help keep readers abreast of developments within Taiwan and abroad.

Awareness and understanding of these different viewpoints and active participation in the debate over conservation methods is central to conservation's ultimate success or failure. While conservation work can never be said to be 'complete,' Taiwan has made major strides over the last decade and has much to contribute to the international conservation community. The articles in *Sinorama's Animals and the Chinese* and *A New Age for Wildlife Conservation in Taiwan* detail Taiwan's evolution from a reputed "wildlife terminator" to an active partner in international conservation efforts and provide valuable information for those interested in the history and possible future directions of wildlife conservation in Taiwan. □

TRAFFIC Taipei
National Representative

目次 CONTENTS

生態保育系列（三）

台灣保育動物新傳

A New Age for Wildlife
Conservation in Taiwan

此龍非彼龍？

——恐龍熱戲說中國龍

文·胡珍妮　圖·薛繼光

　　美國電影「侏羅紀公園」如熱浪一般，掀起了全世界對恐龍的好奇與興趣。

　　而隨著不少恐龍化石的陸續出土，中國大陸已成爲僅次於北美洲的「恐龍寶庫」。對地質學者及古生物研究者而言，這遍地素材無疑是令人雀躍的珍寶，對幾千年來素以「龍的後裔」自稱、對龍懷有深厚依戀卻又不知其所以然的中國老鄉來說，茶飯之餘，也開始試圖在這波熱潮話題中爲「

* * *

*B*esides breaking records at the box office, the US film **Jurassic Park** *has also stirred up interest in dinosaurs worldwide.*

　　With a steady stream of dinosaur fossils being unearthed, China trails only North America as a "treasure trove" of their bones. For geologists and paleontologists, these finds are cause for celebration, and for Chinese generally, who have for millennia described themselves as descended from dragons and who have deep feelings of attachment to them even if they don't know why, these fossils have provided food for thought in idle moments around the dinner table. The burning question: Is

The Dinosaur Craze and the Chinese Dragon

「二龍戲珠」是中國器物上流行的吉祥圖案，演變自民間「耍龍燈」的民俗活動，為慶豐年、討吉祥之意。
"Two dragons playing with a pearl" has long been an auspicious motif on Chinese objects of all kinds. It evolves from the folk custom of "swinging dragon lanterns" to celebrate an abundant harvest or seek good fortune.

明清時期，龍圖騰的使用相當嚴格，皇帝、貴族、民間的龍圖飾階級分明；這張「明孝宗坐像」中的龍有五爪，是皇帝專用的權威形制。（故宮博物院提供）

During the Ming and Qing dynasties, uses of the dragon totem were strictly regulated, with separate sets of rules for emperor, nobility and commonfolk. A five-clawed dragon, as in this painting of the Ming ruler Xiaozong, could only be used by the emperor. (photo courtesy of the National Palace Museum)

龍」尋找溯源正名的可能性：「老祖宗龍」與「古生物龍」之間，到底有沒有關連？

「恐龍跟龍沒有關係，將兩者聯想在一起，應該是『龍』字的誤導，」重量級的大陸恐龍研究專家，中國科學院古脊椎動物與古人類研究所研究員董枝明，近年隨著大陸恐龍展在世界各地巡展演講時，常會遇到觀眾提出這方面的問題，多年的科學訓練往往使他不假思索地做出以上的回答。

他分析，中文的「恐龍」一辭是由日本人從西洋文字Dinosauria（恐怖的蜥蜴）首先翻譯，中國再從日文借用來的，因此恐「龍」與「龍」純粹是文字上的巧合；再從時間上看，恐龍是六千五百萬年前絕滅的「一大群已死的爬蟲類動物」，而中國的龍是六千年前才產生的文化圖騰，兩者相差六千萬年，因此此「龍」與彼「龍」根本是兩碼子事。

臺灣的業餘恐龍研究者張武順說得更絕：「如果當初把Dinosauria翻譯成『恐蜥』，大概就不會有這種問題啦。」

科學研究者一下子推翻了兩者聯想的可能，但臺中國立自然科學博物館研究員程延年及副研究員張譽騰，最近卻開始認真思索這個課題，恐龍與龍，除了字面上的巧合以外，有沒有實質上的連結呢？

恐龍之鄉

一九○二年，一位俄國沙皇軍隊中的上校從黑龍江地區漁民手中收集到幾塊巨大的恐龍化石之後，便引起多位中外古生物學家對中國地層挖掘的興趣。繼黑龍江滿洲龍的出土，山東、四川、蒙古、雲南、新疆的準噶爾盆地及塔里木盆地、察哈爾、寧夏……各省，都陸續發掘出大量恐龍化石。九十年來，除了福建及臺灣以外，

there any connection between the dragons their ancestors worshipped and the extinct reptiles the dinosaurs?

"There's no connection between dragons and dinosaurs," stresses Dong Zhiming, a curator of dinosaurs at the Institute of Vertebrate Paleontology and Paleoanthropology at the Academia Sinica in Beijing, an expert on mainland China's dinosaurs. "These two things have been mistakenly connected because the Chinese character for 'dragon' is one of the two characters in 'dinosaur.'" Over the past few years, as Dong has accompanied a traveling exhibit of mainland dinosaurs around the world, he has often encountered this kind of question, and the answer, informed by his many years of scientific training, comes automatically.

Konglong, the Chinese for dinosaur, which literally means "fearsome dragon," came into Chinese via the Japanese translation of Greek "Dinosauria" or "fearsome lizard," Dong explains. And so in Chinese it is purely coincidental that dragon and dinosaur share a character. In the grand scope of time, the dinosaurs were a major group of reptile species that went extinct 65 million years ago. The Chinese dragon, on the other hand, only first became a cultural totem about 6000 years ago. With a gap of 60 million years, dragons and dinosaurs are surely two altogether different beasts.

Chang Wu-shun, a Taiwanese amateur researcher of dinosaurs, gets right to the point: "If 'dinosauria' had been translated as *kongxi* [fearsome lizard], there probably never would have been this problem." While most scientists likewise dismiss any connection, researchers Cheng Yen-nien and Chang Yu-teng, who work at the Taichung Provincial Science Museum, have recently been diligently investigating whether there is a connection other than the coincidence of a shared character.

The homeland of dinosaurs

Since 1902, when a Russian army colonel

中國幅員上可說處處皆是「產地」。以號稱「恐龍之鄉」的四川省爲例，單在自貢市伍家壩一地，就有上百隻恐龍的骨骸。

一九九三年，大陸更爆發了一件震驚世人的「恐龍事件」，河南省西峽縣大批縣民不知其然地將土裡挖出的「黑石蛋」當藥材賤價拋售，直到挖賣出數千枚之後，才由南京海關查獲，原來這些被稱爲「石膽」的黑蛋竟是被全世界視爲珍寶的恐龍蛋！北京中國科學院緊急前往考察，結果發現四十平方公里的西峽盆地中，埋藏的恐龍蛋可能高達數萬枚，與目前全世界總共發現的五百枚相較，規模之大令人咋舌，可稱之爲「恐龍聚落」而不愧。

恐龍生存的地質學年代爲中生代，而中國大陸有「發育」良好的中生代地層，因此恐龍化石的蘊藏量特別豐富。根據研究，到目前爲止在大陸發掘出的恐龍品類豐富，已有百多種，占世界出土恐龍種數的六分之一。而這些化石橫跨的世代，則從恐龍初現地球的二億三千萬年前三疊紀晚期，到六千五百萬年前白堊紀恐龍大滅絕的前夕，爲期約一億六千萬年地球霸主的活動生態，都可在中國大地上找到軌跡。

作爲恐龍時代的重要舞臺，當地球主宰者從當年的「巨型爬蟲類」，歷經物換星移、滄海桑田後，新生代的主宰者──人類誕生，並同樣在這塊古老大地繁衍生息，當年的恐龍遺跡已經被埋藏在地層底下。但是，一個不知起自哪個荒邈世紀的圖騰形象，卻自中國遠古代代流傳下來……

詭秘尊貴的龍

在龍文化已流傳了數千年的今天，雍容繁麗、神乎其技的形象幾乎已成爲龍的「標準概念」。《說文解字》裡形容：「龍，鱗蟲之長，能幽能明，能細能巨，能短能長，春分而登天，秋分而潛淵。」指出了龍幻化萬千的神通；而《古今圖書集成

discovered some large dinosaur bones in the hands of fishermen, both Chinese and foreign scientists have carried out digs in the mainland. In the 90 years since that find in Heilongjiang of the *Mandschurosaurus amurensis*, there have been major finds one after another in Shandong, Sichuan, Mongolia, Yunnan, the Talimu and Junggar Basins of Xinjiang, Chahaer, Ningxia and elsewhere—in fact in every Chinese province except Fujian and Taiwan. Take Sichuan, which is known as "the homeland of dinosaurs." More than 100 dinosaur skeletons have been unearthed just in Zigong's Wujia district.

In 1993, another dinosaur incident on the mainland startled people worldwide. When digging, country folk in Henan's Xishan County came across "black stone eggs," which they then went on to sell as an ingredient for Chinese medicine. It was only after thousands had been dug up and sold that a Nanjing customs inspector discovered that these black "stone eggs" were in fact being viewed as priceless dinosaur eggs elsewhere in the world! Brought in to make an assessment, a team from Beijing's Academia Sinica determined that the 40-square-kilometer Xishan Basin held perhaps tens of thousands of dinosaur eggs. In comparison to the some 500 that had been discovered worldwide up to that point, it was a mind-boggling figure, making the region worthy of the title "dinosaur town."

The dinosaurs lived during the Mesozoic era, during which time China was particularly well suited for them. Here their fossils are numerous, and many species have been identified—already more than 100, or one-sixth of those discovered worldwide. The fossils span their entire realm, from when they first appeared on earth about 230 million years ago during the end of the Triassic period, to their twilight age 65 million years ago in the Cretaceous: a stretch of some 160 million years when they ruled the planet.

People, the lords of the planet in this day and age, have, like those giant reptiles of yesteryear, thrived and multiplied in this ancient land. But it

龍圖騰深入民間，無所不在；在廟宇屋脊的尾端，常可見到水龍上揚的裝飾。
The Chinese totem of the dragon has left a deep imprint on its people, and is found everywhere there are Chinese. You can often see dragons craning their necks skyward at the end of a temple's peaked roof.

is not known from which strange age people have inherited their totem of the dragon.

A mysterious and respected beast

By now the dragon culture has already been passed along for several thousand years, and the image of the dragon as a noble beast with god-like powers has become the standard view. Look it up in *Shuowen Jiezi*, an ancient etymological dictionary: "The dragon, the biggest of scaled animals, can be visible or invisible, thick or thin, short or long. In the spring it rises to heaven; in the fall it plummets to the oceans' depths." Giving testimony to the dragon's amazing ability of transforming itself into a myriad of incarnations, the *Gujin Tushu Jicheng* (*Complete Collection of Graphs and Writings of Ancient and Modern Times*) describes the dragon as a strange beast with "the antlers of a deer, head of a camel (or horse), eyes of a ghost (or shrimp), body of a snake, belly of a crab, scales of a carp, claws of an eagle, paws of a tiger, ears of a cow . . . ." Wu Rukang, a research professor at the Institute of Vertebrate Paleontology and Paleoanthropology of Beijing's Academia Sinica, puts it this way: "It combines the most horrible features found on creatures both on land and in water."

Possessing the ability to ascend to heaven or burrow into the earth and combining the spirit and most exalted postures of numerous beasts, it has for several thousand years symbolized emperors, who, like dragons, cannot be denied respect. But these characteristics ascribed to the dragon that are associated with the powerful and noble were not his by birthright. Back in the

19

歷代器物上都有龍
的圖飾，這是台中
自然科學博物館中
陳列的仿宋代渾天
儀模型。

The dragon has
appeared on
Chinese artifacts
throughout the ages.
This is a copy of a
Sung armillary
sphere on display in
the Taichung Natural
Science Museum.

》中則說「龍是一角似鹿、頭似駝（或說似馬）、眼似鬼（或說似蝦）、身似蛇、腹似蟹、鱗似鯉、爪似鷹、掌似虎、耳似牛……」的奇物，套句北京中科院古脊椎動物與古人類研究員吳汝康的說法：「集合了所有海陸空最厲害的動物特徵。」

如此登天遁地、總集百獸之靈的崇高姿態，數千年來一直被用來輝映帝王天子凜不可侵的尊榮。但這種權貴獨享的專利並不是龍自始即具有的。事實上，商周時代的龍極為簡單樸拙，雖名列神話中的「四靈」（龍、鳳、龜、麟）之一，但在百獸中並不特別。直到後來漢高祖劉邦自稱身世是由母親劉媼「夢與龍交」之後，龍才變成皇家的圖騰，並因此身價飛漲百倍；後經歷朝歷代不斷添加神話與繁複絢爛的圖像，到宋朝才正式統一形制，成為權貴的極致表徵。

因此，兩千年來為「龍的傳人」所熟知的龍形象並非龍的「本來面目」，要追溯龍的起源，必須回到龍紋初現的殷商史前時代搜尋蛛絲馬跡。

問歷史龍為何物

內蒙的三星他拉村紅山文化遺址，於民國六十年出土了一件約六千年前的玉雕龍，一圈俐落圓弧的龍體，龍首上長鬃披向頸脊，整體造型頗有馬頭蛇身的味道。

而在歷史相隔約三千年後的河南省殷墟掘出的甲骨文碎片上，則可清楚地看到一百二十種「龍」字的正體及變體寫法，「甲骨文字中，凡作為飛禽走獸爬蟲之類的獨體象形字，幾乎都是師法自然物所造的，」臺北故宮博物院器物處處長張光遠指出，像虎、豹、鹿、象、牛、羊、犬、豬、雞、鳩、鷹、鳳、蛇、蠍、蜘蛛等等，都是「有其字必有其物」，反觀「龍」曾是一完整的獨體象形字來看，「應可相信先民造字之時，應該見過真龍的形狀。」

Shang and Chou dynasties, the dragon was really quite simple. Though its name was listed among the mythical "four spirits"—dragon, phoenix, tortoise and Chinese unicorn—among beasts it was nothing special. It wasn't until the mother of Liu Pang, the founder of the Han dynasty, dreamed that a dragon fathered her child that it became a totem of the emperor. As a result its stock shot up. Future generations continually added to its mythical powers and image. By the Sung Dynasty it was a symbol of those with power and prosperity and its look was close to the standard depiction of today.

Thus for 2000 years the descendants of the dragon have not known its original appearance. For that you've got to search back before the Shang dynasty.

What beast was this dragon of history?

In 1971, in the Inner Mongolian village of Sanxingtala, archaeologists unearthed a 6000-year-old carved jade dragon—with a round body and long hair along its neck bone. Its overall appearance suggests a horse's head on a snake's body. And in the writing on the fragments of oracle bones dug up in a Shang dynasty site in Henan and made 3000 years ago, 120 different ways of writing the character for dragon are clearly visible. "On oracle bones," says Chang Kuang-yuan, curator of the Department of Antiquities at the National Palace Museum, "the characters for every kind of animal were based on their shapes."

For example, tiger, leopard, deer, elephant, cow, sheep, dog, pig, chicken, dove, eagle, phoenix, snake, scorpion and spider are all drawn as individual images. "If there's the character, there's got to be the beast," so "you ought to be able to conclude that the first people writing characters had actually seen the form of a real dragon." One can observe more than 20 different species of animals represented on the bronze vessels found in Shang and Chou sites, and each one is a depiction of an actual animal "to the point where we can be bold enough to say

在商周廢墟出土的銅器花紋中，則可觀察到廿餘種動物造型，每一種都有實物相應，「甚至我們可以大膽的說鳳就是孔雀，」張光遠認為，龍應該也是一種真實的動物。

不只文化研究者抱持這種開放的觀點，臺中自然科學博物館研究員程延年博士也相信，「中國的老祖宗師法自然，觀察鳥獸生態以造型，因此龍應該也是有所依據才對。」

也就是說，自中華文化的源始就有了龍，但問題的關鍵在於，到底老祖宗造龍字、塑龍形，依據的實物是什麼？

蛇？海馬？長頸鹿？

紅山文化的玉龍、甲骨文中的龍字，及河南省濮陽縣仰韶文化墓址中挖掘出來以蚌殼堆疊的金龍，甚至太湖地區發現的四千多年前的良渚玉器中，不約而同地都可見龍的雛形。儘管時差三千年，地隔數百哩，這些龍的頭型及有無長腳雖各異，但他們的體型卻異曲同工都呈長條狀。

「龍是先民蛇崇拜的晉級，」青銅器研究專家袁德星認為，史前時代，中國民族長時間居住在黃河的中上游，天天與蛇為鄰，受蛇的威脅程度遠超過其他猛獸，因此採取「懷柔」政策，乾脆拜蛇以求安撫，並在儀式中對偶像蛇添加想像與裝飾，而成為後來的圖騰龍。

中研院歷史語言研究所助理研究員王道還也指出，從人類學的角度，詭祕陰毒的蛇是人類自遠祖便深懂的敵物，拜蛇儀式在世界各地的先民文化中都可發現，因此龍有可能是蛇崇拜的衍生。

除了蛇的呼聲最高外，又因龍彎曲的體幹，馬般的頭型，也有人認為其原形應是海馬。還有人根據牠的四足爪及巨頭張口之貌而說牠像鱷魚；而牠頭上的角及長長的身軀更有人指為長頸鹿的翻版……。歷

that the Chinese phoenix is a peacock." Chang Kuang-yuan believes that the dragon ought to be a real animal as well.

It's not only cultural researchers who are keeping their minds open on this issue. Dr. Cheng Yen-nien, a researcher for the Taichung National Science Museum, agrees with Chang. "Our ancestors based their depictions of animals on observations of these animals in their natural habitats. Why should they have done differently for dragons?"

It is evident, then, that dragons go back to the beginnings of Chinese culture, but the key question is, what animal were the ancient Chinese basing the dragon on?

A snake? A seahorse? A giraffe?

Besides the jade dragon from the Hongshan culture and the dragon characters on oracle bones, in a burial ground of the Yangshao culture in Puyang County of Henan, they have dug up a gold dragon made of stacked clam shells, and in the Taihu lake area they have even discovered a dragon on a 4000-year-old Liangzhu jade artifact. Seemingly without any connection to each other, forms of the dragon have been discovered all over what was ancient China. Even when there is a time difference of 3000 years and a distance of many hundred miles, though two dragons may differ in the shape of their heads or length of their legs and may be ornamented differently, they share the same long shape.

"Dragons were our ancestors' next step up from worshipping snakes," avers Yuan Te-hsing, an expert on bronzes. Before recorded history, the Han Chinese lived along the mid and upper stretches of the Yellow River and came into contact with snakes every day. The danger posed by them far exceeded those of other wild animals, and so they adopted a policy of "conciliation," appeasing snakes through worship. People imaginatively ornamented the snake idols used in these ceremonies, adaptations which would lead in time to dragon totems.

Wang Tao-huan, an assistant researcher in

十八世紀歐洲掀起一股中國熱，英國的布萊頓別宮收藏了大批仿中國的藝術品，這個長了翅膀的金龍，洋味十足。

Things Chinese were all the rage in 18th century Europe. England's Brighton Pavilion has many examples of chinoiserie. This winged gold dragon has a distinctly Western flavor. (photo by Cheng Yuan-ching)

the Institute of History and Philology of the Academia Sinica, takes an anthropological tack in pointing out that the stealthy and cunning snake has been man's arch enemy since ancient times. Snake worshipping ceremonies can be found in aboriginal cultures all over the world, and the dragon may be an extension of such worship.

Although those in the snake's camp are in the majority, there are dissenters. Some, pointing to the dragon's bending torso and its horse-like head, say it was originally modeled after a seahorse. The dragon's claws, giant head and open mouth make others see an alligator in its past, while still others, looking at the antlers on its head and its long body, behold an adaptation of the giraffe. What a hot topic of conversation this has been over the ages! One imaginative theory even holds that dragons are bolts of lightning.

As large numbers of dinosaur bones have been unearthed this century in China, views from a proper perspective of the more complete skeletons have given many a startling and eerie sense of recognition. If the Chinese painted the dragon based on an awe-inspiring subject and artists creatively enhanced their rendering of it, dinosaurs skeletons might just be what excited the imaginations of the ancient Chinese to depict dragons.

人類和恐龍相較極為渺小，中國人的祖先創造龍、敬畏龍，是否就是被其龐然骨骸所啓發？ Known links between man and the dinosaurs are minuscule. Ancestors of today's Chinese created dragons and stood in awe of them. Could their imaginations have been stirred by dinosaur skeletons?

史上長年以來眾說紛紜，莫衷一是；而最有想像力的說法，則有「龍就是閃電」一說。

直到近一世紀，恐龍化石在中國大量出土，某些在大地土壤中排列尚稱規則的龐然長條脊椎化石，從高處俯看的確讓人不禁產生猛然驚覺的熟悉感：若說龍的原形是種能令先民觸目敬畏，除了據實形繪又有空間添加豐富聯想創造力的根據物，那麼巨形的恐龍骨骼，有沒有可能也是激發先民想像的原動力？

龍墜於地

中國歷史上的確有發現恐龍化石的記載。在西晉時代常璩所撰寫的《華陽國志》中，就記載四川五城縣出龍骨，並描述了一則故事：「龍升其山，值天門閉，不達，墜死於此，後沒地中，故掘取得龍骨。」而五城即今日的四川省三臺縣，此地的岩層正是中生代侏羅紀的紅色陸相地層。恐龍專家董枝明同意，以今天的地質古生物知識來判斷，文中的「龍骨」應該就是恐龍化石無疑。可見人們在沒有現代古生物學知識的背景下，也可以憑著一架大致完整的恐龍化石試圖還其原形，而與龍的意象附會串連。

《華陽國志》是中國最早的恐龍化石紀錄，而藥典史籍上也有很多「龍骨」的記載，雖然經後人考證，這些骨頭多是大型哺乳類動物（如犀、象、鹿、牛、馬）的化石，但也不排除其中夾雜恐龍骨的可能性。

由於千萬年來的地質升降作用及河川沖積，恐龍的化石大部分零散殘缺，少部分大體完整，但可以想見的是，當先民無意中發現一具龐然骨架時，其心中驚駭的程度必不遜於科學昌明的今人，並會試圖以經驗所及的知識穿鑿附會，予以解釋。

位於長江三峽的浣縣，當枯水季節潮水

The dragon falls to earth

In Chinese history there are indeed records of discovering dinosaur fossils. During the Western Qin dynasty, Chang Zhu wrote in *Hua Yang Guozhi* that a dragon skeleton was found in Wucheng County in Sichuan. He related the following story: "The dragon flew up above the mountains until he came to hit the gates of heaven. The gates were closed and he couldn't get in, so he fell to earth in the place where his bones were dug up."

Wucheng is now in Sichuan's Santai County and its rock stratum is indeed from the Jurassic. Dong Zhiming agrees that in light of today's geological and paleontological knowledge, the dragon bones mentioned were probably the fossilized skeleton of a dinosaur. It is easy to imagine how people without benefit of modern paleontology might have put together a dinosaur skeleton and made conjectures as to its basic shape. And it wouldn't have been too big a leap to connect it to their image of a dragon.

While *Hua Yang Guozhi* holds the oldest reference to a Chinese dinosaur fossil, in books about ancient medicine there are also often references made to "dragon bones." Although recent investigations have shown that most of these were the bones of large mammals (such as rhinos, elephants, deer, cows and horses), one needn't eliminate the possibility that some of these were dinosaur bones.

Because of the rising and falling of geological strata and the alluviation of rivers, most dinosaur skeletons exist only in fragments; very few are complete. But it is easy to imagine that the ancient Chinese were no less astonished by finding a "dragon skeleton" than their scientifically enlightened descendants are today when finding a dinosaur fossil. And they were sure to have drawn on all of their experience in making hypotheses about them.

When the water level falls during the dry season in Wan County, site of the Yangtze River's Three Gorges, it exposes 16 or 17 vertebrae of a

低落時，岩壁上自古以來就清清楚楚地嵌著十六、七節巨大的脊椎骨骼，當地人不知其爲何物，世世代代一貫稱之「霸王鞭」，認爲那是西楚霸王項羽擲鞭斷江的遺跡。到了現代經學者考證，證實是一節蜥腳類（恐龍的一類）的尾椎。可見恐龍骨暴露在大地上的機率並不算太低，只是先民沒有文字記載流傳罷了。

爲龍正身

玉器研究學者那志良認爲，龍能在早期被先民奉做圖騰，一定有令人望之生畏的條件。他認爲海馬太小，鱷魚也不夠看，唯有恐龍化石的氣魄可與倫比。而先民有沒有可能根據這些爬蟲類的化石去衍生發展爲圖騰呢？董枝明只爲難地笑說：「我是研究科學性恐龍的，人文的龍要問人文學者。」

恐龍與龍，一屬科學領域，一被界定爲「人文」範疇，一向是兩門平行發展的學問，從來無人跨越門檻做嚴謹的研究，但臺中自然科學博物館已計劃在民國八十四年的「大演化與大滅絕」、一場關於地球物種演進的展覽中，試圖從科學的角度，爲中國圖騰龍尋溯起源與定位，顯示了這個課題的研究價值。

「但這個答案終究死無對證，」負責展覽籌備的古生物博士程延年對於研究結果的局限性已有心理準備，把握並不大。

相隔六千萬年，中國人自太古時代便識得的「龍」，有沒有可能是「恐龍」精魂的重現呢？或許，這只是龍的附會又一椿；或許，是人類學上一個石破天驚的發現，而這一切則有待科學家慢慢去驗證了。

□

（原載民國83年2月光華雜誌）

skeleton. Not knowing their true origin, local people called them "the Whip of Xiang Yu the Tyrant," believing that this is where the last emperor of Chu cast down his whip and cut his throat, collapsing into the river. In the modern era, scientists have determined that these are tail bones of a sauropod. Dinosaur bones are not so deep that the odds are against any of them ever becoming exposed; it's just that the earliest residents of China had no written language to record their finds.

Giving the dragon his due

Na Chih-liang, who researches jade implements, believes that since the dragon was able to achieve the status of a totem among the early Chinese, it must have been based on something that really scared the daylights out of people. Seahorses, he reasons, are too small and alligators not fearsome enough looking. Only the fossilized skeletons of dinosaurs are close enough in spirit. Could it be that the totem of the dragon was derived from the skeletal remains of dinosaurs? "I just research scientific dinosaurs," Dong Zhiming answers evasively. "For humanity's dragon, you've got to ask people in the humanities."

The dinosaur and the dragon: one is in the realm of science, the other the humanities. So far no one has pursued rigorous scholarly research down these two paths at once. But the Provincial Science Museum in Taichung plans an exhibit in 1995 about the evolution of the world's species titled "The Great Evolution and the Great Extinctions," which will try from a scientific perspective to seek out the roots and position of the dragon totem in Chinese society.

"Yet in the final analysis the lack of evidence makes any theory on the subject inconclusive," says Cheng Yen-nien, who is responsible for organizing the exhibit. He is already preparing himself for limited results so as to avoid disappointment. The odds of success are low.

A gulf of 60 million years separates man from the dinosaur. Is it possible that the dragon

「侏羅紀公園」掀起恐龍熱，兒童們看恐龍電影、玩恐龍玩具、學恐龍怪叫。

Jurassic Park has really stirred up interest in dinosaurs. Children are watching dinosaur movies, playing with dinosaur toys, and even imitating their strange roars.

（下）大陸出土的恐龍展，近年在世界各地巡迴大受歡迎，圖為中影文化城「侏羅紀展覽會」的展覽現場。

A traveling exhibition of dinosaurs from mainland China has been a hit all over the world these past couple of years. The photo shows its Jurassic Exhibit.

the ancient Chinese knew was the reappearance in spirit of the dinosaurs? Is this another theory too fantastic to be true, or is it just awaiting a major anthropological discovery to gain wide acceptance? ☐

(Jenny Hu/photos by Hsueh Chi-kuang/
tr. by Jonathan Barnard/
first published in February 1994)

從過去部落社會的圖騰，到民間吉祥、避邪的象徵，老虎不只是中國叢林裡最兇猛的動物，老虎造型也充滿中國人的生活。（翁清火提供）

From a totem of old tribal society to a folk symbol to bring good fortune and drive out evil, the tiger is not only the fiercest animal in China's jungles—its image is found everywhere in Chinese people's lives. (courtesy of Weng Ching-huo)

虎的傳人——中國人與老虎

Children of the Tiger—
The Chinese and the Tiger

文・張靜茹

隨著「華盛頓公約組織」將老虎列入保育名單、與農委會禁止國人使用虎骨等老虎產製品，未來，老虎將實質的從許多中國人生活中消失；但老虎形象卻不會在中國人的精神生活上隱去。大陸中國美術館副館長曹振峰甚至說：「中國人不僅是龍的傳人，更是虎的傳人。」為什麼？

話說武松出了酒店，路上只見四名獵戶跌跌撞撞奔來，武松攔下來人問起緣由，其中一人說道：朝廷懸賞捉拿老虎，我等前去追捕，沒想到好個下山猛虎，果真厲害，我四人反被追得一路奔逃至此。武松一聽，扳起臉孔：難道你們不知國際保育公約已經禁止捕殺老虎了？

怎麼中國經典小說《水滸傳》裡的「武松打虎」劇情走了樣？原來，這是臺灣大學掌中戲社團「西田社」為慶祝成立九週年上演的新武松。戲中武松成了保育人士，雖然喝得酩酊大醉，卻腦筋清楚地以環保為重，訓示了獵戶一番，在景陽崗遇著了惡虎，武松則示意地勿再傷

*N*ow that CITES has placed the tiger on the list of protected species, and the ROC's Council of Agriculture has forbidden the country's citizens to use tiger bones and other tiger products, in the future the tiger will effectively disappear from many Chinese people's lives; but the tiger's image will not fade from Chinese people's spiritual lives. Cao Zhenfeng, vice-director of mainland China's Museum of Chinese Art, even says: "The Chinese are not only the children of the dragon, but even more so the children of the tiger." Why is that?

The story goes that when Wu Song came out of the inn, the first thing he saw was four hunters running helter-skelter down the road. When Wu stopped them and asked what they were running from, one of them explained: "The emperor has put up a reward for catching a tiger, and we went to try and catch it. But the tiger came down from the mountain and chased us instead. It was so fierce that we ran all the way here." On hearing these words, Wu Song's face darkened into a frown, and he said: "Surely you know that hunting tigers is forbidden under international con-

商周青銅器裡，老虎
總帶著神祕感，圖為
商朝器物。（故宮博
物院提供）

On Shang dynasty
bronzeware, the tiger
always had an air of
mystique: pictured at
right is a Shang
utensil decorated with
the image of a tiger
(courtesy of the
National Palace
Museum).

人後，昂首挺胸，乘月色踏大步而去。

自從前年國際保育團體以臺灣人殺老虎的錄影帶公諸於世，殺老虎、吃虎肉、扒虎皮、抽虎鞭……已成為許多外人眼裡中國人與老虎唯一的關連。在求好心切下，中國社會裡與虎姑婆同樣有名的人虎故事「武松打虎」，也被藝文界改編成武松「縱虎歸山」，拿來啟示現代中國人，不要再津津樂道「上山打虎真英雄」這樣的中國人形象。

問題是，中國人與老虎的關係不是只有敵對和將之視為資源加以利用而已。

老虎文化，一脈相承

雖然老虎不是中國特有的產物，但生物考古學者發現，在中國大陸華南出土，有一百萬年歷史的虎化石，保有最原始的老虎骨骼，是現代老虎的祖先。生物學者認為，起源於華南之土的老虎，以放射狀往各地遷移，最終在亞洲發展成八個不同的亞種。

若把生物界的發現對應到文化上，從事文化探源的學者也提供了線索，證明中國在遠古部落時期，就與老虎形成了命運共同體。

根據文獻記載，老虎是早期遊牧民族古羌族信奉的圖騰動物。為尋找豐美的水草，崇虎的古羌族，率先進入中原，部分從長江而下的羌人，在江浙創造了六千年前的良渚文化。

今天在中國境內出土的上古文物、器皿，老虎造型非常豐富，許多流落他國的商周青銅器中，虎的形象更是信手拈來，藏在美國佛利爾美術館的西周青銅虎尊就是其中之一。兩千多年前戰國時代與秦朝留下的玉琥、虎符，數量更多不勝數。

研究古文物的「故宮文物月刊」執行編輯簡松村表示，以動物造型而言，中國古代文物中，老虎確實較多。除了中國是老

servation agreements?"

Why this distortion of the episode "Wu Song Kills a Tiger" from the epic Chinese novel *The Water Margin*? In fact, this is a new version of the Wu Song story, created by Taiwan University's glove-puppet theater group the Se Den Society, and performed for the celebration of the society's ninth anniversary. In the new play, Wu Song has become a conservationist. Although roaring drunk, he is clear-headed enough to give the hunters a dressing-down and a lecture about environmental protection, and when he catches up with the fierce tiger on Jingyang Ridge, he just tells it not to hurt humans any more, before striding proudly away.

Ever since the year before last, when an international conservation group released a video film showing people from Taiwan killing a tiger, in many foreigners' eyes the only association between tigers and the Chinese has been their killing tigers, eating their meat, skinning them and cutting off their penises. Eager to make amends, the theater group transformed the tale of Wu Song bare-handedly killing a tiger—which is as familiar to Chinese people as the story of "Great-Aunt Tigress" (who bites off the fingers of children who cry)—into one of Wu Song "letting the tiger return to the mountain." In this way they sought to warn modern Chinese to no longer be so enthusiastic about seeing the "tiger-slayer" as an image of Chinese heroism.

But in fact Chinese people's relationship with tigers was never only one of enmity or of seeing them as a resource to be exploited.

A long tradition of tiger culture

Although tigers are not unique to China, a million-year-old fossilized tiger skeleton which paleobiologists have found in southern China is the most primitive known tiger, and the ancestor of modern tigers. Biologists believe tigers originated in southern China, from where they radiated out in all directions and finally evolved into the eight distinct Asian subspecies.

Paralleling this biological discovery, research-

虎主要分布地區，更重要的，老虎也是中國境內最大型、兇猛的動物，中國的叢林之王非牠莫屬。比起熊，分布密林的虎神出鬼沒，行動更迅捷靈活；至於也被中國人拿來作為民間傳統造型的獅子，則是「外來種」，直到佛教傳入中國，才尾隨而入。在廣大民間的現實生活上，因為最容易受兇猛的老虎威脅，老虎也因此成為中國人重要的信仰神祇。

蠻荒時期，人類抗拒自然界危害的力量很薄弱，對於力強性猛的老虎充滿恐懼，進而產生敬畏，也因此賦予某種程度的神性化，商周時期的石雕、銅器，就都強調虎爪的尖銳、虎面的猙獰，「這是文化初期，人類對虎的主要印象，」故宮博物院書畫處長林柏亭認為。

但對後人更具意義的是，這種早期由圖騰崇拜開始的虎文化，隨著時代發展，在中國社會一直有新的面貌出現。

天上龍，地上虎

曹振峰指出，早期虎神原本也是主宰宇宙萬物和人類生命的神靈，在商代的民族綜合體中，與龍同被人賦予上達九天、降福袪災的職能。

大陸安陽博物館出版的刊物指出，高揚自然、天地之神力的商周青銅器上的饕餮紋：「說它是龍便是龍，說它是虎便是虎。」只是，當中國進入農業社會，農耕生產方式造成人們對不可知的自然日愈依賴，虎的地位遂漸漸由抽象的龍替代，出現了龍虎分離的情形。

特別是秦以後，龍被王室所壟斷，成了帝王化身、權力象徵，由此龍被捧上了天，虎便隱入民間。

但龍虎相爭，雖然神虎降入凡塵，牠卻沒有消失，反而出現了全民性的造虎運動，世代不衰，在中國人日常與禮儀生活中，老虎成為自娛性的審美對象，並由過去

ers studying the origins of culture have also found evidence to indicate that even back in the tribal period of remote antiquity, people shared a community of fate with tigers.

According to written records, the tiger was worshipped as a totem by early nomadic herdsmen of the ancient Qiang tribe. In their search for lusher pastures, the Qiang became the first people to enter China's central plains, and 6000 years ago some Qiang people who followed the Yangtze downriver created the Liangzhu culture in what is now Zhejiang Province.

Ancient artifacts and utensils unearthed within China today are often richly decorated with tiger motifs, and tiger images are very easy to find among the many articles of Shang and Zhou dynasty bronzeware which have found their way overseas. The Western Zhou bronze tiger *zun* (drinking cup) in the collection of America's Freer Art Gallery is one example. And countless jade tigers and tiger amulets have survived from the Warring States period and the Qin dynasty over 2000 years ago.

Chien Sung-tsun, a researcher of ancient artifacts and executive editor of *The National Palace Museum Monthly of Chinese Art*, says that the tiger is indeed one of the more commonly appearing animal motifs on ancient Chinese artifacts. Besides the fact that China was one of the main areas in which the tiger lived, more importantly the tiger was the largest and fiercest animal found within China, and the undisputed king of China's jungles. Compared with the bear, the more abundant tiger faded in and out of the forests in ghostly fashion, and was quicker and more agile in its movements. As for the lion, another source of traditional folk motifs for the Chinese, it was an "immigrant" which came into China's mythology in the wake of Buddhism. Because the ferocious tiger was the animal most likely to threaten ordinary people in their real lives, it became one of the most important spirits in which the Chinese believed.

In the earliest days, mankind's power to fend

off natural dangers was very weak, and people were terrified of the strength and ferocity of the tiger. This fear gave rise to respect, and a certain degree of mystification. The stone carvings and bronzeware of the Shang and Zhou dynasties all emphasize the tiger's sharp claws and fierce countenance. "At the dawn of civilization, this was humankind's main impression of the tiger," believes Lin Po-ting, curator of painting and calligraphy at the National Palace Museum.

But more interestingly for us today, the tiger culture which sprang from this early totem worship continued to developed with Chinese society over the ages, always appearing in new guises.

Dragons in heaven, tigers on earth

Cao Zhenfeng notes that in early times tiger spirits were worshipped as the masters of the universe, of all living things and of the lives of human beings. Among the tribes of the Shang dynasty, the tiger was credited with powers on a par with those of the dragon to ascend to the highest heavens, bring good fortune and drive out evil.

A publication of the Anyang museum in mainland China states that the *taotie* patterns (the *taotie* is a ferocious and gluttonous mythical beast) on Shang and Zhou dynasty bronzeware, which express the mystical power of nature, heaven and earth, "could be dragons or could just as well be

萬華龍山寺建寺二百五十年，老虎花燈也來湊熱鬧。（本刊資料）
When Lungshan Temple in Wanhua celebrated its 250th birthday, this tiger float added to the excitement. (*Sinorama* file photo)

的猙獰，逐漸成為造型憨厚、傻氣的民間虎。「在這個意義上，虎文化反而發展了，」曹振峰認為。

在大陸鄉村，今天仍可見到小孩兒穿著媽媽做的虎頭鞋、圍著虎頭圍涎、戴著虎頭帽、虎頭手套，手拿虎頭布玩具，睡虎頭枕，個個虎頭虎腦。

中國境內沒有一種動物像民藝虎，在民間生活中流傳如此之廣。由陝西到南方福建惠安，少數民族如雲南各族，都可以發現充滿自然情感、擺脫嬌柔造作的民藝虎。「這些實用與藝術兼具的民藝品的依據，主要來自商周時期軍士的銅盔、甲冑、銅鉞上的虎頭紋，」曹振峰指出。

鳳飛飛的護身符

老虎具有的圖騰意義，流入民間，也在各地廣泛地變成避邪驅魔與吉祥的象徵。

至今中國仍保有在端午節掛艾草紮成的艾虎，和以雄黃在孩兒額頭上畫「王」字代表虎來避邪的千年習俗；過去地方不安寧，就以「虎」字碑來鎮邪。離我們最近的例子是，臺灣東北角的草嶺古道，就有清朝將軍陳亮光題的虎字碑。老虎也常被畫在門上驅祟，具有門神的作用，觀光客最愛的萬華龍山寺，就有相對襯的龍牆、虎壁作為守護神。

雖然獅子進入中國後，取代了老虎部分

tigers." But when China entered the agricultural age, farming made people more and more dependent on nature with all its vagaries, and the tiger's status was gradually usurped by the more abstract dragon. Thus the dragon and tiger became separated.

From the Qin dynasty onwards especially, the dragon was monopolized by the royal family and became the embodiment of the emperor and the symbol of his power. From this time on the dragon was elevated to a heavenly status, while the tiger found its home among the people.

But although this struggle between the dragon and the tiger ended with the tiger spirit being cast down into the world of men, this was not the end of its career, for the practice of creating tiger images spread throughout the people and continued down the ages. In Chinese people's daily lives and in their rituals, the tiger became an object of artistic appreciation, and its representation gradually developed from a ferocious beast into the cuddly, buffoonish tiger of folk art. "In this sense, tiger culture actually progressed," opines Cao Zhenfeng.

In the mainland countryside today, one can still see children wearing tiger-head shoes, tiger-head bibs, tiger-head caps and tiger-head gloves made by their mothers, and holding tiger-head cloth toys and sleeping on tiger-head pillows.

In China, no other animal is as widely seen in people's everyday lives as the tiger of folk art. From Shaanxi in the north to Hui'an in Fujian Province in the south, or among the minority peoples of Yunnan, folk art tigers redolent with natural, unaffected emotion can be found everywhere. "The origins of these folk craft products, which are both useful and artistic, lie mainly in the tiger-head designs on the bronze helmets, the armor and the bronze battleaxes of Shang and Zhou dynasty soldiers," observes Cao Zhenfeng.

Feng Fei-fei's guardian spirit

The tiger's significance as a totem was taken up by the common people, and throughout China it developed into a symbol which was believed to drive out evil and demons and to bring good fortune.

To this day, China has maintained the age-old customs at the Dragon Boat Festival of hanging up a tiger braided from Chinese mugwort, and painting the character 王 (*wang*, "king"), representing the tiger, on children's foreheads to protect them from evil. In times past, if a locality was turbulent, a stele with the character 虎 (*hu*, "tiger") would be erected to pacify the evil influence. The nearest example is on the old Tsaoling military road in the northeast corner of Taiwan, where there is a stele with the character *hu* written by the Qing dynasty general Chen Liangguang. The tiger was often also painted on doors as a door god to drive away evil spirits, and Lungshan Temple in Wanhua, a favorite with tourists, has a dragon and a tiger wall standing next to each other as guardian spirits.

After the lion found its way into Chinese mythology, it usurped some of the tiger's functions, such as the "wind lions" used to protect houses from evil spirits. "But in fact previously this kind of role had always been played by tigers," remarks Yuan Chang-rue, curator of the anthropology department at Taiwan Provincial Museum.

The tiger is not absent from Taiwan's folk culture either. At a time of international accusations that more than half the Chinese herbal medicine shops in Taiwan sell tiger bones, very few people know that the most widely revered animal spirit in Taiwanese folk beliefs is Huyeh, an incarnation of the tiger. According to surveys by scholars of folk customs, 70% of temples in Taiwan contain Huyeh images. This is because the spirits most widely revered by the people of Taiwan—Fu Te Cheng Shen (the Spirit of Happiness and Virtue), Pao Sheng Ta Ti (the Emperor Protector of Life) and Tsai Shen Yeh (the Spirit of Wealth)—all ride on the backs of fierce tigers or sit on tiger thrones. In all these spirits' temples, Huyeh figures are found below the spirit niche. Some believe that this is because temples are places where the spirits of the world of light gather, and Huyeh has the power to subdue the ghosts and demons of the un-

湯火關　鬼門關

白虎關　無情關

埋兒關　雷公關

問今年運道如何？小心白虎關難過，可是和鬼門關一樣凶險。（楊文卿攝）

How will my luck be this year? Watch out for the white tiger gate—it's as dangerous as the gates of hell. (photo by Yang Wen-ching)

的地位，民間屋宅也出現辟邪的風獅爺，「但過去這樣的角色其實都是老虎在扮演，」省立博物館人類學組長阮昌銳說。

走入民間的老虎文化在臺灣更不缺乏。當國際指責臺灣百分之五十以上的中藥房都賣虎骨時，很少人知道，臺灣民間信仰裡被崇拜最多的動物神，正是老虎化身的虎爺。根據民俗學者調查，臺灣廟宇百分之七十都供祀有虎爺，因為威猛的老虎是民間被普遍奉祀的福德正神、保生大帝、財神爺的座騎，在這些神明專屬的廟裡，神龕下都供奉著虎爺，有人認為廟是集陽界神明之處，虎爺能威伏地下陰界鬼怪，因此有「壇下將軍」之稱。

虎爺也被討海人視為守護神；由於身為保生大帝的部將「黑虎將軍」，也具有治癒毒瘡，消滅瘟疫的能力，土地公廟的虎爺則有驅癩鎮廟和孩童觸摸虎腮可以治療腮腺炎的說法。民間師父雕出的虎爺往往造型可愛，如此小孩才敢安心撫其面腮。因為常伴武財神趙公明身邊，許多大家樂、六合彩賭徒也都拜虎爺；據說，名噪一時的歌星鳳飛飛初出茅廬時，在拜過基隆信義堂的虎爺後，不久果然闖出名堂，在歌壇揚名立萬。

矛盾的綜合體

不論作為歲時節日中應景之物、傳統裝飾圖案，或遍佈大陸農家的民藝品、臺灣廟裡萬能的虎爺，都具有整個遠古民族符號傳承的意義，是六千年的良渚文化與三千年前的商周器物紋飾，經過民族遷移、融合、衝突一脈相傳而來。今天民俗學者追溯祭祀虎爺習俗，就傳承自周朝郊祀，當田工告成，天子就合聚八神報饗之，稱作八蠟，其中第五種神是貓虎，因為牠們捕食傷害禾苗的野鼠野獸，保護農作。

到今天，虎的地位仍然持續與龍相抗衡，「生龍活虎」不時來一場「龍爭虎鬥」

derground world of darkness. Hence he is also called "the general below the altar."

Huyeh is also seen as a guardian spirit of fisher folk. As a servant of Pao Sheng Ta Ti, the "black tiger general" also has the power to cure abscesses and drive out fevers, while the Huyehs in Earth God temples are reputed to banish fevers and keep peace in the temple. It is also said that if children with mumps stroke the tiger's cheeks they will be cured. The folk artisans who carve the Huyeh figures usually give them a lovable appearance so that children will not be afraid to touch their faces. Because Huyeh is often seen beside Zhao Gongming, the martial spirit of wealth, many gamblers who bet on lotteries such as *dajiale* or *liuhecai* also pray to Huyeh. It is said that when Feng Fei-fei had just started out on her singing career, she prayed to Huyeh at Keelung's Hsin Yi Tang Temple, and not long afterwards rose to stardom.

A contradictory amalgamation

Whether in the form of the tiger motifs on seasonal objects at the Chinese New Year and on traditional decorations, the folk craft products to be found in villages all over mainland China, or the all-powerful Huyehs of Taiwan's temples, these tigers all share the significance of transmitting an ancient national symbol. The same patterns decorate artifacts from the Liangzhu culture of 6000 years ago and the Shang and Zhou dynasties of 3000 years ago, and have been passed down to the present day through all the tribal migrations, fusions and conflicts of history. For instance, today's scholars of folk culture trace the custom of praying to Huyeh back to the rural rites of the Zhou dynasty. After the harvest was completed, the Son of Heaven would report to eight kinds of spirits, of which the fifth were the cats and tigers, for they protected crops by eating the rodents and wild animals which might damage the seedlings.

Even today, the tiger's status still counterbalances that of the dragon. The expression "as alive as dragons and tigers" describes people brimming with vitality, while "fighting like dragons and tigers" describes a pitched battle between evenly matched foes; in basketball tall players are nicknamed "heavenly dragons," and short players "earthly tigers"; on TV there is the variety show *Big Brother Dragon and Little Brother Tiger*; the Song dynasty judge Bao Qingtian had both a dragon-head guillotine and a tiger-head guillotine to behead miscreants of royal blood; in Buddhism there are arhats to defeat both dragons and tigers; while among the 12 animals of the Chinese zodiac, the tiger comes before the dragon. Thus it is hardly surprising if one scholar sees the Chinese as not only the children of the dragon, but also of the tiger.

But although the tiger, which is a genuine part of Chinese people's lives, has been elevated on the spiritual plane to an object of folk veneration and belief, unlike the dragon the tiger is also killed for its bones as medicine, and its other organs are indiscriminately taken to be eaten as tonics. This has given many people of other nations a mistaken impression of Chinese medicinal culture. Why should there be such a discrepancy between Chinese people's treatment of the tiger on the spiritual plane and in real life?

In an outspoken article, Cao Zhenfeng has written: "In China's history, there has been a contradictory conception of the tiger. It has been both feared and venerated, both hunted and worshipped. The tiger was both a portent of disaster and an omen of good fortune. . . . No other animal in Chinese culture is such a blatantly contradictory amalgamation."

In fact there is nothing strange about our contradictory attitudes towards the tiger. They are the product of many wild animals' and mankind's having evolved together since before the dawn of civilization.

Only running wild deep in the mountains

Chen Wang-heng, author of the book *Fierce and Stern Beauty—Chinese Bronze Art*, observes that in primitive society, because humans lacked the physical strength to overpower animals such as tigers, bears and panthers, they did their best to avoid them, and did not usually treat them as a

，籃球場上有天龍地虎；電視綜藝節目有龍兄虎弟；宋朝包青天對付作惡的皇族，不但有龍頭鍘，也有虎頭鍘伺候；佛教裡有降龍羅漢，伏虎羅漢也不遜色；十二生肖之中，虎還跑在龍的前面呢。難怪學者要認為中國人不只是龍的傳人，也是虎的傳人了。

不過，和龍不一樣的是，真實存在中國人生活中的老虎，在精神上雖提升為民間的信仰對象，民間卻也殺虎取骨治病，更肆無忌憚的利用虎爺身上器官進補，還因此讓外人對中醫藥文化產生誤解。為什麼中國人對待老虎在精神與實質上會有這樣的衝突？

曹振峰在一篇文章裡開宗明義的就說：「在我國歷史上，對虎有種矛盾的觀念，既懼怕牠，又崇拜牠，既捕殺牠，又信賴牠；虎是不祥之物，又是吉祥之物，……在中國沒有任何一種生物像虎一樣，是如此突出的矛盾綜合體。」

其實，在老虎身上出現的矛盾，並不奇怪，那正是今天許多野生動物與人類由蒙昧時期一路進化而來所造成。

橫行只在深山裡

《獰厲之美——中國青銅藝術》一書作者陳望衡指出，在原始社會，因為人在生理素質上力量比不過虎、熊、豹這些動物，既不足以征服，也就避之唯恐不及，一般是不將之作為食物的主要來源。

但在生產效率低的漁獵社會，面對殘酷的大自然和物資短缺，人們也會一步步逐漸放寬可以利用的資源陣營，例如中國東北的鄂倫春人，早期是禁止吃熊與老虎的

虎落平陽被人欺？除了動物園，今天老虎幾乎只能以圖像出現世間。圖為職棒比賽進行中，大虎字報清楚昭告著「我們是三商虎隊的球迷」。（黃麗梨攝）
Is the tiger away from the mountains at the mercy of humans? Except in zoos, tigers today are seen almost only in pictures. Here we see a large "tiger" character identifying supporters of the San Shang Tigers professional baseball team at a game. (photo by Lily Huang)

民族，但逐漸的，熊肉也可以用來充飢，熊皮可以用來禦寒，但經常處於生命與飢餓威脅之中的民族，對於動物既需要又害怕，也產生許多打獵的禁忌。至今鄂倫春人依然禁止吃熊頭，也不許直呼老虎名諱，而有各種官、老爺、神等充滿敬意的稱呼。

當民智漸開，人們了解疾病不是莫名的天譴，可以靠人力治癒，因此神農嘗百草，由各種自然資源去尋找藥材，過去老虎數量又多，《本草綱目》中就提到老虎說「本經不載所出，今多，山林處皆有之。」在沒有鮮奶、鈣質不足的時代，虎骨成為補強筋骨的藥材，其實無可厚非，只是傳襲至今，在老虎數量銳減後，前幾年大陸、韓國、臺灣都還

major source of food.

But in hunting and fishing society with its low productivity, faced with the harsh realities of nature and a lack of material resources, people gradually extended the range of resources they could use. For instance, the Oroqen people of northeast China once had a taboo against eating bears and tigers, but gradually came to eat bear meat and use bear skins for clothing. But a people which faces the constant threat of death and hunger both needs animals and fears them, and this has given rise to many hunters' taboos. Today, the Oroqen still do not eat bears' heads, and do not refer to tigers directly by name, instead using respectful titles such as Official, Grandfather or Spirit.

As humanity gradually became more enlightened, people came to understand that diseases were not inexplicable punishments meted out by heaven, but could be cured by human effort. Thus Shen Nong (the reputed inventor of Chinese herbal medicine) is said to have tasted all kinds of plants, seeking medicinal materials from throughout nature. In the past tigers were abundant—the ancient *Compendium of Materia Medica* records in its entry on the tiger: "We need not record their source, for they are many, and can be found wherever there are mountain forests." In an age when there was no fresh milk to drink and people lacked adequate sources of calcium, there was nothing wrong in using tiger bones as a medicine to strengthen the bones and tendons. But the same practice cannot be carried on today, when tigers' numbers have fallen dramatically. Just a few years ago, mainland China, Korea and Taiwan were all still producing so-called "Quince and Tiger Bone Wine," providing an obvious target for conservationists' criticism.

But the main culprits behind the growing mismatch between myth and reality for the tiger have been the invention of tools, advances in hunting techniques, and the growing areas of land cleared for agriculture, which have little by little turned tigers into the victims. As an ancient poet wrote:

"Though ferocious, the tiger is lovable/He only runs wild deep in the mountains." But the mountain areas in which the tiger reigns supreme are growing ever smaller.

Lin Po-ting points out that in the hunting scenes which decorate artifacts from the Spring and Autumn and Warring States periods, one often sees mounted swordsmen fighting tigers, with the tigers in the role of the pursued. It would appear that people's fear of tigers had already lessened considerably since the Shang dynasty, when tigers were often depicted as fierce, ravenous beasts.

The tiger's secularization

As humans gradually cast off their fear of tigers, they became able to appreciate the tiger on equal terms. The tiger's powerful physique, its lithe, graceful movements and beautiful pelt inspired the splendid tiger patterns we still see today in folk art. However, the secularized tiger in China with its enormous area and complex ethnic mix naturally gave rise to a multiplicity of different symbolisms, creating apparent contradictions. This is no different from the imaginary dragon, for although the dragon is said to be holy and inviolable for the Chinese, there are also some stories of evil dragons. Furthermore, compared with the mythical dragon and phoenix, in the past when tigers were common in China, incidents of tigers eating people or people killing tigers occurred frequently, so that humans' conflicting emotions of both hating and worshipping tigers were very much a reality. Thus although people use folk art tiger motifs to protect children, others have used the tiger as the inspiration for such stories as "Great-Aunt Tigress" to frighten children.

Writers love to use others as the channel for their own ideas, and in Chinese literature there is the hair-raising *Encounter With a Tiger*, but also the tiger-praising *Story of a Grateful Tiger*. One can admire the tiger's might and vigor, or use it to satirize many aspects of human life. Among the numerous idiomatic phrases and literary allusions involving tigers, "a tiger father doesn't have dogs

生產所謂的木瓜虎骨酒，遂成爲保育人士攻擊的明顯目標。

但老虎神、形的日漸分離，主要仍是拜工具的發明、狩獵技術的進步、農業開墾面積日漸擴張，老虎在不知不覺間淪爲受害者所致。古人有詩爲證：「猛虎雖猛猶可喜，橫行只在深山裡」，逐漸的，老虎只能在範圍越來越小的山中稱大王。

林柏亭指出，春秋戰國時期器物上的狩獵紋飾，常是騎士揮劍鬥虎，老虎扮演被追逐的角色，看起來，人對虎的畏懼程度，比起商代常出現老虎饕餮的造型，已減低許多。

老虎世俗化

當人類對虎漸漸擺脫恐懼感，也能以平等的觀點去欣賞虎的特性，老虎矯健的體型、靈活優美的動作、鮮麗的皮毛，經過民間工藝轉化成今天我們所見色彩燦爛的民藝虎。但另一方面，世俗化後的老虎，在地方廣大、種族複雜的中國，象徵自然也多元起來，並產生看來矛盾的情形；就像實際上不存在的龍，在中國雖說是神聖不可侵犯，但也有惡龍的故事存在。

而且比起無形的龍、鳳，過去多虎的中國民間，虎吃人、人殺虎的敵對狀態不時發生，人對虎亦恨、亦崇的情感極爲眞實。因此既有民藝虎這樣的虎形象來守護孩子，也就有人會利用老虎形象編出「虎姑婆」這樣的故事嚇唬孩子。

文人又喜借他人手中酒杯，澆自己心中塊壘，文學中遂有驚甫未定的《遭虎篇》，也有歌頌老虎的《義虎傳》；可以讚其威猛，也可以借其來諷刺人生百像。豐富的老虎成語典故中，虎父無犬子是讚詞，養虎貽患、與虎謀皮、羊質虎皮等也點出虎的惡狀。

新上任的臺北市長陳水扁，聘請李作復中將任職兵役處長，因爲他在軍中行事剛

involving tigers, "a tiger father doesn't have dogs for sons" ("a talented father will not have a lackluster son") is laudatory, while "rearing a tiger brings calamity" ("appeasement courts disaster"), "bargaining with a tiger for his coat" ("asking an evil person to act against their own interests"), or "a sheep in a tiger's coat" ("a sheep in wolf's clothing") all point to the evil side of tigers.

The new mayor of Taipei City, Chen

臺灣寺廟裡數量最多的動物神，非虎爺莫屬。城隍爺出巡時，虎爺也會出來護駕。（薛繼光攝）

In Taiwan's temples, the tiger is the commonest animal spirit by far. When the City God makes his inspection tour, the tiger spirit Huyeh plays a part in the procession. (photo by Hsueh Chi-kuang)

as director of the city's Department of Military Service, because of his reputation for fair and upright dealing while in the army, which earned him the nickname "the Tiger." But since ancient times the Chinese have also had the saying that "powerful people are as changeable as tigers," implying that the actions of the powerful are as unpredictable as the patterns on tigers' coat are variable. Wei Chuang (*c.* 836–910) of the Tang dynasty wrote in his *Tracks of the Tiger*: "His white brow often comes to the door by night/His tracks crowd the water's edge/Today I withdrew to a mountain cave/But how is it that there I saw you again, lord?" Here, the tiger is a metaphor for an evil lord.

Apart from being feared, respected, and even used to fight fire with fire by scaring away ill fortune, the tiger is sometimes also avoided as taboo.

正，有「老虎」之稱，但中國人自古也有所謂「大人虎變」的說法，形容大人物行止屈伸，莫測高深，如虎身花紋多彩斑爛。唐朝韋莊的「虎跡」：「白額頻頻夜到門，水邊蹤跡漸成群，我今避世棲巖穴，巖穴如何又見君」在此，虎又被比做惡君了。

除了被畏懼、尊敬，甚至被利用來以惡制惡、嚇阻不祥事物的神獸，老虎有時卻也是人們避諱的對象。蕭麗紅女士的小說《千江有水千江月》中，女主角貞觀的三姨就曾對貞觀說：「等妳大了，妳才不想肖虎呢，虎是特別生肖，遇著家中嫁娶大事，都要避開……」

全方位的利用

人類利用自然資源的方式，往往是全方位並進，而非單一的，在精神上，老虎可以被利用做各種解釋；實質上的功能自然也常被誇大。

今天社會更複雜，老虎的功能也就被附會得更加多樣化，加上人們對自然更了解，老虎的神秘感消失，老虎又所剩無幾，人們也不可能再有與虎面對面搏鬥的機會，就可以更自由的由人的觀點出發，高興老虎象徵是什麼，牠就是什麼。就有人認為虎爺會將錢財咬進門，因此賭場與酒家也都拜起虎爺；跑江湖的將虎鞭的藥效描繪的生猛有力、虎虎生風，事實上，中國藥典從沒有虎鞭可以壯陽的記載。

老虎對中國人的精神、心理療效，也使國際保育團體在指責我們仍非法使用虎骨時鬧出許多誤解。當全世界只剩幾千隻老虎，地球島組織卻指出虎骨滿臺灣。事實上，尚未禁用虎骨以前，臺灣中藥房裡，真正的虎骨恐怕連百分之五都不到，因為虎骨只是一個藥名，虎骨市場上賣的最多的其實是羊骨。

中國醫藥學院教授張賢哲就指出，這不

In Hsiao Li-hung's novel *Water and Moon of a Thousand Rivers*, the main female character Chen-kuan's aunt tells her: "When you're grown up, you'll wish you weren't born in the year of the tiger. The tiger's a special birth sign; whenever anyone in the family gets married, you'll have to keep away."

All-round use

Yuan Chang-rue comments that when humans exploit a natural resource they exploit it to the full, and not just in one way alone. On the spiritual plane, the tiger is pressed into all kinds of roles, and its powers in real life are naturally often exaggerated too.

Today's society is even more complex, and the powers ascribed to the tiger have also become more diverse. As people's understanding of nature has increased, the tiger has lost its mystique, and with so few tigers left there is no longer any likelihood of people finding themselves in a face-to-face struggle with a tiger. Thus people are free to develop their own human perspective and let the tiger symbolize whatever they want it to. Some people think Huyeh will bring money and wealth in through the door gripped between his teeth, and therefore represents the god of wealth; for this reason even casinos and restaurants have started praying to Huyeh; meanwhile quack doctors credit tiger penises with the power to confer remarkable virility, when in fact the reference works of Chinese herbal medicine make no mention whatsoever of tiger penises' having any effect on potency.

Chinese people's faith in the curative powers of the tiger has led to many misunderstandings when international conservation groups have accused us of illegally using tiger bones. At a time when only a few thousand tigers remain alive worldwide, the Earth Island environmental group claimed that Taiwan was awash with tiger bones. In fact, even before the use of tiger bones was banned, the number of real tiger bones in herbal medicine shops was probably less than 5%, for "tiger bone" is just the name of a medicine—the

畫家吳昊的「節日的老虎」，是十足熱鬧、吉祥、又憨厚的民間虎。（吳昊提供）
Painter Wu Hau's *Festive Tiger* is a lively, lucky, lovable folk art tiger. (courtesy of Wu Hau)

bones most commonly sold on Taiwan's tiger bone market are sheep bones. Professor Chang Hsien-che of China Medical College says that this is not trickery on the part of herbal medicine merchants, for Chinese medicine recognizes two categories of "tiger bone": the first is "true tiger bone," which includes tiger, panther and lion bones, and the second is "sundry bones," which includes cattle, horse, pig and dog bones. Both categories are sold in the herbal medicine shops, at different prices. The reason they are all called "tiger bone" is because "tiger bone" sounds much more efficacious than "pig bone" or "dog bone," just as in Chinese medicine there is also the so-called "white tiger," which in fact is a plant and has nothing to do with tigers at all.

Unfortunately foreigners do not understand these subtleties, and think that all the bones on show are tiger bones. Today, the Department of Health has no choice but to call on medicine merchants to respond to the situation by calling the "sundry bones" by their rightful names.

Most Chinese remedies are composite concoctions. "Quince and Tiger Bone Wine" contains a dozen or more ingredients, but the active one is not really tiger bone, for Chinese herbalists have since discovered much more effective tonics for the bones, tendons and muscles than tiger bone. Thus giving up the use of tiger bone would not have much effect on Chinese herbal treatments. Since the use of tiger bones was banned, mainland China has still been producing Quince and Tiger Bone Wine, but with a notice on the bottle reading "Does not contain tiger bone." But because of the way in which some people in Taiwan have exaggerated the curative powers of tiger products, we have had sanctions slapped on us by the United States, however unfairly.

When the tiger leaves the mountains

However, whether they betray a love-hate attitude or are contradictory and confused, the many different ways in which we refer to the tiger in fact

獅子形象隨著佛教進入中國後，奪去虎神不少光彩，但老虎的避邪象徵仍然不衰。圖為草嶺古道的虎字碑。（鐘永和攝）

Buddhism brought the image of the lion into China, robbing the tiger of much of its glamour. But the tiger is still a powerful symbol to drive out evil. Pictured here is a "tiger" character stele on Tsaoling old military road. (photo by Chung Yung-ho)

是中藥商掛羊頭賣狗肉，中醫應用上，虎骨其實包括兩類，一種是包含虎、豹、獅骨的「正虎骨」，另一類則是包括牛、馬、豬、狗骨頭的「雜骨」，在藥行裡兩種有價錢高低之別，之所以統稱虎骨，就因

為虎骨聽來此豬骨、狗骨有療效多了，就像中藥裡有所謂的「白虎」，其實與老虎毫無關係。

可惜外人不懂其中玄機，見到骨就以為都是虎骨，今天衛生署也只有要求藥商不得不因應環境將其他雜骨正名。

中國藥方大都是複方，含有十幾種藥方的木瓜虎骨酒裡，真正發揮功能的其實不是虎骨，因為後來的中醫早就發現療效比虎骨更好的強筋健骨藥材；沒有虎骨，對中醫治病不會有太大影響。自從虎骨禁用，大陸依然生產木瓜虎骨酒，不過酒瓶上都有但書——不含虎骨。臺灣卻因為有人將老虎五花大綁，吹噓虎製品的療效而慘遭美國貿易制裁，說來冤枉。

虎落平陽

不過，無論看起來是愛恨交加或矛盾曖昧，各式各樣有關老虎的說法，其實更證明中國人與虎的關係密切。

《古今圖書集成》記載中國人與動物關係的禽蟲典中，有關老虎詩詞、故事的數量，是其他動物無法一較長短的。

「精神上對老虎的各種情感，都是實際生活中人們與虎接觸的轉化。」簡松村表示，比如原本也分布中國的大型動物犀牛，歷經多戰亂的戰國時代，被捕捉作為盔甲，加上氣候的改變，在漢代就已從中國土地上消失。今天除了疾病上犀角粉的利用，和早期留下的少數犀牛造型文物，中國人生活上早就失去犀牛的蹤影。

只是，今天神虎不只在精神領域上逐漸「虎落平陽被犬欺」，任人編造；實質上，老虎也追隨犀牛腳步，即將在中國這一片母源之地消失，由南方的華南虎，到中、印邊界的印度虎和東北虎，如今整個中國，老虎加起來不到百隻，已到了眾虎死滅的地步。

如果以犀牛為鑑，隨著老虎滅絕，中國人崇虎文化的香煙看來遲早也會斷絕，即使已深入民間文化的老虎信仰不會輕易消失，但沒有了老虎，徒留形式的老虎文化，總還是少了一些什麼吧？ □

（原載民國84年2月光華雜誌）

all go to show how close a relationship the Chinese have with this animal.

In the section in *Gu Jin Tu Shu Ji Cheng* (*Completed Collection of Graphs and Writings of Ancient and Modern Times*) which documents Chinese people's relationships with animals, the poems and stories about tigers far outnumber those about any other creature.

"All the different emotions we feel towards the tiger have sprung from people's real-life contacts with tigers." Chien Sung-tsun notes that the rhinoceros, for example—another large animal which was once found in China—was hunted in the turbulent Warring States period for its skin, which was used for armor. With this pressure, combined with changing climate patterns, by the Han dynasty it had already disappeared from China. Today, apart from the medicinal use of rhinoceros horn powder and a few rhino horn artifacts which have been passed down from ancient times, any trace of the rhinoceros has long disappeared from Chinese people's lives.

It's just that today it is not only on the spiritual plane that the once revered tiger is "down from the mountain and at the mercy of dogs," wide open to fictionalization. In real life too, following in the rhino's footsteps, the tiger is on the verge of disappearing from China, its original home. From the South China tiger in the south to the Bengal tiger on the borders of China and India, and the Siberian tiger, throughout China there are less than 100 tigers in all. The animals are on the very brink of oblivion.

If the rhinoceros is anything to go by, if the tiger disappears, the Chinese cultural tradition of venerating the tiger will also sooner or later be broken. Even though the tiger beliefs which run deep in folk culture will not disappear easily, without the tiger, won't tiger culture, which will remain in form only, be lacking something? □

(Chang Chin-ju/tr. by Robert Taylor/ first published in February 1995)

從武松打虎到武松放虎

From "Wu Song Kills the Tiger" to "Wu Song Lets the Tiger Go"

文‧張靜茹

不約而同的，近來不只臺灣西田社改編武松打虎，大陸亦有皮影劇團上演非常「環保」的——武松放虎。

武松打虎錯了嗎？

北魏敦煌石窟有一面「投身飼虎」的壁畫，故事來自《金光明經》第四卷「捨身品」：描述釋尊前生薩埵那王子，一回與兩個哥哥出遊，見到懸崖下一隻生產後的母虎虛弱的匍伏著。三王子凝視即將餓死的雌虎一段時間後，從懸崖跳下，倒在雌虎面前，雌虎對充滿慈悲心的王子卻不動聲色，王子以為老虎衰弱得無法動口吃他，就用銳利的竹子切割自己喉嚨而死。三王子死前說，「肉體不過是糞袋，對生活沒有任何用處，現在我要把自己的肉體用在有意義的事上，如此，肉體將會成為我度過生死大海的船了。」

好生惡死，人虎皆然

美學教授蔣勳在《美的沉思》書中闡釋，投身飼虎哀憫的人生，是將人與虎並列，等同看待眾生，因為人與眾生一樣，有超脫不掉的生死問題，三王子用最慘烈的方式，直指生命的有無，是在大悲哀與大傷痛中，要人頓悟生命的空無與幻滅。

佛教之所以有這樣的故事，正是認為人

By coincidence, not only has Taiwan's Se Den Society recently rewritten the story of Wu Song killing the tiger; in mainland China there is also a shadow-puppet theater troupe putting on a very "environmentalist" show—Wu Song Lets the Tiger Go. So was Wu Song wrong to kill the tiger?

There is a story in the fourth volume of the *Suvarnaprabhasa Sutra* that describes how Prince Sattva, a previous incarnation of Sakyamuni, was once out walking with his two elder brothers when from the top of a cliff they looked down and saw a tigress lying weakly on the ground with a litter of cubs, on the point of starving to death. The prince gazed at the tigress for a while, then leapt down from the cliff and lay down in front of her. But the tigress did not react at all to his kindhearted action, and believing she was too weak to eat him, the prince used a sharp piece of bamboo to cut his own throat. Before he died, the young prince said: "The body is no more than a bag of excrement, and is of no use at all to one in life. Now I will use my flesh for a worthwhile purpose, and thus it will become a boat for me to cross the great sea between life and death."

Both men and tigers love life and fear death

Professor of aesthetics Chang Hsun, in his book *A Contemplation on Chinese Art*, explains that the prince's compassionate gift of his body to feed the tigress places humans, tigers and all liv-

為了傳遞保育觀念，臺大西田社上演的「新武松」，劇中武松一改打虎英雄的形象，放了老虎。（薛繼光攝）
To impart conservation ideas, in Taiwan University's Se Den Society's *New Wu Song*, Wu Song departs from his image of a tiger-slaying hero, and instead lets the tiger go. (photo by Hsueh Chi-kuang)

與動物並不存在本質性差異，在追求慾望、苦惱和以自我為中心上，人類和動物並無不同，因此要人把慈悲普及到動物身上，當然，這是很不容易的事，也只有釋尊能用自己換取老虎的生命。

由這樣的觀點看來，過去不論是武松打虎，或中國人利用老虎身上器官治病，或吳承恩在《西遊記》第十三回描寫一位雙叉嶺獵戶，為救唐僧，手執鋼叉與嶺上的斑爛虎力鬥，其實都是身為生命總有好生惡死的不得已舉措。

尤其在臻芒草萊時代，人不時受虎威脅，更無法閃避在自己生命與其他生命之間做一個選擇，「猛虎潛深山，長嘯自生風，人謂客行樂，客行苦傷心。」「北山虎有穴，南山虎為群，目光如電聲如雷，倚蕩起伏山之垠，百人一飽不留骨，敗衣墜絮徒紛紛，空谷絕樵聲，長路無行塵……」在這樣的情形下，為了自衛，武松出手打虎，看來是最自然不過的事。

徒手禦虎真英雄

只是，後來的人虎相爭，已非防範猛虎食人，今天國際保育團體拿十幾年前臺灣人殺老虎的錄影帶，指控臺灣是野生動物的黑洞，錄影帶裡，人殺虎的目的是創造一場「殺虎秀」，為的是標售老虎身上的寶，和古人徒手禦虎的不得已豈可相比。

現代武松放走老虎，不只是因為「一紙國際公約規定」，而是到了今天，倚仗著科技，人口大量增加，自然萬物輕而易舉被人類壓倒，老虎岌岌可危，此時再去打虎，贏了，也只有勝之不武差堪形容。

不管藝文界新編的武松，是否能讓武松的生命隨著時代、觀念改變而更加豐富；當人們再不需要為生存時時與自然搏鬥後，現代武松是否偶爾也會懷念自己有過為了生存尊嚴，赤手空拳與老虎奮力搏鬥的時代？ □（原載民國84年2月光華雜誌）

ing beings on an equal footing, for humans are no different from other living beings in facing inevitable death. The young prince used this most tragic method to directly illustrate how little separates life and death. In this way, in the midst of great sorrow and pain, he wished to awaken people to the emptiness and disillusionment of existence.

The story shows that Buddhism makes no distinction between the basic nature of humans and animals. There is no difference between humans and animals in their pursuit of desires, their misery and their self-centeredness, and therefore humans should extend their compassion to animals. Of course this is no easy matter, and only a Buddha could give up his own life to save a tiger's.

From this point of view, in the past, whether it was Wu Song killing a tiger or Chinese people using tiger organs to treat diseases, or, as described in *Journey to the West*, a mountain hunter armed with two pitchforks fighting with a mountain tiger to save the monk Xuan Zang, these were all actions forced upon living beings who preferred life over death.

Especially when man still lived in the forests, people were in constant danger from tigers and had no option but to choose between their own life or another. "The ferocious tiger is hidden deep in the mountains/His long roar whips up the wind/They say the traveler walks in joy/But he walks in fear of death." "The tigers of the northern mountains have caves/The tigers of the southern mountains are many/Their gaze like lightning and their voice like thunder/They live wherever the mountains rise/They eat a hundred yet leave no bones/The sound of the woodcutter is gone from the valley/No walker raises dust on the long road. . ." In such circumstances, for Wu Song to kill the tiger for his own protection really was the most natural thing in the world.

The barehanded hero

But people's later struggles with the tiger have no longer been to protect themselves from ferocious maneaters. When an international conservation group uses a 10-year-old film showing Taiwanese killing a tiger to accuse Taiwan today of being a black hole for wildlife, we cannot deny that the tiger in the film was killed purely for show, to drum up customers for an auction of its body parts. How can this be compared with people in ancient times fighting off tigers to save themselves?

If the modern Wu Song lets the tiger go free, it is not merely to conform to the letter of an international convention, but because today, when science and technology have allowed human populations to soar, the natural world is easily crushed by mankind, and the tiger's very existence has become precarious. If we fight the tiger now, ours will be the hollowest of victories.

Whether or not the theater group's new version can bring the old Wu Sung's life into line with changing times and attitudes, in an era when humans no longer need to struggle constantly with nature merely to survive, will the modern Wu Song occasionally feel nostalgia for an age when for his own survival and honor, he battled barehanded with the tiger—an age of valor? □

(Chang Chin-ju/tr. by Robert Taylor/
first published in February 1995)

* * *

再看我一眼——虎鞭的玄機

Taking Another Look at Tiger Penises

文・張靜茹

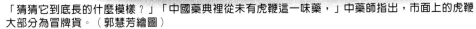

「猜猜它到底長的什麼模樣？」「中國藥典裡從未有虎鞭這一味藥，」中藥師指出，市面上的虎鞭大部分為冒牌貨。（郭慧芳繪圖）
"Guess what it really looks like?" Doctors of Chinese medicine point out that the medical classics make no mention of tiger penis. Most of the marketed tiger penises are impostors. (drawing by Ada Kuo)

虎鞭或牛鞭？消費者可要瞪大眼睛，瞧個仔細！（王煒昶攝）

Buyer Beware. Is it a tiger penis or bull penis? (photo by Wang Wei-chang)

　　或許事涉老虎「隱私」，因此當英國保育團體EIA以十幾年前的影片指證臺灣每年仍然進口老虎、大啖「虎鞭」時；卻沒有人懷疑老虎已如此稀少下，臺灣到哪裡進口「那麼多」虎鞭？

　　三月廿八日出版的美國「時代」雜誌一篇報導老虎的文章提到，富裕的臺灣人付三百美金喝一碗虎鞭湯，因為他們相信如此可以讓自己如老虎般強壯，文中並附有虎鞭照片一張。

　　圖片上黑褐色的虎鞭，卷曲如腸，尾端則帶有許多倒鉤刺，看來，挺能唬人的；只不過中醫師指證歷歷，這張臺灣人吃虎鞭的證據照上，卻是一條「假虎鞭」。

錯把牛鞭當虎鞭？

　　「拿望眼鏡到動物園仔細『觀察』一下老虎就知道那是假的，」中國醫藥學院教授張賢哲說，不論大陸或臺灣，市面上的虎鞭大部分是「沖貨」，賣的人心裡都有數。若以外觀看，假虎鞭往往長度離譜，虎鞭尾端上許多長而明顯的倒刺，是商人以剪刀剪出來的，「老虎生殖器上的倒刺，肉眼難見。」

　　在高雄開業的中醫師許鎮輝說，大部分的虎鞭是由牛或其他動物的腸子偽製的；有一些則是牛鞭冒充。張賢哲認為，別說沒有太多人會花三百美金喝虎鞭湯，以今天老虎之稀少，就算真有人願花錢喝虎鞭湯，「大部分喝的恐怕都是牛鞭湯，」他說自己教中醫、藥二十多年，卻還無緣一見真正的虎鞭。

　　事實上，找遍中國藥典，從來沒有虎鞭這一味中藥，千百年來中醫師從未說過它有特別藥效，現代的中醫師也不會去開這一味藥；虎鞭能「壯陽」的說法，多半是被跑江湖、擺地攤的賣藥人附會出來的。

　　但是想必虎鞭在中、外都太過「隱晦」了，因此大部分的人並不想追究真相，也造成牛鞭假冒的虎鞭，卻被外國媒體振振有辭地攻擊。

再看我一眼！

　　以後想吃虎鞭的人，也許應該謹慎點，不只可能觸犯「野生動物保育法」，若花大錢吃到牛鞭或牛腸子，也未免冤枉；更何況吃了虎鞭是否真能虎虎生風，千百年來老祖先都不曾給予肯定，若吃到牛鞭，「藥效」就更值得研究了。

　　至於EIA，也許他們要以十幾年前的殺虎錄影帶指責臺灣前，應該先拿望遠鏡到動物園去仔細看看老虎？　□

（原載民國83年6月光華雜誌）

Maybe there was so much confusion be-cause it involved tigers' "private parts." When the UK Environmental Investigation Agency (EIA) took a video filmed more than ten years ago as proof that Taiwan still imports tigers and then raised a big ruckus about "tiger penises," how was it that no one doubted how Taiwan could import so many penises of an en-dangered species ?

An article in the March 28 edition of *Time Magazine* about tigers mentioned that wealthy Taiwanese were spending US$300 per bowl of Tiger penis soup to gain the virility of a tiger. The article included a picture of "a tiger penis."

The black-and-brown item in question was curled up like intestines, and its end was barbed. But practitioners of Chinese medicine pointed out what was featured in this picture supposedly proving that Taiwanese ate tiger penises was not the real thing.

The bovine impostor

"Take a pair of binoculars to the zoo to ob-serve a tiger's penis," says Chang Chien-che, a professor at the China Medical College, "and you'll know pretty quick that an impostor was featured in that photo." Whether on the main-land or in Taiwan, the vast majority of tiger pe-nises on the market are all "forgeries." And the sellers know what they're selling. These delec-table dildos are all ridiculously long and capped by dramatic barbs which have obviously been cut by the seller. "The barbs on the reproductive organ of a male tiger are very hard for the eye to see," Chang notes.

Hsu Chen-hui, who practices Chinese medi-cine in Kaoshiung, says that the vast majority of these so-called "tiger penises" are actually fabri-cated from the intestines of cows or other ani-mals. Some of them are actually bull penises, says Chang Hsien-che. And can there be many people willing to spend US$300 for a bowl of tiger penis soup? Even if some will shell out for tiger penis soup when tigers are an endangered species, "What most of them are drinking is bull penis soup." He says that he has been teaching Chinese medicine for 20 years and has never seen an actual tiger penis.

In fact, tiger penis isn't listed in any dictio-nary of Chinese medicine. In the thousands of years that Chinese medicine has been practiced, no one has ever claimed tiger penis has any spe-cial use, and modern doctors of Chinese medi-cine won't prescribe it. The belief that tiger pe-nis increases virility is just an old wives' tale that has been grabbed hold of by medicine peddlers out for a buck.

Because this is a "sensitive" topic for both Chinese and foreigners, most people haven't been interested in actually finding the truth. And so bull penises are being taken for tiger penises, and the foreign media is launching caustic at-tacks.

Take another look!

Perhaps those who want to eat tiger penises should be a little more cautious in the future, not only because they may be breaking the Wildlife Protection Law but because they may be getting ripped off, forking out a pretty penny for bull penis or cow intestines. Never mind the dubious-ness of the claim that they will rise up and roar like a tiger–since no ancient Chinese over thou-sands of years of recorded history ever made such a claim. Perhaps researching "the effective-ness" of bull penis would be more worthwhile.

As for EIA, perhaps before using a video more than a decade old to attack Taiwan, it should first take its binoculars to the zoo for a closer look at the real article.   □

(Chang Chin-ju/tr. by Jonathan Barnard/first published in June 1994)

象牙交易開放了
——保育與利用之間

Trade-Off: Conservation vs. the Ivory Trade

文·張靜茹　圖·鄭元慶

歷經十六、七世紀以
來的浩劫後，大象在
非洲保護區裡安養天
年，族群逐年增加。
至於區外的大部份土
地上，何處覓象群？
圖攝於馬拉威國家公
園。

After the disasters of
the last three
centuries, elephants
have found some
peace in protected
areas, and herds
have grown. But
outside of these
areas, is there
anyplace in Africa you
can find an elephant?
The photo is from a
national park in
Malawi.

過去幾年，台灣在龐大的國際壓力下，已成為世界上管制象牙使用最嚴格的國家。事隔六年，國際象牙禁令卻鬆綁了，台灣似乎白忙了一場。這是象出了問題，還是人的問題？

今年六月，在東非辛巴威舉行的「華盛頓公約」會員國會議上，一百二十三國代表投票，通過將辛巴威、波扎那、那米比亞等三國的非洲象由國際瀕臨絕種生物附錄一類降級為附錄二類，嚴禁非洲象相關產品進行跨國交易的規定，將逐漸放寬。

就在會議通過大象降級不到三個月，台灣又連續查緝到三樁象牙走私案件。其中屏東縣調查站查獲建築商人花千萬元購買的象牙雕刻品，是走私客以佛像、佛珠夾藏方式偷渡進口。不僅類似的走私事件在亞洲頻傳；大象產地國的盜獵事件也層出不窮。去年底，非洲剛果、加彭間就發生近年來最大規模的盜獵，有兩百多隻大象遭到屠殺。

兩百萬個象牙印章！

使用象牙是人類普遍的文化行為，即使不產象的歐洲，從希臘、羅馬時期，象牙雕刻技術已發展極為精緻，象牙從北非經地中海、至歐洲的跨海交易也從未中斷。但本世紀華盛頓公約組織成立後，歐美在野生動物產製品交易的管制日漸嚴格。國際野生物貿易調查委員會的報告指出，近來在世界各國多次大規模搜捕行動裡，「共檢獲五十二公噸、來自二十六國的象牙，其中十八‧八公噸是以亞洲為目的地。」雖然亞洲並非唯一象牙消耗國，但相較起來，消費力強的亞洲國家缺乏交易管制法令，遂成為國際認定的新一波大象終結者。

根據統計，一九八九年，日本就篆刻了兩百萬枚象牙印章，目前日本國內每年仍

In recent years, under strong international pressure, Taiwan has enacted some of the strictest controls in the world covering elephant ivory. Meanwhile, however, the international ivory ban is being relaxed only six years after its declaration, giving the impression that Taiwan has gone to a lot of trouble for nothing. Has the original problem of the elephants changed? Or have people changed their ideas about it?

In June of this year, at the Convention on International Trade in Endangered Species (CITES) conference being held in Zimbabwe, after a vote by the 123 members, elephants in three African countries—Zimbabwe, Botswana and Namibia—were taken out of Appendix I (the most endangered species) and placed in Appendix II (listing less-endangered species). The strict regulations banning international trade in products made from African elephants are to be gradually relaxed.

Less than three months after the reclassification, Taiwan cracked its third major case of ivory smuggling this year. The Pingtung office of the Bureau of Investigation uncovered a case of a construction firm owner who spent tens of millions of NT dollars to purchase ivory carvings. (The items were smuggled encased in Buddhist statuary.) Such cases have been frequent in Asia, as have been cases of poaching in nations that are home to elephants. The largest poaching case thus far was discovered at the end of last year in the Congo and Gabon; 200 elephants had been slain.

Two million ivory name chops

Use of ivory is common across human cultures. Even in Europe, not a source area for ivory, ivory carving was already highly developed in ancient Greece and Rome. The ivory trade from Africa to Europe across the Mediterranean went on uninterrupted for centuries.

However, since the signing of CITES this century, Europe has placed increasingly strict

辛巴威國家公園總部的象牙倉庫，成為「華盛頓公約會議」各國代表參觀的對象。象牙禁售，已在一些東、南非洲國家造成「牙」滿為患。（陳楊文提供）

The storage facility for confiscated elephant ivory belonging to Zimbabwe's national park service was visited by delegates to the CITES meeting held in that country. The ivory trade ban has created a problem of excessive ivory stores for several countries in South and East Africa. (photo courtesy of Vincent Chen)

controls on trade in animal products. A report by Traffic International (a group that monitors wildlife trade) states that large-scale seizures across the world in recent years have netted 52 metric tons, of which only 18.8 tons was destined for Asia. Yet, despite the fact that Asia is not the world's sole ivory-consuming region, the newly developed Asian states, with growing purchasing power and lacking controls on trade, have nonetheless come to be seen internationally as the new "elephant terminators."

In 1989, in Japan alone two million ivory name chops were produced. Currently Japan allows trade of up to 10 tons of ivory for name chops. One person at a large name-chop firm in Taiwan does not even try to deny that his firm has more than 1000 tusks in stock.

High ivory consumption makes elephant herds prey to hunters. As early as 1976, CITES issued a ban on trade in the Asian elephant, of which only 50,000 remained. Though there are still about 600,000 African elephants, it has been impossible to stop poaching and smuggling. In many African countries, elephants are killed for their tusks and then left to rot. In 1989, 103 countries signed an agreement in Lausanne, Switzerland to terminate the existing ivory export quota system.

But with loopholes left amongst the different countries' laws governing ivory trade, poaching

以十噸數量交易中；台灣一家大型刻印店也毫不避諱地表示，庫存的象牙有一千多支，等於五百隻大象所提供！

大規模的消費，使得象群成為獵殺對象，早在一九七六年，華盛頓公約會員國就對地球上只剩五萬頭的亞洲象，下了交易禁令。非洲象雖還有將近六十萬頭，但象牙走私一直未能有效遏止，非洲大陸上許多大象遭獵殺、拔除象牙後曝屍荒郊。一九八九年，一百零三個國家在瑞士洛桑簽約，封閉了原有的象牙出口配額制度。

但在各國象牙管理存有許多漏洞下，盜獵、非法走私並未銷聲匿跡。象牙貿易甚至縮小規模，轉為零散買賣進行。舉例來說，香港居民離境時可攜帶五公斤免課稅手提行李，相當於兩百個象牙印章的重量，每每被利用來偷運象牙。象牙交易牽涉龐大利益，許多國家亦不願配合國際進行嚴格管制。日本就未強制其國人登記象牙，僥倖走私進口的象牙都能就地合法。

誠實有罪？

九○年代以來，台灣更「躍升」為亞洲第一的象牙走私國。野生物調查委員會的非法象牙檢獲記錄中，最近六年以亞洲為目的地遭截獲的大批付運象牙，台灣有七千多公斤，高居日本、中國、香港、南韓、新加坡、泰國七國之冠。

台灣雖是象牙消費市場，但加拿大籍的台北野生物貿易調查委員會主任斐馬克認為，走私數量最高，並不代表台灣是最大市場、最後目的地。事實上，只有台灣連續六年提供完整資料，近三年來其他國家的記錄常是「資料不詳、無法獲得」。

「可以說查緝象牙走私行動在台灣最公開，」斐馬克表示。但正如主管生態保育工作的農委會官員所說，許多加入華盛頓公約組織多年的國家，從未執行法令、甚至不曾制訂國內法管理野生動植物交易。

and smuggling never disappeared. The ivory trade turned to small-scale trade. For example, Hong Kong residents still can take out five kilos of hand-held luggage tax free, equivalent in weight to about 200 ivory chops. This is frequently used to transport ivory. With the large profits involved in the ivory trade, moreover, many countries proved unwilling to cooperate with the strict international standards. Japan has not compelled its citizens to register their ivory, so there is no way to trace smuggled ivory once it is successfully smuggled in.

Honesty is criminal?

In the 1990s, Taiwan has been tagged as the number one ivory smuggling country in Asia. According to Traffic International's records of known cases of ivory smuggling, of shipments of ivory destined for Asian destinations in the last six years, more than 7000 kilos were for Taiwan, more than well-known major ivory consumers like Japan, the PRC, Hong Kong, Korea, Singapore, or Thailand.

However, while Taiwan is indeed a consumer of ivory, the fact that its authorities have uncovered the highest amount of smuggling does not necessarily mean it is the largest market or final destination. This is the view of Marcus Phipps, a Canadian who is director of the Taipei office of Traffic Taipei. In fact, Taiwan is the only territory to have provided complete data for the past six years. Over the past three years in particular, other countries often are recorded as "data not available."

"It could be said that Taiwan is the most open in its investigation of ivory smuggling," states Phipps. Meanwhile, an official at the Council of Agriculture (COA)—the body overseeing wild animal and plant life conservation in Taiwan—says that many long-standing CITES member countries have not enforced the relevant laws, or have even failed to enact domestic legislation governing trade in wild animals. It is ironic, then, that "Taiwan provides information at every session, yet it becomes the focus of attacks."

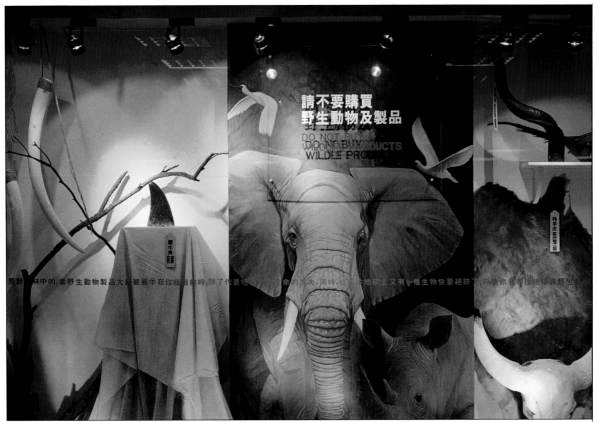

「請不要購買野生動物及製品！」商旅來往的高雄小港機場廣告版如此呼籲。但是象牙的國際貿易就要開放了，到底能不能買？該不該買呢？（張良綱攝）

"Do not buy wildlife products!" implores a poster at Kaohsiung's Hsiaokang Airport. If international ivory trade is permitted again, will consumers buy or not? (photo by Vincent Chang)

In past years, Taiwan has been criticized over rhinoceros horns, tiger parts, and other issues. Thus, the government has strengthened enforcement and amended the wildlife laws, which has led to a drop in large-scale elephant ivory smuggling. "In recent years it has even been common to confiscate small items carried by tourists," says a COA official.

Just as Taiwan has been busy preventing smuggling, the elephant has brought new prob-

lems to the African continent.

Ivory headaches

In a recent Hollywood film, officials and conservationists trapped poachers by making it more profitable for them to try to rob storage facilities of ivory than by poaching elephants in the wild. The film reflects reality. Since the ban on ivory sales, many African countries have found storing confiscated ivory to be a real headache.

「台灣每回提供資料，卻成爲被攻擊的對象。」

過去幾年，在犀牛角、虎骨問題上，台灣備受指責，政府在逐步加強查緝、修改野生動物保護法後，大宗的象牙走私案例已經減少，「近來反而旅客攜帶的小件手鐲、胸花遭沒收的情況較頻繁，」農委會官員表示。

「牙」滿爲患

就在台灣忙著查緝走私，象牙在非洲大陸上卻帶來新的問題。

不久前，美國好萊塢拍了一部影片，片中官方與保育團體竟設法請君入甕、利用「搶庫存象牙比盜獵大象」更有賺頭來誘

騙盜獵者行搶、再行圍捕。電影反映現實，象牙禁售以來，許多非洲國家確已出現「牙」滿爲患的苦惱。

身爲此次華盛頓公約會議地主國的辛巴威，會議之外的活動之一，就是帶著各國人員進入象牙倉庫參觀；南非國家公園也已儲存價值相當兩百萬美金的象牙。根據估計，非洲象牙總存量有五百多公噸之多（相當一萬頭大象象牙）。

除了沒收走私的象牙、打擊象牙交易；南非與辛巴威等東、南部非洲國家大象族群不斷膨脹，是另一個促成象牙解禁的原因。

非洲象族群一度橫跨整個非洲，北由地中海、至南端好望角。撇開人與象更長遠

基隆海關九月中又查獲象牙走私案件。保育團體擔心開放象牙交易，將造成合法掩護非法。（蘇傳槐提供）

Another case of ivory smuggling was uncovered at Keelung Harbor in September. Conservationists are worried that partial legalization of the ivory trade will become a cover for more smuggling. (photo courtesy of Su Chuan-huai)

In Zimbabwe, host of the current CITES round, one of the extra-curricular activities for delegates is to be taken on a tour of ivory warehouses. National parks in South Africa have as much as US$2 million worth of ivory in storage. It is estimated that there are more than 500 metric tons of African elephant ivory in storage (equivalent to about 10,000 elephants).

Besides growing stockpiles of confiscated ivory, another factor encouraging relaxation of the international ivory trade ban is the burgeoning of elephant herds in eastern and southern Africa.

Elephant disaster

The African elephant once roamed the entire continent, from the Mediterranean in the north to the Cape of Good Hope at the southern tip. Leaving aside the earliest relations between man and elephant, it was in the 16th and 17th centuries, when Europeans first penetrated the continent, that the African elephant began to face mass slaughter. After three centuries of killing, the elephant population was devastated. In Cape Town, South Africa, for example, when the government established the national park in 1931, there were only 11 elephants, compared to the historical peak when at least 100,000 elephants roamed the grassy plain.

In the 20th century, African countries have established numerous animal preserves and enacted conservation laws. After World War I, international ivory consumption reached its lowest point, and elephant populations became somewhat stabilized. But the destruction of their habitat and large-scale "recreational" hunting had by then severely scattered and withered the herds.

In the 1970s, as various countries' economies took off, there was a renewed frenzy of ivory purchasing. The African elephant had barely won some breathing space when it faced a new crisis. In 1979, there were still 1.3 million African elephants. By 1987, according to statistics of the International Union for Conservation of Nature and National Resources (IUCN), there were

only about 760,000 head, a decline of nearly half.

While overall numbers were falling however, in the limited areas of the preserves, the populations began to grow. The most famous case is that of elephants in South Africa. At the turn of the century there were only four, but by the 1990s there were more than 9000, of which 82% are concentrated in the renowned Kruger National Park. A 1986 report points out that the elephant population in Kruger Park is growing at 5% per year. And in Kenya, in East Africa, the elephant population is growing at 4% per annum.

Because of the need for agricultural land in Africa, preserves cannot be expanded in size. The elephants—each of whom consumes more than 100 kilos of grass per day—have begun to squeeze out other creatures in the protected areas. The South African government has stated that the enormous "towering baobab tree," of which there were thousands in the park, has disappeared because of drought and damage by elephants. Thus, ironically, even as the elephant is a focus of international conservation efforts, research institutions supported by the international community, working with local governments, have begun so-called "resource management"—culling elephant herds.

Beginning in the 1970s, South Africa began killing about 500 elephants per year. Recently Kenya, Namibia, and Botswana have also begun culling. "Population regulation of elephants will become a necessity during the next century," says an article in the Spring 1997 issue of *Wildlife Society*, published in the US. After protests from animal rights activists, researchers have been searching for a better method of culling than bullets—elephant birth control.

Sales ban kills poaching?

The growth in elephant herds has been a problem for some African countries, and ivory has become a political and economic problem. Because elephants have been forced into rela-

的歷史關係，十六、七世紀歐洲人進入非洲，非洲象面臨了最大的族群屠殺，受難達三世紀之後，僅以南非開普敦灣為例，到一九三一年南非政府在當地成立國家公園，草原上原本至少十萬頭的野象，只剩十一頭。

大象成災

走入二十世紀，非洲國家陸續設置保護區、制訂保護法案；第一次世界大戰後，國際上的象牙消費也降到最低，大象族群才稍微恢復生機。但千百年來棲息地的破壞、大規模的狩獵娛樂活動，已使象群嚴重稀散。

七○年代隨著各國經濟力的飛升，世界上又重新燃起對象牙的蒐購，好不容易喘口氣的非洲象再度面臨生存危機。一九七九年，尚存一百三十萬頭的非洲象，在一九八七年經世界自然保育聯盟「非洲大象與犀牛特別小組」統計，已降為七十六萬多隻，幾乎少了一半。

非洲象總數雖然下降，但是在面積有限的保護區內，大象卻開始增加。特別是在管理制度較健全的東、南非洲國家。最知名的，是南非大象由本世紀初的四隻，到九○年代已增為九千多隻，但百分之八十二都集中在生態旅遊區克魯格國家公園裡。一九八六年就有報告指出，克魯格國家公園象群每年以百分之五的速率成長，位在東非的肯亞，大象也以每年百分之四增加。

由於非洲農地的擴展，保護區面積只減不增，一天消耗一百多公斤糧草的大象，開始擠壓其他生物的生存。南非政府就宣稱，克魯格國家公園裡成千上百的非洲巨樹「猴麵包樹」，因為乾旱與大象的踐躪而消失。也因此，大象縱然成為世人矚目的保育動物，諷刺的是，國際支持的研究單位與當地政府，不得不進行所謂的資源

tively dry land unsuited to agriculture, elephants looking for water often trample farmland, sparking battles between man and beast. Many Kenyans complain that they get no compensation when elephants or other protected animals damage their crops. In 30 years, Zimbabwe has culled 40,000 elephants, but the herds have still doubled in size. The Zimbabwean government has declared that, to protect vegetation from destruction, it can only keep about 30,000 elephants, but the population has grown to 66,000. Elephants there have often been known to chase and threaten people, and local residents have little choice but to fight back. Conflicts between man and animal have come to be seen as the most serious problem in elephant conservation.

Thus the CITES decision to ban ivory sales has been assailed for taking only the elephant into consideration, while neglecting other species, including people. It is not only divorced from reality, it goes against the interests of local residents, exacerbating the friction between elephants and Africans.

In colonial times ivory was a major source of income for African countries. Today, countries that are host to elephants likewise see ivory as an economic asset. One Zimbabwean economist, Brian Child, estimates that Zimbabwe has lost about US$4 million per year during the period of the ban. Thus Zimbabwe has applied to the World Trade Organization asking for compensation.

When there are no ivory revenues, in many countries the budget for elephant conservation is sharply cut. It costs a minimum of US$200 per square kilometer to properly maintain the environment and protect the animals; today actual expenditure is less than 5% of this amount. The dissolution of the conservation net deepens the crisis. In the Garamba National Park in the Central African Republic, the number of elephants poached has doubled since the ivory ban went into effect.

In order to increase revenues, the government

of Zaire has disregarded the decisions of international organizations about elephants and has authorized trading licenses for ivory dealers. While foreign donor organizations asking for donations argue that the ban on international trade in ivory stops poaching, they are wrong, says a report by Traffic. Leaving aside for the moment the economic and legal problems it creates, in purely conservationist terms a ban on ivory sales may actually encourage illegal trading.

Use them or lose them?

In Africa and Asia, it is counterproductive to try to prevent local people from exploiting their natural resources to improve their livelihoods. It does not stop the process of the deterioration of the environment, and it generates local resentment. Thus international conservation groups have been reassessing their actions. "The only way people will treasure and protect their resources, and engage in long-term management of them, is if control of their conservation is placed in the hands of local people and the resources are shown to be of value to the locality." So says Lu Dao-jye, who is currently doing a doctoral dissertation on community conservation. Only by using the assets offered by ivory to promote community-led conservation work can true ecological balance be achieved.

In Africa, the question "Use them or lose them?" has been asked for many years. Botswana, Malawi, Namibia, and Zimbabwe have formed an organization to lobby to restore trade in ivory-related products. "Elephants need water, but people also need water," said Zimbabwean president Robert Mugabe in his opening remarks to the CITES meeting. "Every creature must exist in its own way. For developing countries, natural resources give us hope for future development," he said in encouraging the shifting of the elephant to the less protected level of Appendix II.

The Campfire program being implemented in Zimbabwe has offered confidence to the international community. In the past, the benefits from the sale of elephant products did not accrue to the locality. Today, as Zimbabwe culls from the herds in preserves, more than 20 villages have been given permission to sell elephant meat to increase village incomes. Also, foreign tourists are being taken on elephant hunts, and fee-earning commercial activities are being undertaken. The fact that both the central government and the localities benefit from the Campfire program offers hope to the economically weak countries of Africa.

Similarly, there is increasing international acceptance of the idea of permitting controlled trade, using the sale of elephant ivory to guarantee revenues, and using the revenues to guarantee the continued existence of the elephant. Not only will this undermine the black market, it can convince various governments to proceed with conservation, said a 1995 Traffic International report entitled "Four Years After the CITES Ban: Illegal Killing of Elephants, the Ivory Trade, and Stockpiles."

Marcus Phipps says: "If you don't give the local people an opportunity to survive, what right do international organizations have to criticize them?" Thus, when Botswana, Namibia, and Zimbabwe (all having relatively large stocks of ivory) proposed downgrading the elephant in the CITES appendices, the majority of countries, for a number of considerations, cast affirmative votes.

Flagship animal

Of course, with the overall numbers of African elephants still in decline, not everyone agreed with the downgrading of this creature's protected status. This is especially so because the elephant, the largest land animal, is immediately impressive and touching to people. It is seen internationally as a "flagship" animal. Large creatures are particularly useful for educational purposes, so that the elephant's fate is even more important as a symbol.

Besides those countries which are actually home to elephants, Denmark, the Netherlands,

經營管理：淘汰多餘的大象。

七○年代開始，南非每年射殺大約五百隻大象，近來肯亞也開始淘汰大象，那米比亞、波札那也將跟進。「大象數量的控制將是下一世紀無法避免的事情，」美國出版的「野生動物學報」春季號裡一篇文章寫道。在動物權人士抗議下，研究人員最新的任務是尋找比子彈更好的方式──嘗試給大象避孕。

「禁售」終結「盜獵」？

象群增長，為一些非洲國家帶來困擾，象牙也成為政治、經濟問題。由於大象被逼至不適耕種的缺水地區，為解決無水之苦，不斷侵入農莊，人象大戰，一觸即發。許多肯亞人就抱怨，當包括大象在內的野生動物破壞了他們的農地，他們得不到任何補償。三十年間，辛巴威曾經淘汰四萬多隻大象，象群仍以雙倍速度增加，辛國政府表示，在該國植被不受破壞下，只能容許三萬隻大象，但是野象已增至六萬六千頭，大象在該國甚至追逐、威脅學童生命，當地人不得不對大象展開反擊。「人象衝突」已被視為大象保育的最嚴重問題。

因此華約組織禁售象牙的決定，被攻擊為「一味以物種、生態為主，」不僅不切實際，也完全忽視當地人的利益，更助長了非洲住民與大象的對立。

尤其非洲在殖民時期，象牙一直是最大宗的收入之一，今天大象分布國家在重整自己家園時，同樣視象牙為重要經濟資產。辛巴威一位經濟學者估計，禁售期間辛國每年短少四百萬美金收入，因此去函要求「世界貿易組織」補償辛國損失。

少了象牙收入，許多國家保護大象的預算首當其衝，遭大量削減，每平方公里二百美金以維持保護區生態完整、動物安危的最低要求，都只剩百分之五不到。保護

Germany, the UK, and the US also have elephant conservation groups. In the UK, the group "Elefriends" has gotten signatures from 1.5 million people. "Elefriend zones" have been organized in many countries to block imports of ivory products. The IUCN created an "African

原始森林成為人類住家，野生動物棲息地銳減，人象衝突的種子早已悄悄埋下。

When people take over primeval forest, animals lose their habitats, planting the seeds of friction between man and elephants.

Elephant Emergency Fund" to subsidize urgent elephant conservation activities.

Thus, both supporters and opponents of the proposal to lift the ban on trade in products related to the African elephant have been very active. And it is hard to ignore the views of those opposed. One critic says that the "old Zimbabwe complaint"—"We have so many elephants here, they are destroying our country, so the ivory ban needs to be removed"—is specious: "There is no connection whatsoever between (a claimed) overpopulation in one country, that may be

網絡的瓦解，加深了大象生存危機，中非共和國薩伊西北的嘉淪巴國家公園，近年被盜獵的大象是象牙禁售前的兩倍。

為了增加收入，薩伊政府甚至不顧國際組織的裁定，照樣核發交易許可給象牙商。「外國的捐錢單位四處演說募款，拯救大象，他們相信象牙禁售可以遏止盜獵，但是他們錯了！」國際野生物交易調查委員會出版的報告指出，拋開經濟、法律等層面不看，就保育而言，禁售象牙的手段可能已助長非法交易。

使用或失去

在人口密度高的亞、非洲，限制當地住民利用自然資源以謀生計，對環境惡化沒有幫助，又造成許多反感與反擊，都促使國際保育組織重新調整步伐。「只有保育的管理權回到當地人手上，讓資源對地方產生價值，才可能進而珍惜、保護，進行長期經營管理，」目前以「社區參與及野生動物保護區經營管理」為題進行博士論文的盧道杰表示，利用象牙開闢的資產增進社區主導的保育工作，才可能達成真正的生態平衡。

多年來非洲也不斷發出：「使用牠？或失去牠？」的聲音。波札那、馬拉威、那米比亞、以及辛巴威就結盟成立組織，積極爭取恢復大象相關產製品的交易。「大象要喝水，人也要喝水」，辛巴威總統穆加比在會議開幕致詞說，「每一物種必需以自己的方式生存，對發展中國家，自然資源給我們往前發展的希望，」他催促各國將大象在保育名錄上降級。

近年來在辛巴威實施的「營火計畫」也給了國際信心。長久來出售大象產製品的利益無法歸屬地方，今天辛巴威在淘汰保護區內暴增的大象之際，已有二十幾個村落被允許出售象肉，增加收入，帶領外國觀光客進行大象狩獵、收取費用的商業活動也再度展開。政府與地方利益均霑的「營火計畫」，給經濟衰弱的非洲國家帶來「光明」希望。

同樣的，國際上也逐漸認同開放一個可控制的交易市場，利用象牙買賣保障財政收入，再將經費用來保障大象的構想，「如此不但可以遏阻黑市，也可贏回各國政府意圖保育的決心。」「象牙禁售四年之後」報告中指出。「不給當地人生存的機會，國際組織又怎有權利批評他們？」斐馬克認為。種種理由，因此當象牙庫存量較高的波札那、那米比亞、辛巴威三國提案大象降級時，大部份國家在更多元的考量下投下贊成票。

旗艦動物

當然，在整體非洲象族群仍持續下降的情況下，將非洲象的保育動物排名降級也並非暢通無阻。尤其搧動雙耳的大象容易打動人心，已被保育團體視為保育的「旗艦」動物，大型動物的高教育性價值，也使大象的保育具有更大的象徵意義。

大象分布國之外，丹麥、荷蘭、德國、英國、美國等已開發國家都有大象保護團體。在英國，「大象之友」組織就獲得一百五十萬人簽名響應；許多國家也聯合成立所謂「象友圈」，拒絕象牙入境。世界自然保育聯盟也早就提供一筆「非洲大象緊急資金」，用來援助迫切的大象保育行動。

因此是否解除非洲象禁令，贊成與反對雙方，台面下動作頻頻。持反對意見者的說法也不容忽視：「辛巴威不時老調重彈：我們有太多大象了，牠們快毀滅我們國家了，象牙禁售法案該消除了！但所有人都忽略了，辛巴威需要除去所謂多餘的大象，與開放象牙交易根本是兩回事！」許多人更擔心開放的舉動，將導致狩獵活動再度橫掃非洲。

六月十九日華約會議投票通過將非洲象由保育名錄中「降級」，許多非洲國家出席代表鼓掌歡呼！（陳楊文提供）

When CITES members voted on June 19 to lower the protected status of the African elephant, delighted delegates from many African countries applauded. (photo courtesy of Vincent Chen)

solved by culling, and the removal of the international ban, which will once more start poaching of elephants throughout Africa."

As one might expect, as soon as the lifting of the ban began to be mooted, there were cases of ivory traders hiring local residents to help them poach, expecting to be able to legally sell their take once the ban is lifted. One Japanese person, writing on the Internet, pointed out that since the ban was imposed, ivory has lost value. If trade is legalized, the price will go up again. Some Japanese business people have already imported ivory at the current price, gambling that they will make windfall profits later.

Many conservationists think people have a duty, on humanitarian grounds, to leave the elephants alone. A group called Born Free has been seeking signatures on the Internet, asking people to write to African governments stating that they will refuse to visit any countries that sell ivory. Because the economic and political situations in the countries of western and central Africa are worse than in eastern and southern Africa, many countries are worried that after the ban is lifted there the impact on the elephant will be much more severe, so these concerned countries also cast negative votes at the CITES meeting.

In terms of distribution, it is not easy to do surveys of the "forest elephant" of the forests of Central and West Africa. It is even more difficult to prevent poaching. Most observers are very pessimistic about preserving the forest elephant herds. In fact, the calls for lifting the ban have even touched the Indian elephant. Staff at the In-

果然，早在開放風聲傳出，就發生象牙商人雇用當地居民盜獵，等著大象降級法案通過後將象牙合法出售。一位日本商人為文指出，象牙禁制以來，逐漸失去價值，如果象牙貿易合法化，價格必會上升，一些日本商家已下賭注買入平價象牙，希望遲些獲取豐厚利潤。

一些保育團體也堅持人道立場，認為人類沒有理由再屠殺大象，「象牙是屬於大象的，應該長在大象嘴裡」。名為「生而自由」的保育組織，就上網路到處聯名，要求大家寫信給非洲國家，表明他們將拒絕前往出售象牙的國家旅遊。由於中、西非經濟與政治情況遠差於東、南非各國，擔心開放後引起更多後遺症，也有國家投下反對票。

分佈中、西非洲森林裡的「森林象」不易進行族群調查，更難防止盜獵，對森林象族群的延續，大部分保育人士都持悲觀看法。甚至遠在亞洲的印度象也受開放風聲波及，野生物貿易調查委員會印度辦公室人員發現，近來印度象遭獵殺數量增加，對只有公象才能長出巨型象牙的亞洲象，恐將加重陰盛陽衰、族群難以繁衍的窘況。

不敢戴出門

因此針對各國不同的情況，華盛頓公約會員國雖通過三個非洲國家的大象降級，但目前只允許一項跨國交易：由象牙最大

非洲國家亟思開拓財源，以養活眾多人口；在地方受到挫折的國際保育組織則希望地方可以管理自己的資源，以達到永續利用。兩者一拍即合，大象降級終於通過！
African countries wish to develop their resources to feed their people. International conservation groups, on the other hand, hope localities can be allowed to manage their own resources to achieve sustainable use. The combination of these two forces has allowed the lowering of the elephant's protected status to finally be achieved!

dia office of Traffic have discovered a recent increase in the number of Indian elephants killed by hunters. For the Asian elephant, among whom only the males grow the valuable large tusks, this creates an imbalance in the number of males and females, making propagation of the herds much more difficult.

You can't wear it in public

Faced with different situations in different lands, although CITES has approved removing the elephant from Appendix I in three African countries, still only one type of international trade is permitted: Trade of nearly 60 tons of elephant ivory between Japan, the largest consumer country, and the three nations which most strongly called for a lifting of the ban. (Japan gets the ivory in exchange for donations to the source countries.)

Moreover, the CITES meeting passed a number of provisos. For example, no international ivory trade of any kind will be permitted for the first 18 months from the day the downgrading takes effect. Also, Japan, the designated importer, may only use the ivory for domestic sale; export is prohibited. If the agreement is not respected, and there is an increase in poaching or trade in illegal products, then CITES may at any time ban all ivory trade. "Traders have a heavy responsibility," declares Marcus Phipps. CITES hopes to create a model for managed trade, and its success will determine whether or not the relaxation of the trade ban will continue.

Though in the short run most countries will not be able to resume international trade, people who participated in the recent CITES session got the feeling that "the next session may discuss a complete opening up of ivory trade." Thus, Taiwan's strict controls are being seen by those in the business as cutting their lifeline unnecessarily. Liu Liang-kuo, who runs the Brothers' Chops name chop store in Taipei, says that the harm is already done. Even if trade is restored, the master carvers have already moved on to other jobs. Some even regard Taiwan as being a

"lesson in what *not* to do."

Has Taiwan really made a mistake? Elephant ivory is a major raw material for sculpture and carving, so many countries, aiming to protect their ivory markets, did not ban domestic storage or sale of ivory. "CITES never interfered with domestic trade in any country," says Marcus Phipps. Putting the elephant in Appendix I aimed to block smuggling, not to completely halt domestic trading.

What's interesting is that many people, including those in international conservation groups, assume that Taiwan has banned domestic trade in ivory. But, clarifies a COA official, "We have never banned domestic buying and selling." So why this impression? Because the government did act to dampen demand for ivory.

Television repeatedly showed a government-produced ad depicting a couple about to be married entering the name chop shop, where they are reminded not to buy ivory chops. Also, whereas in most countries, small items need not ordinarily be registered, in Taiwan, sales of even something as small as an ivory name chop must be registered.

Meanwhile, though trade in long-held (and thus never registered) ivory possessions has always been legal, it's hard for people to prove that ivory items in their homes have all been there for quite some time. So many people concluded that "all unregistered ivory in Taiwan must be illegal." The only choice was to put such objects away, because, as a Miss Li (who owns an ivory-beaded necklace) declared, "if you bring them out they will be confiscated."

In addition, the COA issued frequent warnings that even legal elephant ivory or ivory-based goods may not be bought and sold, nor publicly displayed, "without the approval of local authorities." As a result, an ivory cultural artifacts wholesale market was torn down, prompting a protest by the collectors' association.

Many business people with stores of ivory have felt aggrieved by all this. Liu Liang-kuo

消費國日本，以捐款方式與三國交換將近六十公噸的象牙。會議也通過多條但書，例如在大象降級生效日起十八個月，不得進行任何象牙國際交易；被選定為貿易伙伴的日本，進口的象牙只能國內使用，不得外銷。若未遵守協議，或因此造成大象盜獵與非法產製品增加，大會將可隨時關閉交易之門。「商人的責任重大，」斐馬克呼籲，華約組織希望能創造一次良好的交易模式，成功與否將會決定要不要持續開放。

雖然短期內各國仍無法恢復象牙交易，但多位參加此次會議的人士卻感覺出「下一屆會議可能就會討論全面開放」的氣氛，因此台灣嚴格管制象牙交易，被業者視為自斷生路。在台北經營「兄弟之印」篆刻店的劉良國表示，傷害已經造成，未來就算是恢復交易，藝品店師父都已轉行了；甚至有人形容台灣的反應是「錯誤的示範」。

台灣真的錯了嗎？相較於其他物種，巨大的象牙提供了龐大的雕飾品原料，各國為了保護象牙市場，並不禁止國內進行存貨買賣，「華盛頓公約不干涉國內市場，」斐馬克強調，將大象列入第一類，目的是要杜絕走私，而非完全禁絕。

有趣的是，包括國際保育團體在內的許多人士，都以為台灣禁止了象牙的國內交易，事實上，「國內從未禁止買賣，」農委會官員表示。會造成如此印象，其來有自：電視上重複播放即將結婚的情侶走進刻印店，被提醒不應購買象牙印章；大部份國家，小件物品通常不須登記，在台灣，賣出一個小至印章的象牙製品都須登錄註記，一般人家裡的象牙製品難以證明為舊物，因此許多人以為「沒有登記的象牙都算非法」，只能將象牙飾品束之高閣，因為「戴出去，會被沒收！」擁有象牙珠子項鍊的李小姐擔心。農委會曾四處發出

「合法公告象牙或加工品，非經地方主管機關同意，不得買賣或在公共場所陳列」的公文，還因此發生象牙古物由拍賣場被撤下、遭文物收藏協會抗議的事情。

保有許多象牙存貨的商人更覺「冤枉」，劉良國就說，象牙印章是牛角印章的三倍利潤，三、四年前，店裡一天可以賣出十幾個象牙，如今每個禮拜只能售出一、二個，還常有顧客質問他為何賣象牙印章？根據台北野生物貿易調查委員會的估計，目前台灣每年消耗庫存象牙的百分之五、六，二十年內台灣現有象牙存貨將會消耗完畢。年輕的刻印業者卻說，恐怕到他退休也賣不完庫存象牙。

台灣制訂出來的嚴格法令，真能將所有象牙交易納入管理？「所有的人在騙局中互相欺騙，」文物藝術品收藏家協會理事長、耳鼻喉科醫師洪德仁說，許多人擔心象牙被沒收，不願登記，因此交易都在私下進行。

「制度最嚴格的台灣，卻被認為只是變形蟲，」台北野生物貿易調查委員會計劃主任陳楊文表示，過去台灣對大象實際情況與象牙市場並未深入了解；在國際壓力下制訂出的法令，也被視為遭外界刺激一下、才肯動一下。針對象牙未來可能開放，目前農委會已委託野生物貿易調查委員會修正現有象牙管制辦法，讓其更實際可行。

象牙交易不是唯一殺手

象牙交易的收、放，顯示國人對國家資源、對世界資源都缺乏自己的思考；也顯示在國際壓力下立時反應的保育政策是有問題的。同樣的，六〇年代後紛紛獨立的非洲國家，在經濟與文化更加依賴外在世界的同時，也只能跟隨全球發達經濟、加強競爭力的思考模式發展。

今天國際認為適度開放象牙交易的前題

南非國家公園宣稱：大象太多了！公園裡的「猴麵包」樹慘遭大象摧毀，急遽減少。
South African national parks complain: There are too many elephants! The baobab tree has been severely reduced in numbers due to damage inflicted by elephants.

says that the profit on an ivory name chop is three to four times that of one made from a steer horn. Three or four years ago, he could sell more than 10 ivory chops per day. Today he can sell only one or two per week. And often customers ask him why he even sells ivory chops. According to Traffic Taipei, Taiwan consumes about 5-6% of its ivory stocks per year, so it will take two decades to exhaust current stocks. Young carvers fear that things could get even worse: They are afraid that by the time they retire it will be impossible to unload their stocks at all.

However, though legal trade has been curbed, Taiwan's strict laws have still not achieved the goal of bringing all trade under an open, transparent trade system. "Everyone is deceiving everyone else," says Hung Te-jen, a physician who is also president of the Society of Art Col-

lectors. Many people are afraid their ivory will be confiscated, so they don't register it, but a lot of trading goes on in private.

"Although Taiwan may have the strictest regulations, some see it as just window dressing," says Vincent Chen, program officer for Traffic Taipei. Laws passed under international pressure are seen as temporary responses to external stimuli, but Taiwan in fact does not well understand the real situation and the elephant ivory market. Given the possible legalization of the ivory trade, the COA has already commissioned Traffic Taipei to amend existing ivory control regulations so that they will be more in line with reality and more practicable.

Trade in ivory is not the only killer

Taiwan's experience with ivory controls shows that people in Taiwan lack their own un-

大象遊走、生機處處，南非克魯格國家公園已成舉世知名的生態旅遊區，只是這一首開大象保育成功的典範，也只能以實施家庭計畫——給大象避孕收場。

South Africa's Kruger National Park has become a model nature preserve known worldwide. Yet, the very success of its efforts to protect the elephant means that now they must implement elephant "family planning"—birth control.

之一，其實是富裕國家以不能剝奪非洲住民也要進步、也要追求物質生活的方式思考，因此贊同非洲地主國政府支持的生態旅遊、適度打獵、出售象牙。弱勢民族在目前的經濟體系之下，難以堅持自己的生活價值。例如生態旅遊是否考慮到對地方文化的衝擊？非洲游牧民族並不歡迎外國遊客進入、干擾他們在保護區裡的遷移活動。

雖然有人認為弱勢民族沒有什麼選擇機會，但非洲一位人士認為，非洲大象如果消失，對所有人都是可恥的。非洲與其獨有的自然遺產，不是為了經濟才應該被關心，而是非洲住民的子子孫孫，也有權利見到這些資源在他們面前走過，讚美生命的奇蹟，讚美他們身處的非洲，這也是非

Today, advanced-country thinking is behind the new model being promoted for opening up the ivory trade. It is said that environmentalists in rich countries have no right to deprive Africans of their chance to have progress. Based on this justification, there is approval for local government-supported eco-tourism, appropriate levels of hunting and sales of ivory. It seems that under the current global economic structure, weak nations have no way to maintain an alternative value system. Yet, does something like eco-tourism take into account the impact on local cultures? For example, the nomads of Africa do not welcome outsiders who interfere with their movements in protected areas.

Though some might say that disadvantaged groups have little choice but to utilize their resources, one African emphasizes that Africa and its unique resources should not be an object of preservation only if they can be justified on economic grounds. If the African elephant disappears, this would be a loss for all human beings, but especially for the children and grandchildren of the people of Africa. They also have the right to have these resources right there in front of them, to honor the miracle of life, to honor their Africa, and to retain something uniquely African that all people will admire.

In an essay on the Internet, one African wrote painfully about how today tens of millions of people in Africa think it is impossible for people and elephants to peacefully co-exist. But in Africa today, it is hard to find any harmonious relations between man and nature. Today farmers use intensive methods to raise more cattle faster, further straining declining land and water resources. Unable to use the land efficiently, man is rapidly altering the condition of the African environment. This is destroying ecological diversity and causing desertification, and is the ultimate source of the crisis between Africans and their elephants.

Besides the rapid growth in the population of Africa, with its concomitant tree-cutting and ag-

derstanding of national and world resources. It shows that an environmental policy made hastily in response to political pressure is bound to have problems. Similarly, African countries, which successively gained their independence in the 1960s, are dependent on the outside world economically and culturally, and they can only follow along with the thinking of the economically developed countries.

洲所以值得讓人讚美之處。

一位非洲住民在網路上的文章更沈痛：今天成千上百萬的非洲人認爲人和大象是無法共處的，但在非洲，更痛苦的經驗是，人與家畜一樣無法和平相處。今天的農民讓牛快速成長，造成水土流失與土地更加貧瘠。人類無法有效利用土地，使得非洲自然狀態快速改變，生態單一化、土地沙漠化，才是非洲大象與非洲人生存的最大危機。

除了非洲人口快速成長；伐木、農耕活動造成大象棲息地喪失；包括以歐美爲首的華盛頓公約會員國所屬的經濟體，在非洲的長期拓墾，其實更是大象走向滅亡的關鍵。

近來台灣一對前往馬拉威旅遊的夫婦，在朋友陪同下，參觀了有台灣四分之一面積的茶園；過去，角馬、羚羊、象、犀，提供非洲住民蛋白質，今天土地上代之以成群結隊進口的牛、羊、馬。

保育？養牛？

在六年前象牙交易禁止之前，這樣的困窘早就存在。但國際組織除了把焦點集中在象牙與盜獵，將矛頭指向政治上的弱勢族群；並無力改善人們在非洲土地上的不當利用，象群也只能被關在有限的空間裡增生，最後成爲人們眼中的「害蟲」。所謂的保護象群，結果也只能加以避孕、適量淘汰。這就是大象保育的終極目標？

「寄望象群回復到歷史上的記載數量，已不切實際，」或許正如一份有關非洲象的報告所說。失去的自然，永遠不再回來，除了借紀錄片緬懷壯觀的象群在水草豐美的非洲草原上汲水清洗身軀，套用報告的說法，「非洲象的處境，或許只能召喚每個人都想想：什麼是人與其他生物之間關係的解答？」　　　　□

（原載民國86年10月光華雜誌）

ricultural activities, the clearing being done by economic entities from Europe and America, the leading forces in CITES, are even more critical in the elephant's path to eradication.

A Taiwan couple who recently traveled in Malawi, accompanied by friends, toured a tea plantation there that is one-fourth as large of all of Taiwan. In the past, Africa was home to gazelles, elephants, and rhinoceroses, who provided local people with protein. Today, imported cattle, sheep, and horses occupy the land.

Conservation? Or cattle?

These problems already existed even before the ivory ban was imposed six years ago. But the international community has put the focus on ivory and poaching, and aimed at disadvantaged groups. They have done nothing to change land-use patterns in Africa. Elephants can only procreate and survive inside fenced-in protected zones, ultimately coming to be seen as "pests." The result of this so-called conservation of elephants is birth control and culling. Is this what elephant conservation has come to?

It isn't practical to hope that elephant herds in Africa can return to historical levels, says the report "Four Years After the CITES Ban." Lost nature cannot be restored. But maybe we can do more than just view the images in documentaries showing awesome elephants washing themselves in rivers on the rich African plain. Maybe, paraphrasing the report's conclusion, the situation of the African elephant can cause us to think on the question of what the relationship between man and other life forms should be.　　□

(Chang Chin-ju/
photos by Cheng Yuan-ching/
tr. by Phil Newell/
first published in October 1997)

時不「象」予？

Making Peace with the Elephant

文‧張靜茹

PHALABORWA

克魯格國家公園外的市鎮以一對大象牙作為地標。不擔心象牙被偷？放心，不過是對假牙！（鄭元慶攝）

A town on the outskirts of the Kruger National Park uses a pair of elephant tusks as a landmark. Worried that it might be stolen? Relax, it's not really ivory. (photo by Cheng Yuanching)

73

喜愛象牙是亞洲傳統？中國人卻也說過「太平有象」。

從演化長河來看，人類與大象，是弱肉強食，更是唇齒相依……。

歷史早有明鑑：喜歡象牙是會惹禍上身的。

都是象牙惹的禍？

今日台灣因為消費象牙、犀角等野生物產製品遭「培利法案」修理，就此在國際保育史上留下不可磨滅的污點；三千多年前，商朝紂王寵幸妲己，鑿酒池、懸肉林，酒色荒淫。太史公的春秋之筆也未放過紂王少為人知的另一項罪名──使用象牙產製品。

話說紂王命工匠雕鏤象牙筷子，當工匠帶著精心完成的象箸進宮，先天下之憂而憂的箕子瞧見了，怵目驚心，發此聯想：今天雖只造了一雙小小的象牙筷子，為了與它匹配，必得再造同等珍貴的玉杯，玉杯旁更要鋪滿象鼻、龍肝、鳳髓，緊接著，若不穿上錦衣玉袍、高坐瓊室瑤臺裡享用，又豈襯得出象箸玉杯與龍肝鳳髓的珍貴難得？象牙筷子，是奢侈的開端，是亡國的開始，紂王又豈能共謀大事？箕子想到此，止不住寒顫，拔起腿逃之夭夭了。

《韓非子》與《史記》都記載了這一則「象箸玉杯」的典故。深刻體認「福禍相倚」道理的中國人認為，能夠享受珍貴象牙的人要是不懂惜福，也可能因為象牙惹來無窮後患。諸子百家爭鳴的春秋時代，《左傳》更用「象齒焚身」暗喻人斂聚萬貫錢財，易招火焚身，就如「匹夫無罪，懷璧其罪」的大象，長著一對人見人愛的長牙，得時時提防殺身之禍！

只惜仁人君子對象牙戒慎恐懼，卻不表示社會大眾都能認同。言者諄諄，聽者藐藐，箕子的預言成真，紂王成了末代皇帝

，代之而起的周朝王室，為示隆重，製造象牙酒杯進行春郊獻祭。「先秦時代，以象牙製棋」《辭源》記載了象棋名稱的由來。至於文人手上的象牙筆，直呼「象管」。朝代一路而下，牙雕飾品更是美不勝收，發展到明、清，技巧爐火純青，特別是層層轉轉相疊的象牙套球，雕工舉世無雙。中華航空公司曾借象牙球作廣告，敬告消費者：空服員的細心體貼如牙雕手工般一絲不苟，飛行再遙遠，也能忘掉旅途勞頓。

面對中國淵遠流長的「象牙文化」，在台灣面臨國際保育團體痛擊時，去年中央研究院民族所發表了「象牙與犀牛角──環保概念對中華文化衝激」一文，嚴肅提醒來自異域、不解中國國情的「國際友人」：在物質不豐的中國，以野生動物進補與作為工藝材料已有長久歷史，因此斷不可以劇烈的社會革命手段，而應採「溫和方式進行說服台灣漢族改掉這些不好的行為」。

製造象牙工藝品，是台灣漢族應該改掉的不好行為？

你是我的全部？

無巧不成書，《史記》裡亡國之君無法抗拒象牙筷子；被譽為「西方最偉大的文學創作」《奧德賽》中，參加特洛伊戰爭的伊薩卡國王奧德賽則十分想念家裡乾淨舒服的象牙床。據傳《奧德賽》作者、希臘大詩人荷馬首創象牙elephas一字，正是大象英文elephant的字源。

用象牙稱呼大象，果真是司馬昭之心，路人皆知？都只為古希臘人「沒見過大象走路，也用過象牙產製品」。不產大象的地中海文化，征服了遍地大象的北非，隨著地中海貿易，象牙喧賓奪主，比主子大象先放洋歐洲，「進口象牙」也為西方藝術記錄下每個時代的風格。

過去供獵人「殺伐旅」取樂的大象，在被列入國際瀕臨絕種動物名錄後，成了生態旅遊招徠遊客的主角。克魯格國家公園內，成群的遊客自然不會放過欣賞「造物主最偉大的作品」。（鄭元慶攝）

Once the object of hunters on safari, since being named an endangered species, the elephant has become a major tourist attraction. Inside Kruger National Park, tourists can't pass up a chance to see "Nature's great masterpiece." (photo by Cheng Yuan-ching)

*I**s the love of ivory an Asian tradition? The Chinese have an expression that says that world peace will have a* xiang *(象) which means both "symbol" and "elephant."*

In evolution and in human-elephant relations, it is the strongest who survive. But now, perhaps people and elephants need one another to survive. . . .

From the earliest days of recorded history there are examples which clearly demonstrate that the love of ivory is self-destructive.

All ivory's fault?

Not long ago, Taiwan came under Pelly Amendment sanctions for its consumption of ivory, rhino horn and other wildlife products, tar-ring Taiwan's name in the annals of international wildlife conservation. Three thousand years ago, King Zhou of the Shang dynasty spoiled his concubine Daji with pools of wine and forests of meat. In writing of these events during the Spring and Autumn Period (722-481 BCE), the great historian Sima Qian was also unable to forgive another, lesser-known crime of King Zhou's—his use of ivory to manufacture goods.

King Zhou ordered a craftsman to make him a set of chopsticks from ivory. When this craftsman had finished and brought these exquisite chopsticks into the palace, the responsible and patriotic minister Jizi saw them and was frightened. The chopsticks had set off an unpleasant train of thought: Today, it's only a small pair of ivory

希臘之後，羅馬、基督教、拜占庭，紛紛建立象牙買賣中心、象牙製作坊。接著文藝復興、巴洛克，直到本世紀初，「布魯賽爾和巴黎的新藝術風格興起，象牙結合珠寶金屬，呈現出奇特的矯飾氣質……」西方牙雕琳瑯滿目，無怪乎相較之下，美國出版的《大美百科全書》深感與有榮焉，評曰：「中國的牙雕手工細雕細矣，卻缺乏藝術內涵。」

法國動物史學者也來插上一腳，為產象國打抱不平，認為有最豐富大象資源的非洲是利用象牙最少的國家。證諸事實，今天北非埃及等地出土的牙雕，卻從日用品以至精美器物一應俱全。這又怎麼說？

或許應該說：人類在進化成為地球「統治者」之際，對大象所採取的手段都差不多？

象牙，多少人為你瘋狂

有人形容，對於現生的大象，人類有如造成恐龍滅絕的那一顆大殞石。若將大象的生活史拉長，持平而言，在人類文明興起時，大象早感嘆時不我予。

人類用掉不計其數的象牙，卻自我中心作祟，普及各地圖書室的《大美百科全書》白紙黑字寫道：「象牙的兩大特色是耐久與無其他用途，只適合製成雕刻飾物。」無其他用途？月牙形的長牙對大象恰如雙手，蒙它相助，已絕跡的長毛象掘凍土裡的苔蘚裹腹，非洲象、亞洲象靠它掘地裡的鹽塊補充鹽分，有這一對「工具兼武器」防衛獅子、猛虎，再配合巨大無比的身軀，大象一度稱霸地球。

彼時，人類躲在洞穴，覬覦眼前成群來往的巨大「肉山」，肚子餓了，半人半猿的老祖先赤手空拳、或手持最原始的工具，圍捕落單的大象。象肉之外，石器時代缺乏五花八門的物料，洪荒世界的弱勢族群人類物盡其用、利用象牙，想來極其自

chopsticks. But to match them, the king will need a precious jade cup. Next to the jade cup, he'll have to have dishes of elephant's nose, dragon's liver, and phoenix's marrow to make the table complete. If he doesn't have silk clothing and jade robes to wear, and a magnificent hall to feast in, how can he provide an appropriate setting for such rarities as ivory chopsticks and dragon's liver? Ivory chopsticks are the beginning of luxury and indulgence and the beginning of the end for the country. How can I continue to serve King Zhou? When his thoughts arrived at this point, Jizi felt a chill travel down his spine and fled the palace.

Han Feizi and the *Historical Records* both record the story of the ivory chopsticks. The idea that good fortune and disaster are inextricably linked is etched deep in the heart of the Chinese people. For this reason, the Chinese feel that if those who are wealthy enough to have precious ivory chopsticks don't appreciate their good fortune, they may soon experience the endless troubles that ivory can bring. In the Spring and Autumn Period, the Golden Age of Chinese philosophy, *Spring and Autumn with Commentary by Tso Chiu-ming* uses the story of the elephant's teeth bringing trouble on it to hint at the troubles that the accumulation of wealth brings to people. The elephant, who has done nothing wrong, gets into trouble simply because he possesses something valuable. He has grown a pair of ivory tusks which are admired by everyone, and so must constantly be on his guard against being killed.

It's just a shame that the wariness with which the philosophers and men of learning treated ivory was not shared by society as a whole. They spoke of its dangers earnestly, but the public listened with disdain. Jizi's prediction came true and King Zhou (紂) was the last of the Shang kings. They were replaced by the Zhou (周) dynasty, which, in order to express the grandness and solemnity of certain spring rituals in the countryside, incorporated the use of ivory wine-cups into those ceremonies. As one dynasty gave way to another, the beauty of decorative ivory carvings became overwhelming. Ivory carving techniques developed until they reached a pinnacle in the Ming and Qing dynasties. Particularly in the carving of multi-layered ivory spheres in which layers are carved inside one another, the Chinese ivory craftsmen were without peer. In modern times, China Airlines has even used these ivory spheres in advertisements to imply that their in-flight service personnel are as attentive to the "little things" as an ivory craftsman is to his carving.

China's ancient ivory culture is currently facing a painful attack from international conservation groups. In response, last year the Academia Sinica's Institute of Ethnology put out a paper entitled, "Ivory and Rhino Horn—the Conflict between Environmental Protection and Chinese Culture." The paper was a stern reminder to people of other parts of the world who don't understand the sentiments of the Chinese people. According to the paper, the use of the body parts of wild animals as nutritional supplements and as raw materials for craftsmen has a long history in Chinese culture. For this reason, the Chinese people shouldn't be pushed to undergo a social revolution, but instead "the Chinese people of Taiwan should be gently persuaded to change this bad behavior."

Is the manufacture of ivory handicrafts a "bad behavior" that needs to be changed?

All of me?

Coincidentally, *Historical Records*, with its tale of the king who lost his kingdom because he couldn't resist a pair of ivory chopsticks, is not the only ancient record to mention ivory. The Western classic *The Odyssey* also records how much Odysseus missed his clean and comfortable ivory bed at home. The great Greek poet Homer was the first to use the word "elephas" for ivory which is the origin of the English word "elephant."

From this derivation, it is all too obvious what people's real interest in the elephant was. In the case of the ancient Greeks, they had never seen elephants, instead having only used goods made of ivory. The European side of the Mediterranean

is not home to elephants. The cultures that originated there did, however, conquer North Africa where elephants were common. And as Mediterranean trade developed, elephant tusks went where elephants did not—across the sea into Europe. Imported ivory products also reflected the changing fashions of different ages in Western art.

Following the Greeks, the Romans, the Christians and the Byzantines each established ivory trading and manufacturing centers. Western ivory carving came in all shapes and kinds through the Renaissance and the Baroque. It even carried down to the beginning of this century, of which it is written in the *Encyclopedia Americana* that a new fashion arose in Paris and Brussels, that of using ivory together with precious metal and jewels. It goes on to say that the style has an especially affected air. . . . But in contrast to its praise of Western ivory arts, the encyclopedia says that while Chinese ivory carving was very finely done, it possessed no artistic content.

Robert Delort, a French scholar and the author of *The Life and Lore of the Elephant*, writes that Africa, the continent with the most abundant "elephant resources," is nonetheless the region which least exploits the elephant. But, in fact, ivory carvings unearthed in modern times in North Africa (including Egypt) prove that ivory has been used to make everything from everyday utensils to fine works of art. What can one say to that?

Perhaps one can say that, regardless of their race or tribe, when humans become "masters of their environment" they all deal with elephants in about the same way.

Crazy about ivory

Some people have said that to the modern elephant, humans are like the asteroid that made the dinosaurs extinct. To be fair, if one looks at the history of the elephant on earth, by the time human civilization began to develop, the elephant had already become somewhat anachronistic.

Nobody can say how much ivory humans have used, but from a very anthropocentric perspective the *Encyclopedia Americana* says that ivory has

然。

英文字裡以「象牙婚」讚譽牽手走過三十年的婚姻，就因爲純潔乳白的象牙，與黃金、鑽石等貴重金屬是永不變質、白首偕老的象徵。「世界自然保育聯盟」的資料也稱許象牙是動物世界的「白金」，石器時代就對人類產生價值。

七千多年前中國土地上的「河姆渡文化」就製作了象牙工藝品；在沒有大象的法國，還挖掘出兩萬五千年前克羅馬農人的象牙加工器物呢！原來，人類利用過的象牙還不只是出自現存的非洲象與亞洲象。當今人互責彼此過度掠奪大象，地球上已有將近四百種大象走入歷史。

最早的始祖象起源於六千萬年前的北非，大象祖先曾飄洋過海，周遊世界絕大多數地方，甚至彈丸之地台灣，都挖掘出大象化石。環境變遷、氣候變化，許多出土化石可以解釋，大象的消失也是大自然演化下的必然。

「好象」要當兵？

十七世紀英國詩人約翰·唐稱讚大象是「造物主最偉大的作品」，極思進化的人類祖先自然不會放過這麼好的「資源」。至於通過漫長進化之路，而臻「文明」之境的人類，對待大象更加花招百出，當然也不僅是採「二分法」的只愛象牙、不見大象。

「人類對大象的第一個念頭，就是訓練象來替人們打仗。」考據人與象關係的專家認爲。雖不中，亦不遠？

有人認爲中國象棋另一名稱的由來，正因爲古人揮象克敵。果然，驍勇的殷商戰士直上象背進軍東夷；《三國演義》裡，雲南王孟獲的先鋒元帥騎著大象衝鋒陷陣；以馴象駕車縱橫戰場，在中國就稱「象車」。無獨有偶，能攻善戰的羅馬大將凱撒，也在象背上綁著戰車，入侵不列顛，

only two major characteristics—its durability and its uselessness for anything other than being made into decorative carvings. No other use? An elephant's crescent-shaped tusks are like a pair of hands to the animal. The extinct woolly mammoth used them to dig through the frozen ground for moss to fill its belly. Modern elephants use their tusks to dig in the earth for salt. Their tusks are also weapons with which they may defend themselves against lions and tigers. With their tusks and their enormous bulk, elephants were once the kings of the world.

At that time, humans were still hiding in caves, coveting the "mountains of meat" walking about in herds before their eyes. These hungry proto-humans, half-man and half-ape, empty-handed or armed with only the most primitive tools, might surround and kill a solitary elephant. Given that stone-age man lacked the most rudimentary materials, it was only natural that he would not only consume the elephant's meat, but also make use of its tusks.

In English, an "ivory wedding anniversary" commemorates 30 years of marriage. Pure and milky white, ivory, like gold and diamonds, possesses a material character which doesn't change over time and is a symbol of a long marriage. Data from the International Union for the Conservation of Nature and Natural Resources confirms that ivory is the animal world's white gold, one which had value to humankind as early as the stone age.

Seven thousand years ago in what is now China, the Hemudu culture was already producing ivory handicrafts. In France, where there are no elephants, 25,000-year-old Cro-Magnon ivory utensils have been discovered. The ivory that has been used by humans through history is not all derived from the currently extant African and Asian elephants. While modern people blame one another for recent over-exploitation of elephants, in its history the Earth has already seen 400 species of elephant become extinct.

The earliest ancestors of the elephant appeared in North Africa about 60 million years ago. Ancestors of the modern elephant spread to nearly all parts of the world, even crossing oceans. Elephant fossils have even been excavated in Taiwan. But the Earth's environment and climate changed and the fossil record demonstrates that the disappearance of earlier species of elephant was the result of natural processes.

On the battlefield

In the 17th century John Donne called the elephant "Nature's great masterpiece." How could humanity's ancestors, always seeking to move ahead, resist exploiting such a "resource"? Humans, who have strode the long evolutionary path to civilization, have different ways of treating elephants which, of course, are not limited to a mere love of ivory by people who have never seen an elephant.

"Humanity's first thoughts on the elephant were of how to train it to fight in wars," feels one expert on the relations between man and the elephant. He may not be exactly right, but then neither is he far wrong.

Some people think that Chinese chess, literally "elephant chess," owes its name not to its ivory chess pieces, but to the ancient use of elephants on the battlefield. Fierce Shang-dynasty warriors rode elephants into battle in their attacks on eastern barbarians. In the *Romance of the Three Kingdoms*, generals in the army of the king of Yunnan, Meng Huo, led their attacking troops on elephants. Elephants were trained to pull chariots across the battlefield. In China, such chariots became known as "elephant chariots." Coincidentally, the great Roman leader Julius Caesar also bound military carriages to the backs of elephants and used them to invade Britain. But this was only

出自現代台灣雕刻師手下的象牙球。（歷史博物館提供）
The picture shows an ivory sphere carved in modern Taiwan. (courtesy of the National Museum of History)

只因為更早之前，北非迦太基名將漢尼拔率領軍隊與三十七頭大象，翻越阿爾卑斯山突襲羅馬，兵力遠勝迦太基的羅馬帝國遭到重創，此後不忘教訓，有樣學樣，也驅使「進口象」上戰場。

不過，靠體型嚇阻敵人的大象是素食者，正常情況下，不具殺伐征戰的攻擊性，在殘酷的戰場上也就不甚可靠。象主被殺後，群象無首，軍心大亂，加上受傷及驚嚇，無心戀戰，四處逃命，往往敵友不分踩撞傷人。

來看喔！大象作秀

局限於軀體不夠「靈動」，大象服役在人類歷史上逐漸無疾而終，但人類從未放棄試圖駕馭陸地上最龐大的動物。

在中國，大舜孝心動天，大象也為之動容，前來助耕，雖有異議之士批評後人不應為聖賢穿鑿附會、製造神話；但亞洲象確實被教會農事。古埃及人已發現印度象比非洲象適合作為「役畜」。至於被認為野性難馴的非洲象，人類一樣百折不撓，十九世紀末，比利時國王下令在比屬剛果成立象訓練站，為比國披荊斬棘、拓展非洲內陸貿易。

在泱泱大唐，詩聖杜甫臨場素描受過訓練的大象如何「作秀」：群象舉起雙足異常巍峨，揮動長鼻發出噓吸之聲。巍巍身軀上，象眼如星，閃閃發光。大象小象隨著音樂節奏移動，奔跑如百獸風馳，地面灰塵隨之忽起忽落，引人駐足，竟至萬夫雲集。大象跳舞，可是唐代宴會慶典上的佐興節目。

千年後，蘇彝士運河開通，歐洲商人深入黑暗大陸，將非洲當成供應野生動物的大本營，出售珍奇異獸至世界各地馬戲團、博物館、動物園。遊客也以觀賞造物主最偉大的作品表演金雞獨立、長鼻頂球為樂。動物園裡，兒童不斷興奮的叫嚷聲中

，獸欄裡的大象伸出靈巧長鼻捲食人們手上的花生、香蕉。好萊塢電影公司也不遠千里，把外景營地移置群象漫步、汲水互濺的非洲草原上，藉著影片將斯情斯景傳送到每個家庭。

終日無所事事的歐美大亨，終於將以象取樂發展到「顛峰」。跟隨探險家腳步，有閒階級將開暇與金錢投入非洲的狩獵旅行，爭相以槍械征服龐然巨象，奪得最高榮譽。獵人在滿足了追逐動物的樂趣後，帶著戰利品——象牙和象腿返家，象牙做為客廳擺設，象腿是現成的雨傘桶、字紙簍。

低級商品

正如獵人在非洲殺象為樂，奪得地球控制權的人類，缺乏控制的行為演變成大象劊子手，使用象牙，也就成了保護動物人士口中應該杜絕的惡習。

獲取象牙，原本不一定得大批屠殺活生生的象群，自然老死的大象，象牙長得格外巨大，何況，既有生命，就有死亡，生命不就是互相提供、循環不已？中國有個民間故事，說的是一頭大象載著幫牠取出腳底木刺的恩人進山，搭土挖出數十根象牙作為報答。

「開化」後的人類，物質欲望探不到極限，又是動物世界裡唯一發明出商業拓展的物種，市場一經開創，象牙成為普遍的加工原料，消耗量跟著無止境擴大。「人類為了獵取象牙所流的血，比爭取任何原料時都來得多，」法國出版的《大象——世界的支柱》書中寫道。從腓尼基人來回於地中海經營貿易後，北非大象在羅馬時代就消失了。法國查里曼大帝時期，設象牙工作坊產製聖餅盒、十字架與書面，象牙求過於供，但人類對慈愛天主表達虔敬之心的宗教祝禱飾物豈能缺貨，法國北方海岸的海象也只好奉上雙牙。

after the famed Carthaginian general Hannibal had crossed the Alps with 37 elephants in a sneak attack on Rome. In spite of the Romans' superior military strength, they suffered serious losses in the attack. After such an unforgettable lesson, the Romans "imported" elephants for military use.

But the elephant is an herbivore which relies on its tremendous size to put enemies to flight. Under normal circumstances, it is not an aggressive animal, and on the battlefield, it is not very reliable. If its master were killed, a troupe of elephants would be left without a leader. Losing heart for battle, injured and frightened, they might scatter in all directions, trampling friend and foe alike as they fled the field.

An elephant show

Limited by their relatively clumsy bodies, elephants were gradually "phased out" of military service. But humans did not give up training the world's largest land animal.

According to Chinese legend, the filiality of Da Shun, a legendary Chinese king, not only moved heaven, but also the hearts of the elephants which then began to work in the fields for men. Although some are critical of such stories, saying that people should not get carried away with their legend making, it is a fact that the Asian elephant has been trained to work in the fields. The ancient Egyptians, too, noted that the Indian elephant was more suited to domestication than the African elephant. But even in the case of the difficult-to-train African elephant, failure hasn't deterred people from trying. At the end of the 19th century, the King of Belgium ordered the establishment of elephant training centers in the Belgian Congo. The objective of this program was to use elephants to build roads and open the African interior to trade.

With the opening of the Suez Canal, European businessmen began to penetrate the darkest parts of the African interior. The Europeans treated Africa as their principal supplier of wild animals. Rare and valuable animals were sold to circuses, museums and zoos all over the world where visitors went to see "Nature's great masterpiece"

stand on one leg, a ball perched upon its trunk. At zoos, amidst the excited chattering of children, elephants extended their nimble trunks out from their pens to be fed peanuts and bananas. Hollywood's movie studios weren't far behind, transporting outdoor sets to where herds of elephants roamed and sprayed one another with water on the plains of Africa. Through these films, Hollywood brought the look and feel of Africa and the elephant in the wild to families everywhere.

Wealthy Europeans and Americans with little to occupy their time finally brought "elephant entertainment" to its zenith. Following in the footsteps of the great explorers, the leisured class threw their time and their money into African safaris, competing for the opportunity to "conquer" the giant elephant with their guns and attain the highest "honor." After satiating their desire to stalk wild beasts, hunters would return home with the "spoils of war"—elephant tusks and elephant feet. The tusks would be used to decorate living rooms while the feet would be made into umbrella holders or wastepaper baskets.

Low-class goods

Killing elephants for sport is an example of the "out-of-control" behavior of humans as masters of the planet. The assassination of elephants and the use of their ivory are just the kind of "bad habits" that animal conservationists want to put a stop to.

Originally, the acquisition of ivory didn't necessarily entail the wholesale slaughter of elephants. Besides which, the tusks of elephants that have died naturally of old age are especially large. Moreover, where there is life, there is also death in a never-ending cycle. Why hurry the deaths of the elephants? There is a Chinese folk tale which tells of an elephant taking a man who had removed a thorn from its foot into the mountains. There the elephant unearthed some tens of tusks for the man in repayment of his kindness.

The desire of "civilized" humanity for material goods is insatiable. Man is also the only animal to have developed commerce. Ivory has been a common raw material since the earliest days of mar-

亞洲象裡，雌象門牙不增長，部份地區的公象，門牙也不突出，非洲象牙也隨著絲路進入亞洲，希臘歷史學家希羅多德曾描述「蠻荒異域」埃及攜特產象牙來朝宗主國波斯；畫面一轉，西域蕃國進貢象牙等奇珍異物的隊伍，也曾是大唐盛世宮廷畫家筆下爭相描繪的景象。

直到二十世紀，「西方偉大的象牙雕刻藝術若非沒落失傳，便是淪為低級商品，」《大美百科全書》感嘆西方一種藝術的失落。至於象牙淪為何種「低級商品」呢？十九、二十世紀之交，塑膠尚未發明，歐美撞球遊戲盛行，母象的細長象牙被視為製造勻稱撞球的上好材料；無數象牙也成為鋼琴家手下靈活彈跳的雪白琴鍵，今天護象最力的美國因此一度成為象牙最大消費國，佔世界消耗總量的百分之三十，其中百分之八十來自盜獵！風水輪流轉，今日亞洲靠著傲視國際的經濟力，象牙已從過往帝王貴冑的奢侈品，成為人人都能「一印在手」的日常之物。

化友為敵

總算，人類發現，人口擴增、毀林開荒、無窮的物質欲望，是個連鎖反應，加速大象消失，也威脅自身生存，於是一反專為大象吹奏葬曲，改而鼓吹起阻止濫殺動物的號角聲來。體型龐大的象更被生物學家稱許為「聰慧異常、記憶力驚人、具有正義感……」，品質簡直比人種更優良。美國共和黨不就以大象為「黨代表」？有人說這種演變具有高度戲劇性，但強大的事物被當成神祇膜拜，也非當下愛護動物人士開的頭，產象國長期來依賴大象、進而培養出的情感早傳為佳話。

非洲祖魯人一向視大象為尊崇的代名詞；印度人普遍認為睜開眼睛可以看到大象是幸運的，記錄佛陀前身的《本生經》，提到佛陀曾生成象身，佛教徒也認為摸象有助開悟，今天亞洲一些廟宇中還養著象。難怪有保育人士難掩感傷，認為象群因為棲息地銳減，侵入人類土地，使得人與象化友為敵，「實為東南亞與南亞的生態悲劇。」

中國也是個例子。戰國時代韓非解釋中國「象」字之所以代表事物的外形，因為當時人們已不容易親見活生生的象，只能按其圖想像模樣，所以凡意想事物，都叫做象。當人們發現象竟是「獸之最大者」，更借其比喻包容於天地間犖犖大者如山川日月的種種外形，最後經轉訓為事物的表象。

三千年前亞洲象曾廣佈黃河流域，但東漢末年天才兒童曹沖利用水的浮力得知象重，其時許慎寫《說文解字》，已經說明「象，而出南越」，南方才有大批野象出沒。「曹沖秤象」和「瞎子摸象」都是隨著佛家故事，由保有較多象的南亞傳來。

大陸作家古華一篇寫故鄉湖南嘉禾「二象村」的文章就提到，「說是更早些時候，家鄉的森林裡有大象出沒，孔雀開屏，參天古樹枝頭落滿朵朵彩雲似的金雞。」後來有了人煙，大象、孔雀、金雞只得朝更西、更南邊的山林一路遷徙而去，最終只剩些地名、山名、水名，徒留遐想。

今天全中國野象獨於於雲南西雙版納，屈指可數的兩百多頭象群還具有「雙重國籍」，「當偷獵者的槍聲一響、毀林開荒的黑煙一起，野象就逃往寮國，反之，則逃向中國。」一位作家描述。

太平有象！

由恐龍、大象到人類，此消彼長，說不定是造物主刻意讓生命代謝，讓地球更多采多姿？為此，大象的潰敗，人類或許也不需太過傷感？只不過，倒是可以想想，龐大如大象、巨大如恐龍都會化為塵灰，聰明如人類，能保證自己與造物主永世不

kets, and its consumption has grown continuously. Robert Delort writes that the blood shed in the pursuit of ivory far exceeds that shed in acquiring any other material. The ivory trade was conducted by the Phoenicians in the Mediterranean, but by the Roman era, the North African elephant had disappeared. During the reign of Charlemagne, ivory-working centers produced sacred vessels, crosses and covers for Bibles. Demand for ivory exceeded supply. But it simply was not acceptable that the trappings with which people showed their reverence for their benevolent deity be in short supply, and so the walrus of France's northern coast generously donated its tusks.

As for the Asian elephant, its females do not grow large tusks, and in some regions nor do the males. The Greek historian Heroditus once described how the "barbarians" of Egypt sent ivory as tribute to Persia; and court painters of the Tang dynasty also depicted scenes of envoys from lands to China's west coming to the sumptuous imperial palaces of that age bearing strange and precious gifts, including ivory.

According to the *Encyclopedia Americana*, by the 20th century, where they had not disappeared altogether the West's magnificent ivory-carving arts had degenerated and ivory itself had become a vulgar product. In the 19th and early 20th centuries, plastic had not yet been invented, and in both Europe and America the tusks of female elephants were seen as the perfect material for the manufacture of billiard balls. Immeasurable amounts of ivory were also turned into the "ivories" under pianists' fingers. The world's strongest proponent of elephant conservation, the United States, was at one time also its largest consumer of ivory, taking 30% of the world's ivory production, of which 80% came from poachers. But times change. In today's Asia, proud of its international economic might, ivory, once exclusively a luxury of the aristocracy, is now used to manufacture the sort of name chops used everyday.

Friends become enemies

People finally realize that the increase of human population, the destruction of forests to open up land for farming, and the unlimited desire for material goods are connected to one another. They recognize that the disappearance of the elephant threatens their own survival. The elephants' requiem has turned into a call for a stop to the killing of animals. Biologists admire the giant beast for its unusual intelligence, its excellent memory, and its sense of justice. . . . It seems that elephants are better than people. And isn't the elephant the symbol of America's Republican Party? Some say that this kind of change is dramatic. But taking large animals to be gods is not something that started with the conservationists. Countries which are home to elephants have relied on them for a long time and this reliance has given rise to deep feelings for the elephants.

Among the Zulus of Africa, the word "elephant" connotes respect and admiration. Indians commonly believe that seeing an elephant on first opening one's eyes in the morning is lucky. A Buddhist sutra which records the Buddha's previous lives mentions the Buddha taking the form of an elephant. Buddhists also believe that touching an elephant can help one along the road to enlightenment. In modern Asia, some temples raise elephants on temple grounds. Given these kinds of sentiments about elephants, it's no wonder that conservationists are saddened by the plight of the elephant. Its stomping grounds are being reduced and its encroachments on land used by people are turning one-time friends into enemies. For some, this is a tragedy for Southeast and South Asia.

China is another example. Three thousand years ago, Asian elephants roamed in the Yellow River basin. And at the end of the Eastern Han dynasty, the child-genius Cao Chong is said to have used displacement to weigh an elephant. But at that time, Xu Shen also stated explicitly in his *Shuo Wen Jie Zi* that "elephants come from Nanyue [Vietnam]." In China, herds of wild elephants could only be seen in the south. Stories such as "Cao Chong Weighs an Elephant" and "Blind Men Touch an Elephant" actually came to

中國文字意象豐富，大象溫和、厚重的造型與性格，讓中國人將之與花瓶聯想成「太平有象」。（故宮博物院提供）

"Peace has its sign." In China, in addition to its practical value, the elephant eases the hearts of the common people. (courtesy of the National Palace Museum)

滅？

中國人的「太平有象」說不定誤打誤撞，提供了答案。中國歷代皇帝在寶座之旁，照例會置放金屬製的兩隻象，象背馱著花瓶，諧音為「太平有象」。皇帝至庶民都祈求天下太平吧？

《資治通鑑》上記載，唐朝大和六年，皇帝在延英殿，問宰相牛僧孺，天下何時太平？有何跡象可尋？牛僧孺回答：太平無象。天下太平，並無一定的標準，今天

四夷並未入侵，百姓不至流散，雖非盛世，也算小康，陛下若還要求更上層樓，就非臣等能力所及。太平無象，成了諷刺統治者粉飾昇平的用語。後代皇帝怕遭人恥笑無德「無象」，瓶、象結合成的具體文物「太平有象」，就被隨時擺在王座旁提醒自己——或者，也討個吉利吧！

太平有象，太平有象，沒有了象，人間可還有太平？ □

（原載民國86年10月光華雜誌）

China along with Buddhism from South Asia where elephants still lived.

The mainland Chinese writer Gu Hua, in an essay entitled "Two Elephants Village" about his hometown of Jiahe in Hunan Province, mentions, "People say that some time ago in the forests around my hometown there were elephants, and peacocks spreading their tails, and that the old trees almost scraped the sky, their branches draped in golden birds like colored-cloud blossoms." Later, as people spread through the area, the elephants, the peacocks and the golden birds could only move away into the mountains and forests to the south and west. In the end, all that remained of the animals were memories and the names of some villages, mountains and waters.

In the Warring States Period, Han Fei, a famous scholar, explained how the word *xiang* (象), which means "elephant; image; external appearance" came to acquire the meaning of "external appearance." According to Han Fei, at that time, seeing an elephant with one's own eyes was already a rarity; it was only from pictures that one could know what an elephant looked like. For this reason, any thing that one thought about or imagined was called *xiang*. When people realized that elephants were the largest beast living on the land, the metaphor was extended to include the evident instances of things, such as the appearance of mountains, rivers, the sun and the moon. After more twists and turns, the word came to mean "the external appearance of things."

In today's China, wild elephants remain only in the Xishuangbanna area of Yunnan Province. The herd that remains consists of only 200 or so animals. These elephants have dual nationality. "When they hear the sound of poachers' guns, or when the smoke of people clearing the forest begins to rise, the wild elephants flee towards Laos. Or they flee towards China," says a scholar of animal behavior.

A symbol of peace

From dinosaurs to elephants to people, animals have disappeared and animals have arisen. Perhaps the creator is letting life renew itself, or making the Earth more colorful and varied. For this reason, perhaps humans shouldn't be too saddened by the failure of the elephant to survive. But it's worth thinking about. If the giants of the Earth, the dinosaurs and the elephants can become extinct, how can we guarantee that the intelligent, the humans, will be eternal like the creator?

The Chinese expression "peace has its symbol [*xiang*]" perhaps may inadvertently be turned into reality. Next to the throne of the emperors throughout Chinese history there were two metal elephants. On the back of each was a flower vase. The figures made a play on the sound of *tai ping you xiang*, "peace has its symbol." World peace was something prayed for by both emperors and commoners alike.

In the *Comprehensive Mirror for Aid in Government* it is recorded that in the sixth year of the Dahe period of the Tang dynasty, while the emperor was at his Yan Ying Palace he asked his prime minister, Niu Sengru, when there would be peace in the world and where he could look for a sign. Niu answered, "Peace has no sign. World peace has no absolute standard. Now, the empire is not being invaded by the tribes on our borders. The people are not wandering. While the empire is not at its zenith, it is doing well. If Your Majesty wishes to take the empire to yet a higher level, I fear this minister's abilities are insufficient to the task." Niu's response that "peace has no sign" was later used ironically to speak of rulers who tried to pretend things were better than they really were. Later emperors feared becoming known to their people as no-ability, "no-sign" idiots. The vase and the elephant come together in a concrete expression of the idea that "peace has its sign." Always by the side of the emperor, they reminded him of this—or perhaps just brought him some luck.

Peace has its sign. But without the elephant, can people have peace?

(Chang Chin-ju/tr. Scott Williams/ first published in October 1997)

熊膽——國際保育新焦點

UNBEARABLE
On the Trade in Ursine Gall

文‧張靜茹　圖‧薛繼光

　　目前華盛頓公約組織已將全世界現存的八種熊都列入保育名單，而「熊膽」在中國卻有長久的使用歷史，因為在醫療上發揮功能，今天市場上也仍有穩定的需求。

　　熊膽目前使用情況到底如何？中醫師、藥商如何看熊膽的管制使用？臺灣又如何因應？

* * *

CITES has listed all eight species of bears as protected animals. Yet the Chinese have a long history of using bear gall in traditional medicines. There is a well-established market and steady demand for it.

How is bear gall being used these days? How do Chinese herbal doctors and dealers in Chinese medicine view controls on its use? And what should Taiwan do about it?

繼犀牛、老虎之後，熊已成為國際亟於保護的野生動物，熊膽的交易也因此受到關注。

On the heels of the rhino and tiger, the bear has become the object of urgent international conservation efforts, and as a consequence, the trade in bear gall has attracted notice.

雖然許多國人只聞熊膽之名，但仍有不少中藥含有熊膽成分。圖為熊膽藥材與大陸生產的盒裝引流膽粉。

Bear gall medicines and boxed "drained gall powder" from the mainland. While many ROC citizens' knowledge of bear gall may go only as far as having heard of it, it is an ingredient of many traditional Chinese medicines.

在去年十一月的華盛頓公約組織會議上，三年前燃起臺灣犀角戰役的英國環境調查協會，毫不留情地批評臺灣保育努力仍然不足外，更提到臺灣公然非法銷售熊膽。被列入華約組織附錄名單的熊，按規定不應販賣、公開陳列相關產品；但在他們查訪臺灣的六十家中藥店中，就有四分之一的中藥店賣熊膽。

有人擔心臺灣中藥店的熊膽，會成為國際保育組織作秀的新目標；不過，這次政府處理熊膽的腳步卻與犀角有一些不同。

針對還未引起軒然大波的熊膽，除農委會已訂出熊膽管理辦法，衛生署去年初也發函給中醫師，要求不再開具含有熊膽的藥方；並請中國醫藥學院進行熊膽存量調查；衛生署更引進辨識真假熊膽的技術，希望能確實掌握國內熊膽真正存量；近來更邀集中醫、藥各界，商討用完現有熊膽存量的時間表。

看來在處理熊膽事上，我們已設法建立一個好的模式；不過比之犀角、虎骨的管制，熊膽問題卻更複雜，也很難說服中醫師、藥商，甚至許多國人。

熊膽，點名了！

雖然包括貓熊、北極熊、黑熊、棕熊等全世界八種熊科動物都在華約組織的保育名單內，但並非全部都被歸在第一類（瀕臨絕種類）——除了研究、學術的使用，嚴禁國際性的商業交易。

At last November's meeting of CITES, the British Environmental Investigation Agency (EIA), which had played the leading role in sparking the rhino horn controversy here three years ago, mercilessly attacked Taiwan's conservation efforts as insufficient, noting that Taiwan allows bear gall to be sold and displayed openly, in violation of the law. Though all species of bears are protected, an EIA survey of 60 herbal pharmacies in Taiwan revealed that one-fourth sold bear gall.

People worry that the bear gall in Taiwan's herbal pharmacies will become the next target for attacks by international conservationists. But this time around the government is taking a different tack.

Working to avert a crisis, the Department of Health has gone well beyond regulations controlling bear gall's use set by the Council of Agriculture. Early last year the department sent letters to Chinese herbal doctors, asking them to stop prescribing ursine gall altogether. Commissioning professors at China Medical College to proceed with a study about the amount of bear gall stockpiled in Taiwan, it introduced technology to distinguish the genuine from the ersatz. Recently the department invited Chinese herbalists and pharmacists to discuss a timetable for finishing off existing stocks.

Regarding bear gall, Taiwan has established a good regulatory model. But controlling the use of bear gall presents many more difficulties than restricting the use of rhino horn and tiger bone, and it will be much harder to convince Chinese herbal doctors, pharmacists and many citizens to obey such regulations.

A roll call for bear gall

Although all eight species of bear are on CITES protected lists, only seven (including the panda, polar, and Asian black and brown bears) are on the first list (the endangered species list), which bans all trade in them except for purposes of research.

The American black bear is the exception. With a population estimated at 500,000, it, unlike other bears, is not threatened with imminent extinction, and the US and Canadian governments permit hunters to kill 40,000 black bears a year. They once even allowed export of bear gall to such Asian markets as South Korea, mainland China, Japan, Hong Kong and Taiwan.

The year before last CITES put the North American black bear on its second list. Unlike endangered animals, these can be exported and imported as long as they have proper papers attesting to their origins. But conservation groups have recently been pushing to get the species moved up to the first list, so as to bring about an outright ban on the bear trade.

Asian black and brown bears, found mostly in mainland China and North Korea, are the biggest source of gall. Because both places have a tradition of using bear gall in medicines, they long ago began raising bears in captivity and attaching tubes to extract their gall, producing so-called "drainage gall." But since all Asian bear species are endangered, international trade in drainage gall from bear farms is illegal.

As Chinese pharmacists see it, Westerners get thrills from hunting American black bears but try to prevent Asians from treating illness with bear gall, whose medicinal effects have long been documented and which can be drained without threatening the bear's life. At the root of the problem they see racism.

Also part of Western medicine

According to Tang dynasty medical documents, bear gall was then already commonly used to treat illness. In traditional Chinese medicine, bear gall has a wide range of applications for both serious and minor ailments—from use in first aid to eliminating toxins, protecting the liver, and treating stomach ailments, diarrhea and jaundice.

Yet in Taiwan today, Western medicine has eclipsed Chinese medicine in importance, and while many Taiwanese may have heard of bear gall, they may know little of what it does. According to Department of Health statistics, there are more than 19 different registered medicines that

例外的是北美黑熊。由於估計現存野外數量仍有五十萬隻，絕種壓力不如其他熊危急，地主國美國與加拿大仍准其國人每年獵殺四萬頭，也曾經允許出口熊膽到南韓、大陸、日本、香港、中華民國等亞洲國家。

前年華約組織將北美黑熊列入附錄第二類（珍貴稀有類），和保育第一類不同的是，按規定只要有華約組織與進、出口國政府同意文件，來源清楚，仍可出口；但保育團體近來卻運作希望將之升級為第一類，好徹底根除熊產製品的貿易行為。

此外，熊膽最大宗來源是亞洲黑熊與棕熊，主要產地大陸與北韓，由於都有熊膽這味傳統藥材，多年前就進行人工養殖，以導管引流活熊膽汁，生產所謂的「引流膽」。但亞洲熊都被列在保育第一類的名單上，因此國際上買賣取自養殖場的引流膽，仍被視為非法行為。

在中藥商看來，西方仍維持獵殺北美黑熊取樂，卻運作要讓亞洲不能使用熊膽治病，可以說是根本上的歧視，至於禁止不直接傷及熊生命的引流膽，看起來更沒有道理。更何況熊膽的有效成分早經證實。

西藥也有它

根據唐朝《藥性本草》記載，當時熊膽已被普遍用來治病，在中醫傳統上，熊膽被視為涼性藥品，效用廣泛，不論重症、輕疾，從急救到健胃、解毒、寶肝，治瀉痢、黃膽病都能派上用場。

今天臺灣看西醫的人遠遠超過中醫，許多人對熊膽也只聞其名，但根據衛生署統計，現有許可證照的藥品中，還有十九種含有熊膽。除了腸胃藥粉，電視廣告常出現預防小孩感冒、受驚，和助鎮靜的八寶散，開放大陸探親後，成為家家必備、傷筋勞骨一擦即減輕痛症的「正骨水」，都多多少少含有熊膽成分，今天它更被用來與麝香等藥材，做成五寶散，治療肝病、癌症。

在西方還懷疑犀角、虎骨的療效時，同樣受中藥文化影響深遠的日本，卻在一九二七年就由熊膽中分離出具有療效的特殊成分「脫氧熊膽酸（UDCA）」。

一九五五年，東京TANABE公司由牛膽中合成此一成分，並開始生產具有治療肝病、消化器官，以熊膽為藥名的URSO。一九七○年代，日本與德國共同證實該藥對治療膽結石的效能，今天西醫已普遍以其代替開刀。

可惜成分純、藥效強、價格便宜的URSO，已經不被視為中藥。自然物的熊膽，成分複雜，發揮功能的也不只是單一成分，而且中醫治療觀念強調自然、緩和，開的藥劑都為複方，URSO這種單一使用的合成藥，並未能取代熊膽。

黑熊進了山產店

當然，熊族因為有一顆與眾不同的膽，在亞洲面臨的滅種壓力也並未解除。

以臺灣本身為例，師大生物系教授王穎在一九八五至一九八八年進行山產店調查，曾在十家店裡發現總共九十幾隻熊待處理的膽、骨頭、肉和皮，在師大探訪的九十幾個獵人中，超過一半表示他們獵捕過黑熊。

一九八九年臺灣通過野生動物保育法後，仍然出現零星的獵捕紀錄，一九九○年拉拉山就有三隻黑熊被捕殺後取走熊膽。去年臺灣還召開了一場稀有動物臺灣黑熊的保育研討會。

許多熊膽消費地由於不產熊或自家的熊減少，必須由國外進口熊膽，也加重非消費國家的獵捕壓力。一個熊膽不過三、四兩重，根據國貿局資料統計，一九七九到八四年間，臺灣曾經由泰國、加拿大進口六千多公斤的熊膽。

今年初保育團體曾在臺北舉辦保護野熊活動，圖為保育團體展示大陸將熊關在籠內抽取膽汁的模型。（關懷生命協會提供）

This exhibit of how mainland farms cage bears to drain their gall was shown at one of the "save-the-bears" activities sponsored by conservation groups in Taipei early this year. (photo courtesy of Life Conservationist Association of ROC)

use bear gall as an ingredient, including powder for the digestive tract, the "Papaosan" children's sedative and cold medicine advertised on television, and the "Chengkushui" ointment (said to relieve sore bones and muscles on touch) that has appeared in medicine cabinets all over the island since the mainland was opened to travelers from Taiwan. All of these contain some amount of bear gall. Today bear gall is also combined with musk and other medicinal ingredients to make "Wupaosan," which is used to treat liver disease and cancer.

While Westerners have questioned the medical effects of rhino horn and tiger bone, the Japanese, with a long tradition of using Chinese medicine, were able in 1927 to isolate an active medicinal component of bear gall: ursodeoxycholic acid (UDCA).

In 1955 the Tanabe company of Tokyo started using cow's gall to synthesize UDCA, which it used to make a medicine to treat liver disease and problems with the digestive tract. They called the product "Urso," a shortened version of the scientific name. In the 1970s Japan and Germany jointly proved its effectiveness in treating gall stones, and now Western doctors commonly prescribe the drug instead of operating.

Unfortunately, though it is pure, effective and cheap, the Chinese don't consider Urso to be Chinese medicine. The ingredients of bear gall are very complex, and doctors of Chinese medicine believe that no one of its components can bring the intended effects. Furthermore, traditional Chinese medicine stresses natural, gradual solutions, and

在各種亞洲熊日愈減少後，如今北極熊也成了熊膽的來源。（張良綱攝）

With all species of Asian bears on the decline, even the polar bear has become a source for gall. (photo by Vincent Chang)

　　去年六月，「美化環境基金會」執行長丁天奎至越南進行國人在當地消費山產的調查，在河內專門販賣野生動物產製品的街上，他詢問是否有熊膽出售，商店老闆立刻表示：「如果需要量不是太多，二十個以內可以馬上給你。」

它來自四方

　　雖然熊的銳減，不只是因為過度獵捕，獵熊的目的也不只為了熊膽，熊掌、熊皮等市場交易仍然存在；但熊膽長期作為傳統藥材，一直有一定的需求量。

prescriptions are always combinations of ingredients. A single medicine like Urso cannot take the place of bear gall.

Bears in the game shops

And of course the drug has done nothing to resolve the problem of bears being threatened with extinction in Asia because of their extraordinary galls.

Take Taiwan. Wang Ying, a professor of biology at Taiwan Normal University, carried out a study of wild game shops from 1985-1988. In ten shops he found the galls, bones, meat and skins of some 90 bears. Of the more than 90 hunters interviewed by the university, more than half admitted to having hunted bear.

Even after the Legislative Yuan passed the Wildlife Conservation Law in 1989, there have been scattered reports of hunting. In 1990 three dead bears were found on Lala Mountain. Hunters had killed them and removed their galls. Last year Taiwan held a seminar about protecting the rare Formosan black bear.

Many consuming nations have to import bear gall, because they either have no bears from which to take gall or harvest insufficient quantities of it. This puts greater pressure on the bear populations of non-consuming nations. A bear gall weighs about 150-200 grams, and Board of Foreign Trade statistics for 1979-84 show that Taiwan imported more than 6000 kilograms from Thailand and Canada.

In June of last year the administrative director of the Beautiful Taiwan Foundation, Ting Tien-kuei, went to Vietnam to carry out a survey on Taiwanese consumption of wildlife there. On a street in Hanoi lined with wild game shops, he asked a shop owner if he could buy some bear galls. The immediate reply: "As long as you don't want too many. I can give you 20 right now."

From all over

Of course the sharp decline in bear populations is not just a result of overhunting. And hunters aren't only after the galls: There is also a market for bear paws and bear skins. But ursine gall has long been used as an ingredient in traditional medicines, and demand has been constant.

In one report, the World Wildlife Fund noted that with great economic growth in Asia and with liver cancer in some Asian countries running at thirty times or more Western rates, "The next ten years will be critical to the fate of many bear populations in Asia." Perhaps CITES has had no choice but to put these Asian bear species on the endangered list.

As the number of bears in Asia have decreased, the price of bear products has risen. And now CITES has found that with the single exception of the panda (the most endangered bear with a population of only about 1000) all species are slaughtered to supply the trade in gall—even the polar bear.

Recently North American governments have discovered that for every bear hunted and killed legally there, another is poached. And though some Westerners eat bear meat and collect bear teeth and claws, many dead black bears have been found in North American conservation areas with their galls and paws missing. Last year authorities in Northern California arrested three Koreans for taking a bear's gall and paws without licenses. It was the 35th American black bear they had poached in recent years.

Soon to be endangered

And so America worries that Asian demand for bear parts is causing large-scale poaching of North American bears. Last fall the first "International Symposium on Bear Parts for Medicinal Use" was convened in Seattle, and both mainland China and Taiwan were invited to attend. At the conference, a Canadian police dog trained to sniff out bear gall gave a demonstration of its skills, showing just how seriously the Canadians regard bear gall smuggling.

CITES hopes that putting the North American black bear on its second list will help to keep the trade in bear gall visible and prevent the growth of a black market, a World Wildlife Fund report notes. But too many businessmen are willing to

「世界野生動植物基金會」一份報告指出，由於亞洲經濟日愈飛昇，一些亞洲國家的肝癌罹患率又是西方國家的三十幾倍，「未來十年將會是亞洲許多熊族生死最關鍵的十年。」這也使得華約組織不得不將亞洲熊都列入保育名單。

在亞洲熊數量漸減，價格劇升後，根據華約組織所屬的野生動植物產品鑑別機構發現，如今除了被視為情況最危急、只剩一千隻的貓熊，包括北極熊也都成了熊膽的來源。

北美黑熊要升級

近來北美政府也發現，被盜獵的黑熊數量，不少於合法獵捕的黑熊，也就是說只要有一隻北美黑熊被合法獵捕，平均就會有一隻被盜獵。雖然西方也喜愛收集熊牙、熊爪、吃熊肉，但北美許多自然保護區，常出現少了膽與掌的黑熊殘骸。去年九月，加州政府就在加州北部逮捕了三位沒有打獵執照的韓國人正割取熊膽、熊掌，而那已經是他們近年來非法打死的第三十幾隻黑熊。

美國因此懷疑，因為亞洲國家對熊器官的需求，才會產生北美黑熊被大量盜獵，於是去年曾在西雅圖召開「熊產製品醫療使用會議」，大陸、臺灣都被邀請參加。會場上加拿大保育警察甚至展示能嗅聞、辨別熊膽的警犬，顯示走私熊膽在該國已被重視。

世界野生動植物基金會的報告指出，華約將北美黑熊列入第二類，就是希望熊膽交易能透明化，杜絕黑市。如今商人卻捨正途不由，加上擔心其他已禁用的熊膽被魚目混珠，「偽裝」成合法的北美熊膽販售；保育團體也憂慮開放北美熊膽外銷，將造成市場大量需求，加速北美黑熊走上亞洲熊的後路。西雅圖會議上，就有人建議不如把北美黑熊也升級為保育名錄中的第一類，完全禁止出口。

主管進出口交易的國貿局就表示，「中藥商要有心理準備。」亞洲國家既然將自己資源消耗殆盡，只得受制於人。

只管國際交易

但看來矛盾的是，如果真要徹底保護野熊，華約組織為何不乾脆阻止北美獵殺黑熊？為何焦點只對準熊產製品的國際交易？許多人不了解，今天在國際上對生態保育最有影響力的華盛頓公約組織，成立的宗旨是只針對影響到野生動植物生存的國際貿易行為，進行調查、限制。

尤其自然資源往往牽涉到地方的生計問題，如果地方可以透過科學的調查，合理的利用，讓資源與人共存，華約並不願意多加干涉。

每年被合法獵捕四萬隻的北美黑熊，是當地政府在估算過幼熊出生率可以替補下，達到所謂永續利用的決策，獵人更須遵守嚴格的規範，和付昂貴的費用，才能擁有打獵執照。

「臺北野生物貿易調查委員會」專案負責人盧道杰表示，目前華約唯一涉入地主國進行保育的動物只有犀牛，因為犀牛族群已經無法自然延續，相關製品如犀角的黑市交易又仍然存在。

因此，早期大陸發展熊養殖場，抽取引流膽汁使用，國際並未多加置喙，但大陸開放後，各地中藥商紛紛前往購買熊膽，當地熊場因應市場需求，大量增加，國際保育團體的關切也隨之而來。

黑熊、白熊，都是野熊

今天大陸熊場已分散各省，由東北到雲南、廣東，不分國營、民營，規模有上百隻到幾十隻，根據估計，目前大陸一共養有八千到一萬隻熊，未來的目標將飼養到四萬隻。

deal under the table. Environmentalists fear that unscrupulous traders will only be too happy to sell illegally poached bear gall of endangered species as legally hunted American black bear gall. And the United States and Canada also worry that open export of bear galls will create a greater market demand, speeding up the day that the American black bear follows the tracks of its Asian cousins toward real endangerment. At the Seattle meeting some people suggested that it might be best to put the American bear on the endangered list now, tearing the bear gall trade out at its roots with a total ban.

The ROC Board of Foreign Trade, responsible for overseeing imports and exports, warns, "The Chinese medical community should be prepared." The matter is beyond Asians' control only because Asians have exhausted their own natural resources.

A focus on foreign trade

But there seems to be a double standard. If CITES really wants to protect bears, then why doesn't it outlaw the hunting of bears in North America? Why does it put the focus only on preventing international trade in bear products?

Many people don't understand that CITES, the conservation organization with the greatest international power, usually confines itself only to the effects of international trade in wildlife.

Natural resources frequently involve local livelihood. If a nation conducts its own scientific surveys and ensures reasonable use—so that man peacefully co-exists with nature—then CITES won't interfere.

The 40,000 bears hunted legally every year in North America are what governments there think can be killed while sustaining a steady population through new births. The hunters have to respect very strict hunting guidelines and pay a heavy license fee.

Lu Dau-jye, a task force member for the Taiwan office of TRAFFIC (Trade Records Analysis of Flora and Fauna in Commerce), points out that only once—in the case of the rhino—has CITES

大型動物往往成為自然環境破壞的第一波受害者，各地也風起雲湧般出現護熊運動，圖為國際保育團體發行的護熊標誌。

The bear protection symbols used by international conservation groups as "save-the-bears" activities sweep the world. Large animals are always the first to suffer from environmental destruction.

expanded its concern from trade to domestic conservation policies. The rhino is an exception because its population can no longer be maintained naturally and because black-market demand still exists for its horns and other body parts.

And so, when the mainland opened farms to drain gall from live bears, the international community at first didn't have much to say about it. But after Taiwan relaxed restrictions on visits to the mainland, suppliers from all over the island

有別於取自熊的完整熊膽──中藥商稱爲正膽，引流膽缺乏正膽中的三種有效成分，中藥商也證實引流膽藥效較差；但引流膽價錢只有正膽十分之一，若非急症，業者與病患也逐漸接受。

傳統上，中藥爲避免取自自然的藥材被趕盡殺絕，和來源取得容易，人工養殖原本就很平常。已經退休的中國醫藥學院教授許喬木所寫的中藥書中，甚至教人如何養殖海馬、蛤蚧等動物藥材，如今鹿茸、麝香也多取自養殖族群。

華盛頓公約組織也有規定，保育第一類的野生動物，若經人工繁殖，可以將繁殖部分劃歸第二類，經過申請、核准後即可進行國際交易。

去年在北京舉行的第三屆東亞野熊會議上，大陸就提到將向華約組織申請讓熊場的熊，降爲可以交易的第二類，國內中藥商也抱著引流膽能夠合法使用的希望。

一隻抵三百隻？

可是大陸養殖場熊的來源卻不斷遭到質疑。雖然大陸標榜養一隻熊抽取膽汁，終其一生生產的膽汁量等於三百個熊膽，也就是救了三百隻野外的熊。但野熊的人工繁殖不易進行，「大陸農場熊的主要來源還是由野外抓來的，」參加西雅圖「熊產製品醫療使用會議」的衛生署藥政科長江雙美表示。

盧道杰也表示，人工養殖的野生動物必須不影響到野外族群，華約組織才可能同意讓養殖的熊降級。

大陸爲強力推銷引流膽，在藥材市場需求飽和後，又生產熊膽洗髮精、熊膽茶、熊膽酒等等非醫療商品，更引起保育組織反感。曾經前往大陸進行熊場訪問的「地球信任組織」代表張念蘇表示，許多熊場掛著巨大廣告招牌，並提供新鮮膽汁讓觀光客當場生飲。

crossed the strait to purchase bear gall. To meet a growing market demand, the number of farms grew, as did the attention they were attracting from international conservation groups.

They're all wild bears

Today farms can be found all across the mainland from the provinces of the northeast to Yunnan and Guangdong in the south. Some are state-run, others private, and each has from several dozen to a hundred bears. A mainland report says these farms now hold 8000 to 10,000 bears, with the population projected to rise to 40,000.

But Chinese herbal pharmacists distinguish between this drained gall and the gall taken from wild bears, which they call "true gall." Drained gall, they say, lacks three active medicinal ingredients, and they have indeed shown that it is not as effective as true gall. But because it is only a tenth as expensive, consumers and pharmacies alike are gradually taking to using it for chronic illnesses.

Chinese medicine has a long tradition of turning to animals raised by man to secure a steady supply and prevent overhunting. In his books, Hsu Chiao-mu, a professor emeritus at China Medical College, even tells people how to raise sea horses, horned toads and the like. Today musk and pilose antlers are also taken from animals raised in captivity.

A CITES regulation states that first-list animals bred in captivity can be treated as animals on the second list. After submitting an application and getting approval, a nation could proceed with export.

At last year's Asian CITES conference in Beijing, the mainland brought up the idea of applying to CITES to have the farmed bears treated as second-list animals. This would have given Taiwan's Chinese medicine dealers hope of having CITES-sanctioned access to drained gall.

One the equal of 300

But questions surfaced about the source of the bears. Lu Dau-jye points out that CITES only allows domesticated animals to be treated as second-list animals if they have no effect on the wild population. And only under such conditions will CITES approve the mainland's request.

The mainland claims that the drained gall obtained over the course of one of these captive animal's lives is the equivalent of what is taken from 300 hunted wild bears. Hence one bear can save the lives of 300. But it's not easy to breed bears in captivity, and "the main source for these farms is still wild bears," says Jiang Shuang-mei, the director of the Department of Health's medicine section, who attended the Seattle conference.

In order to strengthen sales of drained gall when medical demand for it is sated, the mainland has created such non-medical products as bear gall shampoo, bear gall tea, and bear gall alcohol. These rankle conservation groups even more. Suzie Chang Highley of Earthtrust Taiwan once went to the mainland to investigate bear farms. She says that many have huge signs and offer thirsty tourists fresh bear gall juice.

Very few countries agree with the methods these mainland bear farms employ. Aware of this, the mainland withdrew its application to make its drained gall a second-list animal product before last year's general meeting of CITES.

Besides noting that the bears on these farms are captured in the wild, Chang points out that mainland hotels sell drained bear gall products and Canton even has stores that openly sell whole poached bear galls to Taiwanese businessmen.

Playing the bear gall market

Judy A. Mills, the director of TRAFFIC's Hong Kong office and an expert on the use of bear gall in Asia, acknowledges that many countries are involved in its trade, but she notes that after permitting visits to the mainland, Taiwan became "the principal consumer market for poached and farmed mainland bear gall."

Since the Wildlife Conservation Law went into effect, Taiwan has had no record of bear gall imports, but you can find drained bear gall powder in any herbal pharmacy. Unlike rhino horn, dried bear gall can't be picked up on X-ray machines. Many travellers simply put in it their pockets when they go through customs.

In fact, most ROC citizens have only an "it's-better-than-nothing" attitude toward Chinese medicine. Chinese medicine peddling is a sunset industry: Over the last decade the number of herbal pharmacies in Taipei has declined from 1000 to 700.

Chiang Shuang-mei points out that while estimators are busy adding up the island's bear gall stock, consumption is on the decline, and the Department of Health has discovered that one out of three herbal pharmacies now uses cheap substitutes such as pig, cow or tortoise gall.

But the expectation of a ban has prompted speculation, and the price of bear gall is on the rise, as is smuggling of it. "We are always looking at the herbal pharmacies," Chiang notes. "But we should turn our focus to the speculative activities of the middlemen."

When stocks run out

Currently the Department of Health hopes to control bear gall as it did rhino horn, stamping out smuggling by having pharmacists register their stocks. To avoid having herbal pharmacists lose everything when and if a complete ban is declared (as many did when the sale of rhino horns and tiger bones was prohibited), the department wants to coordinate a timetable to allow the pharmacists to sell off their stocks. It has also commissioned Yang Ming Medical College to proceed with research on substitutes for bear gall.

But such research will yield no results over the short term. Kuo Sung-ken, chairman of the ROC Chinese Medicine Traders' Association, says that though the galls of other animals are used in Chinese medicine, they are not as effective as bear gall. And so allowing for existing stocks to be used up is not enough, he argues. When all the gall is gone, how will the government provide relief?

Chang Hong-jen, a specialist at the Department of Health, notes that though Taiwan is not a CITES member, its international status is very precarious, and at times of controversy it will be the first attacked among countries with similar

由於沒有多少國家認同大陸熊場的作法，大陸也有自知之明，已自行收回原本擬在去年華約會議上提出的申請案。

除了熊場的熊來自野外，張念蘇指出，現在不只大陸旅館裡到處都有引流膽出售，由於臺灣商人要的是一粒粒的熊膽，因此廣州也有商店公開出售盜獵取得的完整熊膽。

炒熊膽如炒股票

雖然牽涉熊膽交易的國家很多，南韓更是熊膽消費量首屈一指的地區；但多年來調查亞洲使用熊膽情形的野生動植物交易調查委員會成員苗朱迪指出，「開放大陸探親後，臺灣已成為大陸熊膽黑市交易與養殖場的最主要消費者。」

自從保育法公告實施後，臺灣從未有熊膽的進口紀錄，但今天人們在任何一家中藥店都可買到盒裝的引流膽粉。乾製的熊膽不像犀角可以由 X 光掃瞄出來，許多旅客就將之裝在口袋帶進海關。

事實上，今天許多國人只在聊勝於無的情況下看中醫、吃中藥，中藥商有如夕陽行業，過去十年臺北市的中藥行就由一千家減少到七百多家。

江雙美表示，雖然國內熊膽存量尚在估計中，但用量越來越少，衛生署也發現有三分之一中藥店用的是價格較便宜的豬膽、牛膽、海龜膽等替代品。但是預期禁用熊膽的心理，反讓熊膽像股票一樣被炒起來，挺而走險的走私因此多起來，「我們一直把焦點放在中藥商，但應該注意的是中間商的炒作，」江雙美說。

存貨用完後怎麼辦？

目前衛生署希望像管理犀角一樣，由中藥商自行登記現有的熊膽存量，以杜絕走私。為了不再重蹈即刻禁用犀角、虎骨，讓中藥商平白損失的覆轍，衛生署將協調一個時限，讓業者用完現有存貨，並委託陽明醫學院進行熊膽替代品的研究。

但藥品的開發短時間難有成果。臺灣省中藥商公會理事長郭松根就表示，雖然雜膽用的很多，但效能終究無法與真正熊膽比較，因此即使現存貨源准予出售，但市面上的熊膽用完後，政府又將如何因應？

無奈的衛生署技監張鴻仁表示，臺灣雖非華約組織會員，但國際地位艱難，有問題總是先被開刀，「不過我們畢竟是國際社會一份子，未來引流膽、北美熊膽能否使用，還是要看國際上的態度而定。」

在衛生署與中藥商溝通後，也有製藥廠已經停止與日本合作生產含有熊膽的漢方胃腸藥。但也有中、醫藥商因為接著犀角、虎骨之後，連鎖般的輪到熊膽，反應有如驚弓之鳥。一位住北投的中藥商就說，現在中醫師開的藥單上，即使有熊膽，也不會以熊膽二字出現了。

一起來救熊

由於全球性的自然環境破壞，食物鏈上層的大型動物，往往成為第一波受害者。除了澳洲與南極，熊原本遍及各大洲，牠的滅絕，代表的是全人類對整個地球環境的輕忽，國際上推動熊的保護活動，具有一定的代表性意義。

尤其在犀牛、老虎、大象的保護逐漸被全球認知，並成為國際合作行動，如今保育團體不僅注意熊膽的交易，也在世界各地推動不訓練野熊表演、不獵捕等等全方位的護熊活動，「套句俗話，現在不談熊，就落伍了，」國內保育團體「關懷生命協會」指出。

中藥商也只有面對現實，否則，不只是世界性的護熊活動已不會停下腳步，未來可能只有日本合成的人工熊膽，而沒有正牌的中藥熊膽了。　　　　□

（原載民國84年8月光華雜誌）

records. "But we are after all a member of the international community. Whether or not we can use North American bear gall and drained gall from the mainland will depend upon international opinion."

After the Department of Health opened up channels of communication to the Chinese medicine industry, some factories have already stopped joint ventures with Japanese companies to make bear-gall-based stomach medicines. But after having lost their rhino-horn and tiger-bone business, some traders fear that the same fate is in store for bear's gall. One Peitou pharmacist says that even if a Chinese doctor's prescription calls for bear gall, he won't write the characters out.

Working together to save the bears

As natural environments all over the world are damaged, large animals at the top of the food chain are always the first to suffer. The bear is found on all continents except Antarctica and Australia, and its extinction would pointedly display mankind's neglect of the environment. Hence, international efforts to save the bear are fraught with symbolic meaning.

Steps to save the rhino, tiger and elephant are becoming recognized globally and are leading to international cooperation. If conservation groups around the world promote across-the-board steps to save bears, working not only to curtail the trade in gall but also to ban the hunting and training of wild bears, "then you'll be behind the times if you're not talking about bears," says a representative of the Life Conservationist Association of the ROC.

Chinese medicine traders are beginning to face the music. If they turn away and cover their ears, it won't just add tempo to the save-the-bear anthem; it might even result in all bear gall being pulled off the market, leaving behind only the Japanese synthesized stuff.

(Chang Chin-ju/photos by Hsueh Chi-kuang/ tr. by Jonathan Barnard/ first published in August 1995)

何不讓熊寶寶不僅是小朋友的玩具，也能與人類一樣，在自然界中佔有一席之地。

If the teddy bear is not to be the only species to survive, bears, like people, must have ample space in which to live.

海豚生與死
Save the Dolphins!

文·王文娟　圖·張良綱

在台灣東海岸，經常可以看到海豚迴游，跳躍嬉戲。
（黃昭欽攝）

Dolphins can frequently be seen swimming and playing off Taiwan's east coast. (photo by Huang Chao-chin)

101

過去澎湖曾發生過幾次海豚大規模擱淺。在西嶼鄉鄉民代表會前任秘書薛先正的相簿中，留下民國四十六年農曆初一，有1074頭海豚擱淺於內垵村的歷史記錄。
In the past, there were many large-scale dolphin beachings around Penghu. A photo taken on lunar New Year's Day of 1957, kept in a photo album by Hsueh Hsien-cheng, secretary of a local township assembly, shows a beaching of 1074 dolphins.

今年一月下旬，農委會野生動物保護小組連續在雲林和台東，查獲多達一萬二千多公斤的海豚肉，嫌犯之一吳萬教以違反「野生動物保育法」被收押禁見。

消息經由路透社報導公告於國際「海洋哺乳動物網路」之後，許多關心鯨類的保育團體和學術單位，紛紛與國內協助這次海豚肉鑑定的台大動物系教授周蓮香聯絡。而她登錄於網路上的結果報告，也被網路負責人主動再次傳送，顯示這次事件受到國際關心的程度。

為什麼海豚是吃不得、抓不得的？海豚事件是否會成為另一個野生動物保育的新戰場？

In mid-January of this year, the Wildlife Protection Unit of the Council of Agriculture (COA) confiscated more than 12,000 kilograms of dolphin meat in raids in Yunlin and Taitung counties. One of the suspects in the case, Wu Wan-chiao, was arrested for violating the Wildlife Conservation Law.

After the story got onto the Internet via Reuters, many conservation groups and academics concerned about the fate of cetaceans got in touch with local scholar Chou Lien-siang, a professor in the Department of Zoology at National Taiwan University who was on this occasion responsible for verifying that it was indeed dolphin meat. When her final report went out over the Internet, people picked up the story and passed it along on their own initiative, suggesting the degree of international concern over this incident.

Why can't you catch or eat dolphins? Will the dolphin become the next major focus of the effort to protect wild animals in Taiwan?

Dusk. Under their leader Charles Chang, the members of the Wildlife Protection Unit of the Council of Agriculture have been hunkered down for many days in Yunlin County's Ssuhu Rural Township with local government and police officials, monitoring the activities of Wu Wan-chiao. After they familiarize themselves with his schedule and habits, they decide to act. At the moment they move he is in a ramshackle workshop, using an electric saw to cut off dolphins' heads, after which he chops up the meat. When he is caught in the act, there are still seven entire dolphins he has not yet had time to process. The authorities then open up his storage freezer, only to find that there is such a large stockpile that it takes a long time just to calculate the amount.

Who is this "butcher"? As Chen Juei-yung, in charge of wildlife conservation affairs for the Yunlin County Bureau of Agriculture, says, Wu is "a simple man."

Based on records of transactions, Charles Chang judges that Wu was a major middleman in the dolphin meat trade, buying from fishermen for resale to seafood restaurants in Yunlin and Chiayi, on Taiwan's west coast. Will the dolphin, like the shark and the bear, be another sacrifice in the quest for culinary delicacies by people in Taiwan?

The dauphin and the lazy daughter-in-law

In the West, dolphins are seen as friendly and intelligent animals. There are many tales of dolphins rescuing drowning people or helping fishermen. The hunter Orion made his way into the heavens riding a dolphin. In ancient Greece, killing a dolphin was held to be as serious an offense as killing a man. And in the French royal court, the heir to the throne was honored with the name "Dauphin" (dolphin).

In the Orient, in ancient records, the early Chinese personified the dolphin, depicting it as a lively creature. Moreover, these records clearly state that dolphin meat is not suitable for eating. In a Chinese tale, a man named Bo Ya is playing the zither, hoping in vain for an appreciative audience, until a dolphin comes along who hears and understands his music. Also, dolphins were said to appear to warn people of impending disaster.

According to another legend, reported in the *Shu Yi Ji* (*Records of the Strange*), the dolphin is the transformation of a woman, surnamed Yang, who was drowned by her mother-in-law. Thus it also carries the name "lazy daughter-in-law fish." Perhaps the dolphin's large amount of body fat is reminiscent of a daughter-in-law who is not hard-working enough! Because Chinese found dolphin fat "repellent," they said that only "barbarians" would eat dolphin. Chinese only used the dolphin to get oil for lamps or for mixing with lime to repair boats.

So why do people in Taiwan today eat something their ancestors didn't think of as edible? Yang Hong-chia was the earliest in post-WWII Taiwan to study cetaceans. He speculates that

黃昏時分。農委會野生動物保育小組成員在組長張有長率領下，和地方政府、警察單位，於雲林縣四湖鄉守候多日、摸清吳萬教的作息後，決定採取行動。那時，他正在簡陋的工寮，用電鋸將海豚頭分割，再把其餘的部份切塊。結果當場被逮個正著，剩下七隻完整的海豚來不及處理。隨後辦案人員開啓了他儲放屠體的冷凍庫，還因爲數量太過龐大而無法一時清點完畢。

然而這位「屠夫」，根據當時也在場的雲林縣政府農業局野生動物保育業務承辦人陳瑞永的描述，卻是「他是古意（老實）人啦。」

從帳冊和往來紀錄中，張有長斷定，吳萬教應該是大盤商，主要將貨批發到西海岸雲林、嘉義的海產店。難道，海豚肉又如同鯊魚、熊掌一樣，成爲台灣人追求美食的犧牲品？

海豚王子vs.懶婦魚

海豚在歐美國家，一直被視爲友善而聰明的動物，有許多海豚拯救溺水者和幫助漁民捕魚的傳說流傳在民間。獵人歐萊恩就是騎著海豚到天上變成獵戶座的。

古希臘人認爲殺害海豚和謀害人命同罪，而法國王室的傳統，國王的長子都被授與「海豚」的封號，成爲「海豚王子」。

在古老的東方，根據中國古籍的記載，我們的老祖先對海豚也有著鮮活而擬人化的描述，並明白指出海豚肉是不適合食用的。

《爾雅》提到，伯牙鼓琴，出聽的知音就是海豚。而海豚也會現身警告人類天災的來臨。

《述異記》有一則傳說：海豚是由一位被婆婆溺斃的媳婦楊氏所化身，又別名「懶婦魚」，可能是因爲從海豚身上肥厚的油脂，聯想到媳婦可能不夠勤勞吧。因爲

牠的肉「肥不中食」、「腥臭不可近」、只有「土人間有能食者」，中國人只利用牠的脂肪點燈照明，或混合石灰修理船隻。那麼今天的台灣人，爲什麼吃起老祖宗不認爲是美食的海豚？日據時代後首先從事台灣鯨類研究的楊鴻嘉推測，可能是四百年前，漢人在唐山過台灣時從福建帶過來的飲食習慣。

福建沿海人世代以討海爲生，可能因地方畜產不豐、海豚肉又肥富油脂，於是逐漸食用而因襲成俗。一九七四年楊鴻嘉到雲林縣北港鎮做調查時，還看過專門販售海豚肉的魚市場。

不過楊老先生特別強調，「海豚肉消費的區域有限，」主要以雲林爲主，各地捕獲的海豚大多集中到這裡。民間普遍認爲海豚肉很滋補，女人坐月子身體虛、老人血液循環不良、手腳冰冷，吃盤老薑、麻油炒海豚肉就有顯著的改善。而在過去不是人人吃得起雞、鴨、豬肉的時代，便宜的海豚肉就成爲貧窮人家補充蛋白質的來源。

然而這種「傳統」需求，在民國七十九年野生動物保育法公告實施後，卻成了新的商機。陳瑞永說，有野保法之前，海豚肉市價大概一台斤四、五十元左右（豬肉約爲七十五元），現在由於變成非法交易，則要賣到四、五百元，足足漲了十倍。一般市場已買不到，到海產店還得是熟客，老闆才會主動提供「內幕消息」。

一千隻算多或少？

海豚和鯨魚同屬鯨目，其下共有約七十九種，「海豚」或「鯨魚」是依體型的大小來稱呼，不具科學意義。而周蓮香的著作《台灣鯨類圖鑑》指出，在台灣附近海域，目前記錄的有太平洋瓶鼻海豚、熱帶斑海豚、花紋海豚……等二十八種海豚。原先牠們大部份被列爲瀕臨絕種的野生動

perhaps the first immigrants to Taiwan brought the habit of eating dolphin with them when they crossed over from Fujian 400 years ago.

People living on the Fujian coast have always relied on the sea for their livelihoods. Perhaps they began eating the dolphin because in their local area meat was scarce, and the dolphin was rich in fat and oil. Eventually eating dolphin became customary. When Yang did a survey in Yunlin in 1974, he found one fish market that specialized in selling dolphin meat.

But Yang emphasizes that "the area of dolphin consumption is very limited." In fact, it is mainly confined to Yunlin, and dolphins caught by fishermen from around Taiwan usually end up in that county. It is widely believed that dolphin meat has great "supplementary value" (as Chinese dietary theory puts it). Women who are still weak just after giving birth, or old people with cold limbs from poor circulation, are said to benefit from dolphin meat cooked up with ginger or sesame oil. Also, back in the days when

not everyone could afford to eat pork, beef, or poultry, inexpensive dolphin meat was a source of protein for the poor.

However, after the promulgation of the Wildlife Conservation Law in 1990, this "traditional" demand became a commercial opportunity. Chen Juei-yung notes that before the law, one catty (0.6 kg) of dolphin meat fetched about NT$50-60 (pork going for about NT$75). But now that the trade is illegal, the price has jumped nearly ten times over, to NT$400-500 per catty. You can't buy it in most ordinary markets, and only old familiar customers at seafood restaurants are "let in on the secret."

Is 1000 a lot?

The dolphin is related to the larger toothed whales, both being part of the order Cetacea. There are 79 species within this order. The terms "dolphin" and "whale" are applied to various cetaceans depending on body size, but there is no scientific discontinuity between the species of Cetacea. Chou Lien-siang's book *Guide to Ceta-*

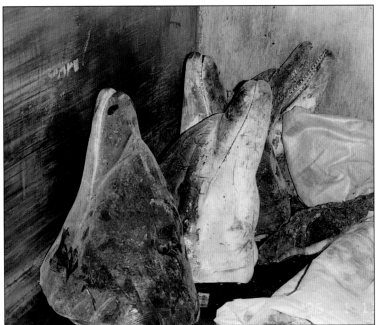

這次農委會在北港查獲多達一萬兩千多公斤的海豚肉，立即引起國內外保育人士的關心。（農委會野生動物保護小組提供）

The confiscation by the Council of Agriculture of 12,000 kilos of dolphin meat in Peikang attracted immediate attention from conservationists at home and abroad. (courtesy of the Wildlife Protection Unit, COA)

物，後來改為珍貴稀有類，如要使用，必須經過聯合國相關單位的認可。

從族群數量來看，台灣的海豚是不是真的少到「珍貴稀有」？研究鯨類近六年的周蓮香也無法回答「台灣有多少海豚？」「牠們迴游的路線？」「什麼時候比較多？」等這些需要配合大量人力、物力、時間去調查的問題。

鯨類研究在台灣一直相當冷僻，最早投入的楊鴻嘉幾乎都是自行研究，沒有所屬機構台灣省水產試驗所計畫經費的支持。直到民國七十九年以後，才有海洋大學漁業科學系和台大動物系，開始從事資源調查與鑑定，一切都還在起步階段。

海洋大學漁業系研究生黃昭欽從去年七月起，每個月跟著水試所船隻出去調查。至今在台灣西海岸蒐集到二十六個群次，離計算公式所需要的六十個觀察點還有一段距離。

而去年在台灣舉行的「鯨類生態及保育研討會」，與會者曾於六月十九、二十日，搭乘水試所「海富號」及觀光局的「觀海二號」在東海岸觀測。根據估計，這兩天大約就有一千隻海豚在附近出沒。不過這個數據的意義，由於沒有過去的資料作對照，「僅供參考，」黃昭欽說。

海豚在稀有動物檔案中「榜上有名」的原因，並非奠基於周詳的研究評估所做出的決定。翻開海豚保育史，是由漁民、官方、國外保育團體的衝突與妥協所構成。

海龍王的賭注

故事的開端在澎湖。湖西鄉北寮村村長洪國強說，每年農曆年前後，海豚會乘著海潮、追逐小管等浮游性魚類，在澎湖與嘉義、雲林、台南間的澎湖水道迴游。牠們有可能游向屈爪嶼以南、沿著當地人俗稱「竹篙港（路）」的天然水道，經過員貝嶼前進，這條港路外深內淺，而沙港就位於終點。

沙港的老人家說，海豚是「海龍王賭輸的」（意思是天物），給他們加菜。在日據時代，如果員貝漁民遠遠看到了海豚，就通知沙港，大家齊力把魚網接起來出海，用竹篙敲打船緣。因為海豚「沒膽」，會往中間集中，於是就在漁船包圍下慢慢被驅游向沙港所在的淺灘。

馬公高中地理老師、也是地方文史社團澎湖采風工作室一份子的郭金龍說，他於民國五十八、五十九年在湖西國中沙港分部教書時，就親眼目睹這個盛況。學生們遠遠看到很多漁船，就跑到岸邊守候，等待大人們把海豚趕進港，「還有人會跳下水，騎在海豚背上玩呢。」

他們以土地公廟為中心，將擱淺在岸邊的海豚先給員貝三成，剩下的再按出力的多少，由委員會分配。甚至小孩只消在港邊站一站，也都見者有份。「這是他們凝聚村民的一種共同漁獲方式，」郭金龍說，就像是赤崁和湖西一起合作採紫菜一樣，都有三、四百年的傳統。

大約早在一九七四年，國內電視媒體就曾風聞沙港圍捕海豚的「盛會」而加以報導。雖然也引起大眾廣泛的關心，卻由於當時國內保育觀念尚在萌芽階段，討論的熱度並沒有持續很久。

直到民間保育團體「信任地球」（Earth Trust ，前身是「拯救鯨魚」）將他們在一九九〇年拍攝沙港人如何「屠殺」海豚的紀錄片，透過夏威夷總部在美國電視網播出，才引起了國際的注意。

國際視聽

當時著名的環保記者楊憲宏曾在「首都早報」描述其中一段漁民殺「假殺人鯨」（偽虎鯨）的過程：

「海豚被漁民先以小刀割喉，並以鋼筋刺傷口。棄置一旁二、三小時，再拖上舢

ceans of Taiwan points out that 28 species of Cetacea, including the bottlenose dolphin, Risso's dolphin, and the pantropical spotted dolphin, have been recorded in the waters surrounding Taiwan. Originally they were categorized as "endangered species," but have since been listed as "precious and rare species." Permission must be received from the relevant agencies of the United Nations in order to use them.

Are Taiwan's dolphins really so few that they are "precious and rare"? Even Chou Lien-siang, who has been studying cetaceans for more than six years, is unable to answer such questions as: How many dolphins are there around Taiwan? What are their migration routes? When do their numbers peak? These questions will require a lot of manpower, resources, and time to answer accurately.

There has never been much interest in cetacean research in Taiwan. The earliest pioneer, Yang Hung-chia, worked virtually single-handedly, without any financial support in this endeavor from the institution where he worked, the Taiwan Fisheries Research Institute (TFRI). It was only after 1990 that the fisheries department of the National Taiwan Ocean University and the zoology department at National Taiwan University began doing resource surveys, all of which are still in the early stages.

Last July, Huang Chao-chin, a graduate student at Ocean University, began going out with ships of the TFRI each month to do surveys. Thus far he has spotted 26 groups of dolphins. But there is a long way to go before he reaches the full 60 sightings required for an accurate statistical analysis.

Last June 19 and 20, participants in Taiwan's "Third Symposium on Cetacean Ecology and Conservation" surveyed the East Coast aboard the TFRI's ship *Haifu*. It is estimated that about 500-600 dolphins appeared in the area during the survey. However, because there are no previous figures against which to compare, the survey results "are just for reference," advises Huang.

The main reason dolphins have protected status is not because of the results of detailed research and evaluation. When you look back over the history, you can see that dolphin conservation in Taiwan has grown out of conflict and compromise among fishermen, the government, and overseas conservation groups.

The gamble of the Dragon King of the Sea

The story begins in Penghu. Hung Kuo-chiang, mayor of Peiliao Village in Huhsi Rural Township, relates that dolphins come by every year just around the lunar New Year. Riding the currents and pursuing squid and other fish, the dolphins migrate along the sea lanes between Penghu on one side and Tainan, Yunlin, and Chiayi counties on the other. Sometimes they end up following the natural sea route that the locals have come to call "punting pole road." This route, deep outside and shallow inside, passes by Yuanpei Island and terminates at the Penghu town of Shakang.

Old folks around Shakang describe the arrival of the dolphins in their area as "the covering of a gambling debt by the Dragon King of the Sea," who pays up by delivering dolphins for people to eat. Beginning in the Japanese occupation era, when Yuanpei folks saw the dolphins coming, they would signal Shakang, and everyone would take to their fishing boats. By banging their punting poles against the sides of their sampans, they could herd the dolphins—who some call "not very daring"—into the central channel. Surrounded by boats, the dolphins would be steadily forced toward the beach at Shakang.

Kuo Chin-lung is a teacher at Makung High School and also a member of the Penghu Cultural Workshop, a group preserving local history and culture. He recalls that in 1969-1970, when he was teaching at the Shakang branch of the Huhsi Middle School, he saw this spectacle with his own eyes. When the students saw the huge number of fishing boats out at sea, they rushed down to the beach, to watch and wait for the

圍捕海豚，是澎湖員貝和沙港漁民的共同漁獲方式，已經有三、四百年的歷史。（郭金龍攝）

For centuries the people of Yuanpei and Shakang cooperated in encircling dolphins and driving them ashore. (photo by Kuo Chin-lung)

般，用小刀環切斷頭，小刀切及頸動脈時，這頭『假殺人鯨』在大出血中掙扎跳回海中，染紅海水，久久不消。」

同年，美國海洋哺乳類學者培林博士在「國際捕鯨委員會」（簡稱IWC）首次指出了小型鯨類面臨直接獵捕或間接因漁獲而致死之問題嚴重性。

一九四六年由捕鯨國家成立國際捕鯨委員會的目的，是要均分捕鯨業的資源。由於世界上並沒有專門以捕海豚為主的漁業，因此委員會對經濟價值不高的小型鯨類並不重視，只有管制數量稀少的北方瓶鼻海豚。

直到一九五○年代海豚研究開始蓬勃發展，所顯示的數據，使得人們對海豚因瞭解而更加珍惜。在比較人腦、海豚腦和其他陸生哺乳動物腦部結構時，發現海豚腦的皺摺甚至比人還多，可能具備極高的智慧。

✳ ✳ ✳

adults to force the dolphins into the tiny harbor area. "Some people even jumped right into the water and playfully rode on the backs of the dolphins."

Bringing everyone together at the Temple of the God of the Earth, the beached dolphins would be divided up. First Yuanpei was given 30% of the catch, and the rest would be distributed according to how much effort each person put in. Even little kids who just stood off to the side would get a portion. "This was a collective fishing process that helped to cement the community together," explains Kuo. Like the cooperative picking of the laver in Chikan and Huhsi, the dolphin catch was a tradition that went back 300 or 400 years.

There were reports about this "event" on Taiwan television as early as 1974. Although there was some concern about the situation, discussion didn't last long; at that time environmental consciousness was not very strong in Taiwan.

美國夏威夷大學赫門研究室在從事了十五年的研究後，肯定了海豚具有語言結構的高層認知能力，可能有主詞、動詞、形容詞、副詞、受詞等文法結構呢。

漁民眼中的小偷

然而，晚近才受生態保育界矚目的海豚，卻面臨著許多的生存危機。在國際自然及自然資源保育聯盟（簡稱 IUCN）於一九九一年出版的鯨類書籍中，列舉目前威脅海豚族群的因素，主要是直接捕捉、棲地破壞、環境污染和魚網的意外捕獲。

直接捕殺海豚，並非只在台灣發生。根據「信任地球」組織一九九三年出版的「地球專刊」〈國際間捕殺海豚的現況〉的報導，在日本、秘魯、斯里蘭卡、丹麥及智利等世界主要漁場所在的國家，漁民仍利用海豚提供人類消費，或作為捕鯊、捕蟹的魚餌。漁民並聲稱海豚是海上的小偷，和他們競爭漁業資源。「漁業與保育界在世界各大漁場的衝突最直接，」周蓮香說。

但是這仍屬區域性的問題。對海豚族群更大的威脅是來自意外捕獲，其中又以鮪魚業為主要禍首。

兩種主要危及海豚的鮪魚業是在美國、拉丁美洲捕撈黃鰭鮪的圍網漁業，及在北太平洋區捕撈長鰭鮪的流刺網漁業。

由於海豚常常出現在黃鰭鮪的上方，因此被圍網誤捕的機會很大。而後者則是因為海豚誤觸有「幽靈網」之稱的流刺網而大量溺斃。

雖然沒有確實的數據證實海豚族群因此受到絕種的威脅，但在國際上已經形成保護牠們的氛圍。在保育團體的壓力下，美國三大海產公司在一九九〇年聯合起來，拒購讓海豚遭受不必要死亡的鮪魚，並在罐頭上印製「海豚安全」（Dolphin Safe）的標籤，要消費者支持。各大鮪魚漁場

In 1990, however, the practice caused an international uproar when the Hawaii-based private conservation group Earthtrust (formerly "Save the Whales") caught the "slaughter" of dolphins by the people of Shakang on film, and got it broadcast in the US.

An international audience

It was about the same time that the well-known environmental reporter Yang Hsien-hung wrote an article in the *Capitol Morning Post* describing one particular incident of fishermen killing a "false killer whale."

"First the fishermen cut the dolphin's throat and inserted a steel rod into the wound [draining the blood slowly supposedly makes the meat more tender]. After putting the dolphin, still alive, aside for two or three hours, they started to use a knife to decapitate it. When the knife got to the animal's carotid artery, it began to struggle amidst an outpouring of blood. It finally managed to jump into the sea. The water turned red, and remained so for a long time."

It was not only in Taiwan that dolphin deaths at the hands of fishermen began to get serious attention. That same year, Dr. W.F. Perrin, an American marine mammal scholar, gave testimony to the International Whaling Commission (IWC) on this issue. He described for the first time the severity of the problem of small-scale cetaceans being deliberately caught or dying after being accidentally trapped in fishing nets.

The IWC was originally formed in 1946 by whaling nations in order to distribute the resources for the whaling industry. Because no one in the industry specifically aims to catch dolphins, little attention has been given to small cetaceans of low economic value (with the exception of controlling the numbers of the northern bottlenose whale).

Yet, one might ask, why should people object to dolphins being caught any more than other forms of sea life? People first began to understand dolphins—and to think them especially worth treasuring—with the development of dol-

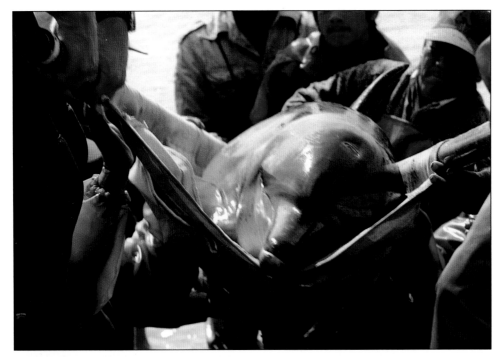

在民國七十年代，漁民將海豚販售到香港海洋公園、野柳海洋世界等水族機構訓練表演。
（郭金龍攝）

In the 1980s, fishermen sold some dolphins to Hong Kong's Ocean Park, Taiwan's Ocean World, and other oceanariums for training and performances. (photo by Kuo Chin-lung)

phin research in the 1960s. Comparisons of the brains of dolphins, monkeys, man, and other mammals showed that dolphins had even more folds in their cerebral cortexes than humans, suggesting that dolphins are highly intelligent. Also, research conducted over a 15-year period at the University of Hawaii confirmed that dolphins have high-level language recognition abilities, and may have a grammar structure including nouns, verbs, adjectives, and direct and indirect objects.

Fish thieves

Despite growing sympathy for dolphins since those days, it was only rather late that they attracted the attention of conservation organiza-tions, and dolphins now face many threats. In a 1991 publication on cetaceans, the International Union for Conservation of Nature and Natural Resources listed the main threats to dolphins as being commercial takes, destruction of their habitats, pollution, and incidental takes.

Deliberate hunting of dolphins is not limited to Taiwan. According to the Fall 1993 issue of Earthtrust's *Earth Journal*, people working the fishing grounds off Japan, Peru, Sri Lanka, Denmark, and Chile all provide dolphins for human consumption, or use them for bait to catch sharks or crabs. Fishermen, who see the dolphins as competitors, even scorn them as "fish thieves." Says Dr. Chou, "You can see the conflicts be-

墨西哥、委內瑞拉等都受到衝擊。

　　而被保育人士指為頻繁使用流刺網的台灣、日本和韓國，也終於同意在一九九二年底在公海上禁用，以降低包括海豚在內的海中生物、海鳥等的意外死亡。

每年三十頭

　　民國七十九年的沙港事件，本質上是從事近海漁撈的台灣漁民，向無法理解國際保護熱最直接的引爆點。雖然農委會也已立即跟進，在同年將海豚列入野保法保護的對象，但紛爭仍未止息。

　　沙港人在八十二年海豚再次經過澎湖時，又圍捕了三十餘頭，改以飼養的方式藉觀光名義賺錢，他們還有一個十二個人組成的海豚管理委員會。後來他們執意留下二頭海豚不肯放生，全體委員因此被判刑。而從民國七十九年飼養的七頭海豚，由於缺乏專業的照顧，在六年之間，只剩下

＊　＊　＊

tween the interests of the fishing industry and those of the dolphin most starkly in major fishing grounds worldwide."

　　But direct hunting has always been limited to certain regions. An even greater threat to dolphin numbers has been incidental death, which is especially serious in the tuna industry.

　　The two main tuna fishing industries that have posed the greatest threats to dolphins are encirclement net fishing off the United States and Latin America, and driftnet fishing in the North Pacific.

　　In the former, dolphins are easily accidentally caught in encirclement nets because of their habit of showing up above the tuna. In the latter, many dolphins have been drowned after being accidentally entangled in driftnets.

　　Although there were no figures to prove that these deaths threatened to make dolphins extinct, there developed a broad sense internationally that they should be protected. In 1990, under

海豚自民國七十九年始已列入被保育野生動物，但漁民仍非法飼養牠們作為觀光資源。雖然和大海只有一網之隔，海豚卻無法回家。

Dolphins were brought under the protection of the Wildlife Conservation Law in 1990, but some people still kept a few (illegally) as tourist attractions. Though separated from the open seas by only a net, these dolphins are not free.

二頭，而這一群海豚所生五、六隻幼兒，只有一隻存活至今。

周蓮香幾次和沙港人協調，目前任職於香港海洋公園的自然保育聯盟鯨類小組主席，也願意免費提供飼養技術，但漁民的反應冷淡。「我們也很盡心在養啊，」負責看顧的歐老先生說。問題的癥結仍在於他們把海豚跟其他魚類都當成生財工具一樣看待。

他們後來也曾透過縣政府，向農委會提出每年捕捉三十條新海豚的觀光計畫，不過因為目前野外海豚族群量尚未估算出來而被駁回。

周蓮香認為，現在要談這些都還太早。當然站在她個人的立場，是相當不贊成的。因為，「那是不是意味每年要死三十條？」

保育「成績單」

海豚現在已是國際保育的焦點，台灣又走過一段艱辛的保育歷程，因此對於這次海豚事件，國外保育團體如英國環境調查協會（簡稱 EIA）、牧海人保育協會及大洋洲學會等，都在網路上與周蓮香聯絡，要求進一步的資料，並認為這是台灣執行野保法的成果之一。

台北野生物貿易調查委員會駐台灣代表斐馬克也說，這次的事件，「是單純的法律問題。」台灣已有野生動物保育法，他看不出國際保育團體有任何介入的必要。

然而這些發展，對熟悉國際環保政治的人士來說，卻還是要捏出一把冷汗。因為在即將來臨的四月，美國要根據去年一年台灣對野生動物保育的「成績單」，重新考慮是否要把我國從培利法案的觀察名單中除名。處於這個敏感時刻，突然爆發的「海豚事件」，是否會對台灣的國際形象造成負面影響？

農委會保育科官員認為，執法是沒有選擇的，雖然可能會傳遞「台灣還有獵殺海豚」的負面訊息，但卻同時足以顯示政府積極執法的決心。

張有長也說，如果今後再得到有關違反野生動物保育法的線索，他仍然會全力偵察。不然，「知情不辦，那不是如同警察吃案嗎？」

海豚謝恩

近幾年由於農委會保育科及地方縣市政府等相關單位的宣導，再加上國人對三年前澎湖事件的重罰仍記憶猶新，大家普遍都已經有「不能再捕捉海豚」的共識。去年一年間，台灣沿海曾發生過幾件鯨類擱淺的事件，分別在新竹南港岸邊、宜蘭縣壯圍鄉沙灘、澎湖縣湖西溝尾（淡水排水溝）及桃園新屋永安海濱，都受到當地政府、警察及軍民的全力救助。根據「中國時報」八十四年十月一日的報導，在永安擱淺的海豚在順利脫險後，「還喜悅地在海面上不斷跳躍，並不時點頭感謝。」

有鑑於類似事件頻繁，周蓮香也寫了一篇鯨類擱淺處置要點投稿到報社，希望能讓專業救助的知識更為普及。

不過，強力取締只能治標，卻不能治本。目前卻又因為執法過於嚴格而產生新的問題。

害怕「上衙門」

「只要漁業存在一天，意外捕獲率就不可能等於零，」周蓮香表示。她前年接受農委會委託，蒐集各地擱淺及意外死亡的鯨類作標本研究，以作為日後台灣鯨類資源分佈的比對資料。

這些標本將有助於「建立我國鯨類基礎生物資料，如生活史、族群結構、及食性等。由生活史與族群結構之研究，可推測鯨類族群是否面臨過度開發壓力，及可能因應措施；由食性之研究可徹底求證漁民

pressure from environmental groups, the largest seafood processing companies in the US agreed not to purchase tuna that was caught in ways causing unnecessary dolphin deaths. They labeled their new products "Dolphin Safe," in an effort to win consumer support. These steps were a major blow to the tuna fishing industries in Mexico and Venezuela.

Meanwhile, Taiwan, Japan, and Korea—lambasted by environmentalists—finally agreed at the end of 1992 to ban driftnet fishing on the high seas in order to reduce accidental deaths of all sea creatures (including dolphins) and seabirds.

Thirty dead per year?

Given these trends, the 1990 Shakang incident described above—involving people who are normally coastal fishermen and thus were unaware of the intensity of the international conservation trends—was explosive. Although the Council of Agriculture reacted immediately to follow up the incident and the same year placed the dolphin under the protection of the Wildlife Conservation Law, the dolphins of Shakang had already become a *cause célèbre*.

In 1993, when the dolphins again swam past Penghu, locals herded about 30 into the harbor, though this time they fed them and kept them alive in hopes of making them a tourist attraction. They even established a management committee. Later, they insisted on keeping two of the dolphins, a violation for which all the members of the committee were found guilty of criminal offenses. Sadly, it is clear the local residents lack specialized knowledge of how to care for dolphins. Of seven dolphins retained after the 1990 incident, only two are still alive; and only one of the five or six calves produced by those dolphins taken in 1990 survives.

Chou Lien-siang has tried many times to discuss alternatives with the citizens of Shakang. Ocean Park of Hong Kong is willing to teach them techniques for the care and feeding of dolphins free of charge. But the locals have been

cool to any such offers. "We are looking after them as best as we can," says old Mr. Ou, in charge of the dolphins. The key to the problem is that the residents still see the dolphins as they see all fish—as living property to be exploited.

Shakang has already applied several times through the county government to the COA for permission to catch 30 dolphins a year to replace the old dolphins as part of a tourism plan. But the request has always been rejected because the number of dolphins in the wild has not yet been ascertained.

Chou Lien-siang says that it is too early to discuss any such plan to take dolphins into captivity. Of course, personally she doesn't approve of the idea, wondering, "Does it mean that 30 dolphins will die each year?"

Put on the brakes?

Now that the dolphin is a focus of international concern, and Taiwan has been through a tough process of improving animal protection, there has been intense interest in this latest incident involving confiscation of dolphin meat. International bodies like the Environmental Investigation Agency, the Sea Shepherd Conservation Society, and the Oceania Project have all contacted Dr. Chou through the Internet for more information.

Thus far most of them see the incident as a successful result of the implementation of Taiwan's conservation laws. As Marcus J. Phipps, representative of TRAFFIC (East Asia-Taipei), says, "it is purely a legal problem." Taiwan already has laws on the book to protect these animals, and he can see no need for international environmentalists to become involved.

Nevertheless, there are those in Taipei, all too familiar with the politics of international conservation organizations, who have broken out in a cold sweat. They know that April approaches, and with it the United States' "report card" on Taiwan's environmental protection efforts over the past year, based on which the US will reconsider whether or not to take Taiwan off the Pelly

115

與海豚在漁獲上之爭執。」周蓮香在農委會期末報告中寫著。

理論上最近正值海豚擱淺季的高峰，但接到的回報卻寥寥可數，特別是澎湖。

澎湖人仍利用流刺網在近海作業。根據台大動物系周蓮香研究室研究助理楊世主在當地的訪談，漁民是有合作的意願，但是他們很怕「上衙門」──面對岸邊檢查哨的盤查，以及後續的報備程序。萬一沒法證明是意外捕獲，搞不好還會吃上官司。那何必辛辛苦苦從海上把海豚整隻拖回來？

船長洪國強曾在去年接獲漁民用無線電傳來捕獲海豚的消息，就立即通知台大動物系派人來作標本處理。他說，「那時許多人跑出來圍觀，派出所還不時接獲『有人在殺海豚』的檢舉。」

但是，今年到目前為止卻沒有任何消息。他私下去詢問，大家都說怕麻煩，捕到乾脆就直接再丟回海中。

周蓮香也特地到澎湖「拜碼頭」，請縣政府和警察單位配合、商請漁民協助標本採集的可能性，希望減輕他們的心理障礙，和建立蒐集網絡。

然而，農委會在今年二月所印製的鯨類保育宣導海報中卻特別加註，「誤捕海洋保育類野生動物，無論死活應即放回海中。」這樣，已溺斃的海豚可以在大海中自然腐化，而一息尚存者也可重獲生機。但對周蓮香來說，標本的取得就更困難了。

準備用來給遊客餵養海豚的鯖魚，因正值人潮稀少的淡季，放在室溫過久，發出陣陣腥臭味。
With the tourist tide at low ebb, fish kept for visitors to feed the dolphins have gone bad, making for a very unpleasant odor.

Amendment watch list. At this sensitive time, will this "dolphin incident" have a negative impact on Taiwan's international image?

Members of the Wildlife Protection Unit say that they have no choice but to enforce the law. Though any new cases might give rise to negative claims like "Taiwan is still hunting and killing dolphins," they will also demonstrate the government's vigor in implementing the law. As Charles Chang stresses, his unit will fully investigate any and all future indications that the conservation law is being violated. Otherwise, "if we knew about a case and did nothing, wouldn't that just be the same thing as the police burying a crime?"

Grateful dolphins

In any case, because of educational efforts by the Wildlife Protection Unit and local city and county governments, and because memories of the stiff punishments meted out three years ago to people in Shakang are still fresh in people's minds, there is already a broad consensus that "dolphins are not to be caught." In the last year, there have been four incidents of cetaceans being beached in four very disparate parts of Taiwan, and in all four incidents local governments, military units, and citizens rushed to the rescue. According to a November 1, 1995 report in the *China Times*, after a dolphin was rescued at Yung-an, Taoyuan County, "it happily leaped out of the sea several times, and occasionally nodded its head up and down, seeming to express its gratitude."

Because of the frequency of such incidents, Dr. Chou wrote a special newspaper article instructing people how to deal with beached cetaceans, so that the public at large could become more educated in specialized rescue techniques.

Yet the comprehensive ban addresses only the symptoms (the capture of dolphins), but does not get to the root of the problem (a full understanding of dolphins and their numbers). Indeed, in one respect, the law has created a problem for dolphin researchers.

Given the fact that, as Dr. Chou notes, "as long as the fishing industry exists, the incidental take will never reach reach zero," two years ago, commissioned by the COA, she began acquiring samples of dead dolphins from beachings and incidental takes to study for future reference in managing Taiwan's cetacean resources.

These samples have proved helpful in establishing basic biological data on local cetaceans. "Such data includes life histories, community structures, and eating habits. From life histories and community structures we can tell whether cetaceans are being put under pressure from overdevelopment, and adopt countermeasures. From eating habits we can get to the bottom of the question of just how much conflict there really is between fishermen and dolphins," wrote Chou in her final report to the COA.

But fishermen are hesitant to report and deliver beached or incidentally taken dolphins. Thus, though this should be the peak season for such reports, there has been silence, notably from Penghu.

Caught in a legal net

Penghu people still use driftnets in coastal waters to catch fish, so they must have some incidental cetacean catches. So why don't they report these? After a visit to the islands, Yang Shih-chu, one of Dr. Chou's research assistants in the Department of Zoology at NTU, says that the fishermen want to cooperate, but they are "afraid of getting involved." They don't want to have to go through a dockside investigation and do all the follow-up procedures. If they can't prove the catch was accidental, they might even face prosecution. So why should they go through the effort of bringing a dolphin all the way back to harbor?

Village mayor Hung Kuo-chiang, also a ship's captain, on one occasion last year heard about an incidental dolphin take over the wireless, and immediately notified the NTU zoology department to send someone to pick up the specimen. When the dolphin was brought back

徒法不足以自行。要保護台灣海域迴游的海豚，唯有回歸科學化的基礎調查，確實掌握牠們的數量、生態以及可能擱淺的原因，並教育漁民有關海豚的常識及保育意義。

趕魚好幫手

早期研究海豚的學者約翰・利理博士曾在一九六〇年代預言，「一、二十年之內，人類將可以和瓶鼻海豚溝通，」並嘗試編纂海豚字典。那麼可不可能有一天，漁民和海豚可以彼此協議、共同分享漁業資源？

這或許不是癡人說夢。在一篇〈高智慧動物——海豚智力、溝通技巧與社會型態之筆記〉中提到，「在巴西海岸，就有一群雌性瓶鼻海豚帶著小海豚跟漁人合作共同捕魚，這種漁人與海豚的合作關係歷時已有將近一百五十年之久！」

「漁人沿著海岸佈下漁網，等候海豚將鯔魚驅向他們；待漁人撒網後，海豚則將一團混亂、企圖逃竄的魚群飽餐一頓。」

也許，當人類懂得向動物學習的那一天，就是海豚戰爭結束的時候吧。　　□

（原載民國85年3月光華雜誌）

罐頭上「Dolphin Safe」的標誌，表示在捕撈鮪魚的過程中，將海豚被誤捕的數量降到最低。

The "Dolphin Safe" label means that the tuna inside was caught using methods that reduce the accidental take of dolphins to a minimum.

to the dock, he says, "a lot of people circled around to gawk. The local police were told by several people, 'There is someone out there killing a dolphin.'"

Thus far this year there have been no reports at all. Hung asked around unofficially, and found out that everyone is afraid of trouble, so if they kill a dolphin by mistake they just throw it straight back into the ocean.

Chou Lien-siang also paid a visit to Penghu to ask local officials to encourage fishermen to bring samples back. She hoped to reduce the psychological obstacles for them and establish a collection network.

Unfortunately, posters produced by the COA

this February say: "If any protected wild animal is accidentally caught, it must be immediately returned to the sea, dead or alive." This means that dead dolphins will return to nature, and injured ones have a chance to live. But this will make it that much harder for Dr. Chou to get her samples.

Legislation alone is not enough. To really protect the dolphins around Taiwan, it is necessary to do basic scientific surveys in order to get a firm handle on their numbers, habits, behavior, and possible reasons for beaching. This information can be used to educate fishermen about dolphins and the goals for protecting them.

Fisherman's friend

In 1960, Dr. John Lilly, one of the first to study dolphins, anticipated that "humans will be able to communicate with the bottlenose dolphin within a decade or two." He even tried to produce a dolphin dictionary. But will there be a day when dolphins and fishermen can reach a *modus vivendi* and share fisheries resources?

This may not be a dream. An *Earth Journal* article entitled "Smarts: Notes on Dolphin Brain Power, Communication Skills, and Social Style," states that, "In coastal Brazil, a group of female bottlenose dolphins and offspring has participated in cooperative hunting with fishermen for nearly 150 years. Fishermen with nets line the shore and wait for dolphins to chase mullet towards them. After the nets are cast, the dolphins feast on the confused fish that manage to escape."

Perhaps the day when people understand how to learn from the animals will be the day the dolphin wars come to an end. ☐

(Jane Wang/
photos by Vincent Chang/
tr. by Phil Newell/
first published March 1996)

大約在四、五十年前，人類開始馴養聰慧好玩的瓶鼻海豚作娛樂表演。

It was about 50 years ago that humans began to train the intelligent, fun-loving bottlenose dolphin to perform.

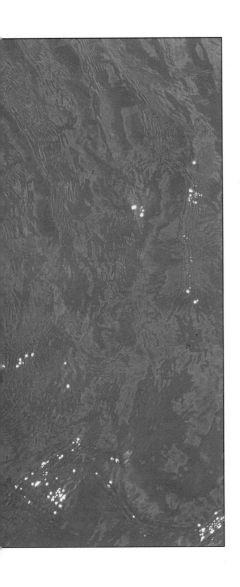

永遠的明星？
——談海豚馴養

Dolphin Stars—
Trained or Abused?

文·王文娟　圖·張良綱

　　在電視、電影或水族館的表演中，海豚總是以聰明、有靈性的姿態出現在人們面前，特別是牠那向上微彎的吻部，就像無時無刻掛著一臉無辜的微笑，惹人愛憐。人們從何時開始馴養海豚？什麼是人類對待牠們最恰當的方式？

＊　＊　＊

On television, in the movies, and in shows at theme parks, dolphins appear as intelligent creatures who can communicate with and relate to humans. In particular, the dolphin's slightly upturned mouth appears to be set in an innocent smile. They attract our sympathy and affection. When did people begin to train dolphins? What is the most appropriate way for people to treat dolphins?

野柳海洋世界，十五年前開幕曾轟動一時，現在夏天的生意也還不錯。
Ocean World was a sensation when it opened 15 years ago in Yehliu. Business is still quite good in the summer.

難得一個冬日晴朗的午后。由半圓形露天看台圍繞的水池中，四條海豚和一隻偽虎鯨正在台灣北海岸野柳海洋世界「上班」，隨著訓練師的手勢和高頻哨音，做著拍尾、接環、合唱……等動作。

觀眾大部分是大人小孩全家出動，利用寒假時分來看表演。節目進行到海豚算術，只見那隻海豚有模有樣地看了白板上的試題「6+4=？」，若有所得地快速轉身，游到面對觀眾的喇叭，開始按出答案。

「1，2，3……」有些小朋友甚至緊張地幫著數出聲音來。當喇叭聲響到十，全場期待的氣氛，頓時化為熱烈的掌聲。孩子們被

It is afternoon on an unusually clear winter's day. In the outdoor pool, surrounded by a semi-circular viewing platform, four dolphins and a false killer whale are "at work" at Ocean World in Yehliu, on Taiwan's northern coast. Following the instructions of their trainer, who carries a high-frequency whistle, the animals engage in tail-fin slapping, ring-catching, choral singing, and other activities.

The audience is mostly made up of families taking advantage of the winter holiday to see the show. When the program reaches the math segment, everyone watches as a dolphin stares at a blackboard—for all the world like an intent little student—with the problem "6+4=?" written there. Then it turns quickly and swims to the horns facing the crowd, where it begins tooting out the correct number.

"One, two, three...." Some little children, getting worried, even count along to help out. When the number of toots gets to ten, the air of tense expectation dissolves into loud applause. Children, entranced by the "cleverness" of the cetacean, clap until their hands are red. Then the dolphin swims quickly over to the pool edge next to the trainer, where it gets what it obviously loves most—"wages," in the form of fish and strokes from the trainer.

Ancestors

Training of performing dolphins has not been going on for a very long time. Whale researcher Yang Hung-chia says that the "ancestral home" of this activity is probably a research institute affiliated with an oceanarium in Florida, in the US. That facility was established in 1938, and it was there that, in 1947, it was first discovered that dolphins have sonar.

The playful nature and linguistic complexity shown by several species of dolphins intrigued researchers. At the same time, as care and feeding techniques improved, researchers began to explore development of dolphin performances. Training began in Asia only after World War II, at an oceanarium in Japan.

There are 32 species of dolphins in the world, but virtually all performing dolphins are of the bottlenose variety. This is because "they are most amenable to being close to people, and they are very playful," explains veteran trainer Jackson W.C. Hui, an advisor to Ocean World.

Many people have joyful memories of seeing dolphin performances as children. The first real dolphin star was probably Flipper, a bottlenose who appeared on American television back in the 1960s. He was best friends with a little boy, and helped out whenever people were in trouble, winning the hearts of countless children.

Yet, in this brief period of less than half a century, with the rise of environmental consciousness, many conservation groups have begun to have doubts about performing dolphins.

One school of thought holds that training dolphins to engage in activities that are not natural just to delight an audience is by definition animal abuse. There were incidents in Japan of trainers using corporal punishment—kicking dolphins or depriving them of food for a day or two—to force the dolphins to conform.

The halibut, not the stick

A trainer by profession, Jackson Hui describes the training of captive dolphins as nothing more than "a good day at work" that gives them a chance to be active. Otherwise they would have nothing to do all day, and, like idle people, could become depressed and die prematurely. He also notes that, due to the impact of conservationist thinking, punishment was dropped as a training method 20 years ago.

Current principles for dolphin training begin with earning their trust by spending several days with them. After that, rewards are used to get the dolphins to learn to do actions within their capabilities at specified times. "We use the psychological principle of conditioned behavior," says Hui. In simple terms, they set targets and use hand gestures to guide the dolphins to do certain actions, after which the dolphins are rewarded with food at the sound of the whistle.

If on a given day the dolphins cannot do what is requested, the trainer will not force them to do so. Hui talks about "Ah Chuang," a male dolphin he trains. Ah Chuang has great learning capacity, but is stubborn and egotistical, and often loses patience after having to do the same action two or three times in a row. When this happens, Hui just walks away and gives Ah Chuang the cold shoulder for an hour or two. By the time he returns, Ah Chuang's attitude is always appreciably more mellow.

Ironically, the thing which most readily creates friction between humans and animals is something beneficial to the animals—medical care. Ocean World veterinarian Chen Te-chin

海豚的「聰明」模樣逗得樂不可支，拍得手掌都脹紅了。而牠卻以最快的速度游回訓練師所在的對岸，顯然更愛的是工作酬勞──訓練師手中的魚和撫摸。

「祖師爺」

人類馴養海豚做表演的時間並不長。研究鯨類分類的楊鴻嘉說，這一行的「祖師爺」，應該是於一九三八年成立、一九四七年首次發現海豚具有聲納的美國佛羅里達海洋水族館附屬研究所。

在研究過程當中，某些品種的海豚好玩的天性及複雜的語言系統引起他們的興趣；同時伴隨著逐漸成熟的飼養技術，水族館開始嘗試發展海豚的表演。而東方的訓練系統，則是二次世界大戰後，從日本沼津南方「中之島」海洋水族館發源。

海豚科約有三十二種海豚，目前各大水族館中的表演明星幾乎非瓶鼻海豚莫屬，因為「牠跟人最容易親近、又喜歡跳躍玩耍。」海洋世界顧問、資深訓練師許永昌說。

海豚表演曾是許多人歡樂的童年回憶，電視史上第一頭海豚明星就出現於一九六○年代。那隻名叫 Flipper 的瓶鼻海豚，最好的朋友是一個小男孩，牠每每在人類碰到麻煩時伸出援手，不知擄獲了多少孩子的心。許多人至今仍記憶猶新。

然而短短五十年不到，隨著野生動物保育意識的抬頭，保育團體卻開始質疑這樣的做法。

有一派人士認為，訓練牠們表演不自然的動作和把戲取悅觀眾，是一種虐待動物的行為。日本就曾發生訓練師用腳踢或一、二天不餵食等體罰措施，逼動物就範的例子。

獎勵代替責罰

站在訓練師的立場，許永昌表示，對飼養的海豚施加訓練，不過是「上班」，讓牠們有活動的機會。不然整天無所是事，可能也會跟人一樣悶出病來。同時，大概受到保育思潮的影響，體罰在二十年前就已經沒人用了。

目前訓練海豚表演的原則，是花幾天時間和他們相處、取得信任後，再用獎勵的方式，要牠們在正確的時間內做出能力所及的動作。「我們是利用心理學『條件反射』的原理，」許永昌解釋。簡單的說，就是用目標棒和手勢引導，達成動作就吹哨子、給予食物犒賞。

如果一時達不到要求，訓練師也不會勉強。許永昌說，「阿壯」是他訓練過學習能力很強的雄海豚，但脾氣卻相當倔強而自我，經常一個動作重複兩、三次就失去耐性。每逢這個時候，他就當下走開，故意冷落牠一、兩個小時，再回來，阿壯的態度就會明顯軟化了。

比較容易造成人和動物間緊張的，反倒是對牠們有益的醫療行為。海洋世界獸醫師陳德勤說，過去要為海豚抽血，必須把牠們弄上岸，由幾位訓練師壓制固定。然而這種接觸行為對海豚來說更為陌生，經常在掙扎中本能地尾鰭一掃，就造成了傷害。

另外，如果有不熟悉的人隨便靠近，海豚也會採取「自衛」。一位同在海洋世界表演的國外退休跳水選手，有一次興起，伸手去逗弄海豚小姐「招財」。牠一驚之下，馬上張嘴露出一顆顆尖尖的牙齒，從水中翻跳出來。陳德勤說，海豚不會攻擊人，招財的「齜牙」，其實只是一種出於害怕的反應。

「招財」和「媽媽」

再看池中，剛剛「收工」的「演員」偽虎鯨和海豚們正在訓練池中追逐嬉戲，然而招財卻獨自抵著池邊一角，隨著水波載

says that at first, when they wanted to take a blood sample, they had to bring the dolphin out of the water and have several trainers hold it steady. But the dolphins found this kind of contact to be too strange, and often quite naturally struggled, flipping their tail fins and causing injury.

Also, if approached by a stranger, dolphins will act in "self-defense." Once a high diver from abroad who works at Ocean World thought it would be fun to reach out and play with a female dolphin called Lucky. Startled, the dolphin immediately displayed its sharp teeth, and jumped backwards out of the water. Chen Te-chin, noting that dolphins will not attack humans, says Lucky's "growl" was in fact a sign of fear.

"Lucky" and "Mom"

Looking back at the pool, the "performers" who have just "gotten off work" are playfully chasing each other around the training pool. But Lucky keeps to herself off to one side of the pool, just floating up and down on the waves. Generally speaking, this is a sign of illness, but Lucky's case is an exception.

Lucky's skin is of a slightly darker color than her colleagues, and her body is somewhat bigger. The white markings on her dorsal fin are scars left from an accidental entanglement in lines years before. The trainer says that in the six years since Lucky joined the park, no one has ever seen her engage in mating behavior, and she isn't much for playing with the others. Perhaps this is because she is a Japanese gilli dolphin, making it harder for her to get along with the others, which are southern bottlenose.

Looking at Lucky's melancholy posture, perhaps she is reminiscing about her days of freedom with her own species in the wild.

Because of a lack of experience raising dolphins, many situations are hard to anticipate and forestall. For example, how do you care for a pregnant dolphin?

In the wild, dolphins about to deliver swim rapidly in order to "squeeze" the calf out. This process takes only about 30 to 60 minutes. But when the female dolphin "Mom" first delivered eight or nine years ago, it took two hours. Hui recalls that "Mom" was overfed and underexercised during her 12-month pregnancy, so that the calf grew too large. The difficulties she had birthing it caused the calf to suffocate.

It seems that "Mom" knew that something was amiss, but she still struggled with her head and back to force the corpse to stick its head out of the water to breathe. When staff members approached, Mom immediately assumed an aggressive posture to protect her baby!

Extremely valuable Willy!

In recent years, wild animals raised in captivity have been given more living space and more natural surroundings. Still, says Marcus Phipps of TRAFFIC, there are still some animal rights groups overseas who wish to close all zoos and sea-world theme parks, with the goal of returning the animals to their natural habitats.

Remember the intelligent and courageous killer whale in *Free Willy*? The movie's star (closely related to the dolphin) was purchased by the filmmakers from a theme park in Mexico that was on the verge of bankruptcy. The success of the film saved the park, but also attracted broad public concern. Since then many people have contributed money to help liberate the real Willy, but the filmmakers know good business when they see it: Although the sequel has been out for a year now, there is still a long way to go before Willy can be free.

Some people have suggested that it is actually better for Willy to stay in captivity. Having been away from the open seas for 15 years, and accustomed to being fed by humans, would he be able to cope with the hard challenges of nature?

Indeed, what should be done with dolphins (which can live for 30 to 40 years) that outlive their performing careers? Chen Te-chin notes that Taiwan's Ocean World has not yet been

浮載沈。一般而言，這是海豚生病的前兆，不過牠的情況卻是例外。

招財的膚色比起同伴們都來得黝黑，體型也較碩大，背鰭上一道白紋是幾年前不小心被繩子纏繞留下的傷疤。訓練師說，招財入園六年多，大家從來沒有觀察到牠有交配的行為，也不太和其他海豚玩在一起，可能是因為牠的品種是日本吉氏海豚，和其他南方瓶鼻海豚相處，有所隔閡。

看招財意興闌珊的模樣，也許正是在思念以前野外的同類和自由的空氣吧。

不過，過去由於飼養經驗不足，有許多狀況是「海洋世界」始料未及而不懂得事先防範的，例如對懷孕海豚的照顧。

在野外的海豚媽媽臨盆時，會快速地游動，將寶寶「擠」出來，這個過程大約只要三十到六十分鐘，但海豚小姐「媽媽」八、九年前的一次生產過程，卻花了兩個小時。許永昌回憶說，那時讓「媽媽」在懷孕十二個月中吃太多，又缺乏運動，因此肚子裡的寶寶長太大而難產，等生下來早已死去。

「媽媽」似乎感覺到有些不對勁，卻仍拼命用背和頭將屍體頂出水面要幫助牠呼吸，有工作人員靠近，「媽媽」馬上做出攻擊的姿態要保護牠的小孩！

威利要回家

即使近幾年來被豢養的野生動物們，已獲得比較開闊的生活空間、更接近自然的環境，但根據來自加拿大的台北野生物貿易調查委員會駐台代表斐馬克的說法，在北美和歐洲仍有一些倡導動物權的團體，希望能促使動物園、海洋水族館停業，以幫助動物重返自然。

還記得電影《威鯨闖天關》中那隻智勇雙全的殺人鯨威利嗎？牠可算是海豚的近親，被片商從墨西哥一家快倒閉的水族館買來拍片。這部賣座影片化解了水族館的

faced with this problem, but expects that "We will allow them to live out their natural lives in the pool. We can't release them into the open sea. That would be immoral."

Water wings

Besides providing entertainment, are there any other benefits to be derived from dolphins raised in captivity? For one thing, specialists

海豚表演帶給人類歡笑，但近來保育界卻不斷質疑，這麼做是否侵害動物權？

Dolphin acts bring lots of happiness to people, but conservationists have begun to wonder whether the dolphins' rights are being infringed.

have discovered that trained dolphins can help improve the quality of life for autistic, learning disabled, or emotionally damaged children.

They may also help in physical therapy. In an article called "Water Wings" in the Fall 1993 *Earth Journal*, author Beth Livermore reports the following story from a marine mammal facility in Florida that hosts the "differently-abled."

A therapist at the facility—which is legally authorized to allow customers to swim with dolphins—treats two children afflicted with cerebral palsy by placing them in the water with three dolphins. The children have impaired muscle control due to injury to the brain. The buoyancy in the water helps the kids exercise, and the dolphins "provide distraction and moti-

127

危機，卻也引起大眾的注意。許多捐款從各地湧入，作為威利放生的基金，然而片商卻不願放棄這個商機。續集早在去年面市，但威利的回家之路還很漫長。

不過也有人質疑，離開大海十五年、習慣被人類豢養的牠，是否還有能力面對大自然嚴酷的生存挑戰？

然而，海豚的壽命可長達三、四十歲，如果海豚老得無法表演，又該何去何從？陳德勤說，雖然海洋世界尚未碰到這樣的情況，不過，「我們會讓牠們在池中怡養天年，不可能再放回大海，那樣是不道德的。」

水中的翅膀

許多人好奇，飼養海豚除了供人欣賞娛樂外，還有什麼意義呢？專家發現，經過訓練的海豚，可以幫助學習，改善自閉症、學習障礙和情緒受傷害的孩子的生活品質。

在「地球專刊」〈水中的翅膀〉一文中提到，美國境內一家可提供顧客和海豚同游、並接待能力異常者的水族機構中，治療師就利用這個方法治療兩個因腦性麻痺而導致肌肉控制功能受損的兒童。由於「水的浮力有助於運動，而動物則使他們的精神不再專注於訓練工作，並使他們產生運動的動機。」結果他們在短時間進步神速。

此外，透過就近和海豚的頻繁接觸，也可以更進一步觀察，探究牠們的行為奧秘，對於將來維護目前已遭人類文明之害的海洋生態十分重要。

根據陳德勤的觀察，每有新海豚加入海洋世界，整群海豚的社會階級就要重新排列。文獻中所記載的野外海豚社會結構，通常是一群媽媽帶著小孩迴游，雄海豚則單獨行動，但在「海洋世界」中則是雄海豚稱「王」。不過在發情期時，母海豚也

有可能稱「女王」。

一直以來，這群海豚的領袖是資格最老的海豚先生「大頭」，但阿壯不甘屈居第二，經常企圖發動「政變」，弄得嬌嫩的皮膚上「戰績」累累。最後還是將牠們隔開，才徹底平息了這場紛爭。

國王雖掌握優先交配權，不過跟在身旁的「敗將」仍有機會，這也與書面資料上「海豚是一夫一妻制」有所出入。

到了每年春、秋兩季的發情期時，海豚小姐會做出尾部朝上的姿勢，向海豚先生示意。有一次因此造成海豚先生方寸大亂、無法專注表演，陳德勤只好將牠隔離。沒想到放出來後，卻沒有海豚先生願意和牠燕好了，一驗血，才發現海豚小姐已經懷孕。「母海豚如何發出懷孕的訊息？」是陳德勤正在研究的課題。

讓牠們快樂

現在世界各國幾乎都明文規定禁止捕捉海豚。台灣自民國七十九年野生動物保育法公告實施後，海洋世界就不能自澎湖購買海豚，於是面臨了貨源缺乏的問題。而近期正在籌備成立的國立海洋生物博物館，也因此無法取得海豚做展示和研究。

目前海洋世界讓海豚在人工環境中自然繁殖，維持族群的生生不息。但為了避免近親交配產生的病變，陳德勤事前會替每隻海豚進行基因鑑定，以釐清血緣關係。

另一個可能的解決方式則是和其他水族機構相互交換，不過這牽涉到品種、習性等複雜的問題，目前的可行性並不高。

然而對於已經被馴養的海豚，究竟人們該如何對待牠們？

從醫療的角度來看，陳德勤表示，把海豚養好要花一輩子的時間。過去陳德勤曾在養牛場服務七年，他認為兩者最大的差別是對待動物價值觀的不同。豬、牛是經濟動物，死了就淘汰；但養海豚就像養人

vation." The children have made "an awful lot of progress in a short amount of time," concludes their therapist.

Another way captive cetaceans may prove useful is that further study and research into their lives may be very important in sustaining the seas, which are already seriously damaged from human activity.

Chen Te-chin has observed that each time a new cetacean enters Ocean World, the social hierarchy has to be readjusted. Studies indicate that in the open seas dolphin social structure usually consists of a group of females with their young, while males are active alone, outside the group. But at Ocean World, the male dolphins are "kings" of the group (though during mating seasons the females could well be "queens").

The leader of the Ocean World dolphins has always been "Big Head," who has the greatest seniority. However, when Ah Chuang arrived he was not satisfied with second place, and was constantly trying to stage a "coup." Today he is covered with "battle scars." In the end the two had to be separated in order to bring an end to the conflict.

Although the king seems to get first dibs on mating, "defeated generals" who stay by his side still have a chance. This is somewhat different from the "monogamous" relationship of dolphins reported in the literature.

During the mating seasons (which occur once in Spring and again in Autumn), the female signals the males by raising her tail. Once, this caused the males to be unable to concentrate on the performance, so the female was separated from them. Unexpectedly, when she was released, none of the males showed any interest. A blood test revealed why—she was already pregnant! Chen Te-chin is now looking into the question, "How do females signal males that they are already pregnant?"

Making them happy

Currently virtually all nations forbid the capture of dolphins. After the passage of Taiwan's Wildlife Conservation Law in 1990, Ocean World could no longer purchase dolphins from Penghu, so the facility now faces a problem of where to get new dolphins. Also, the planned National Aquarium is finding it impossible to acquire specimens for display or research.

In the short term, Ocean World is allowing its dolphins to reproduce naturally to keep the group going. But this raises the problem of mating with close family members, creating the risk of diseases from too narrow a gene pool. Chen Te-chin thus has been doing genetic tests on each cetacean in order to clarify their exact relationships.

One solution to the problem of where to find new blood might be swapping with other marine mammal facilities. But this would raise complex problems of interactions among creatures of different species and habits, so right now the prospects are not so great.

How should people treat dolphins already raised and trained in captivity?

From a veterinary point of view, says Chen Te-chin, taking care of dolphins is a lifetime proposition. Chen previously worked at a cattle ranch for seven years. He says that the biggest difference is people's attitudes towards the animals. Hogs and cattle are seen as economic beasts, and if they die they are culled. But dolphins are treated more like people. They are watched constantly, given immunizations periodically, fed vitamin supplements, and so on. Everything possible is done to look after them.

These days, the target is to "make them happy." Thought is being given to how to make changes in their current environment—such as different toys or obstacles in the water—to spark their curiosity about their environment. For Chen, the greatest reward comes each time he sees a dolphin leap happily out of the water and, perfectly relaxed, "cannonball" back down in a splash of water.

Educational functions

Chou Lien-siang, a professor of zoology at

訓練師運用「條件反射」的原理——做對動作就給魚吃，以獎勵代替責罰，讓海豚達到要求的標準。

Dolphin trainers use the principle of "conditioned response"—awarding fish for doing what is required. Today only rewards, not punishments, are used.

，得隨時注意，定期打預防針、補充維他命等，盡其所能地照顧牠們。

他今年將目標訂在「讓動物快樂」，思索如何在現有的空間下，藉由一些小變化，如玩具的更換、設置路障等，來增加海豚對生活環境的好奇。每當陳德勤看到海豚快樂地跳到半空中、再全身放鬆地掉回水中「炸水」時，就是最大的回饋了。

寓教於樂

台大動物系教授周蓮香認為，為了便利飼養和醫療行為的進行，是有必要訓練海豚一些如定位吃魚、翻身量體溫等簡單的動作。但是飼養的目的應該著重教育功能，讓人類藉機瞭解海豚的行為，發掘牠們的可愛之處，進一步愛護牠們。

佛羅里達的海洋世界在介紹殺人鯨時，一面用幽默的方式，向觀眾提出有關動物行為、生態等問題；一面採用四台攝影機捕捉鏡頭投射在螢幕上，甚至觀眾也會入鏡。

例如旁白說到「殺人鯨一天要消耗身體重量百分之幾的食物？」，畫面就出現觀眾的頭和殺人鯨的嘴巴重疊，看起來就像被吃掉一樣，在大家一片驚笑聲中，主持人立刻補充了一句，「還好牠不吃人。」

曾身歷其境的周蓮香說，每個人的注意力因著參與感而被牢牢吸引，教育和娛樂的目的都達到了。如果僅為了逗趣而做一些如算術、後空翻⋯⋯等不自然的表演，反而容易傳遞錯誤的訊息。

要不要讓海豚「回家」？該不該馴養野生動物？什麼是最理想的人與動物的關係？答案已牽涉到哲學的層次。人類將永遠無法真正瞭解動物的感受，任何訓練也似乎都是要動物來適應人類需求。然而決定用什麼態度面對牠們，只是顯示出人類自己的文明程度吧。　□

（原載民國85年3月光華雜誌）

National Taiwan University, says that for feeding or medical purposes it is necessary to train dolphins in some simple maneuvers—for example, always eating in one specific place, or rolling over to have their temperature taken. But the emphasis in raising dolphins should be on education, not on tricks. People should be informed about dolphins' behavior, and learn their many attractive points, so that they will go further to protect these marine mammals.

In Florida's Sea World, they use humor to educate people about dolphin behavior and ecology. They also have closed-circuit big screen TV to get people close to the animals, and they also get the audience involved.

For example, they do a bit when they introduce the killer whale in which the audience is asked, "What percentage of its body weight does the killer whale eat every day?" Suddenly on the video screen appears the picture of the head of an audience member superimposed on the open mouth of a killer whale, so it looks like the person is about to become whale-lunch. Amidst general laughter, the emcee declares, "Fortunately, killer whales don't eat human beings."

Chou Lien-siang, who has been to Sea World, says that the audience is drawn in by a sense of participation, so that they are educated as well as entertained. If audiences are only entertained with tricks which are not natural for the dolphins, such as simple math or backflips, then people might get the wrong signals.

Should the dolphins be allowed to go home? Should wild animals be trained? What is the ideal relationship between man and animals? These questions begin to involve philosophical issues. People may never know how animals really feel, and all training requires animals to adapt to people's demands. The attitude we take toward them will display our own level of civilization. □

(Jane Wang/photos by Vincent Chang/tr. by Phil Newell/first published March 1996)

宜蘭南方澳漁港內，漁船正卸下捕獲的搥頭鯊（ㄚ髻鮫）。除了魚鰭價格高昂，近年來鯊魚肉也逐漸被消費者接受。

In Ilan County's Nanfang Ao fishing harbor, a fishing boat is just unloading its catch of hammerhead shark. Shark fins have long commanded high prices, and in recent years shark meat has also been gaining consumers' acceptance.

失翼的鯊魚——都是魚翅惹的禍？

Sharks in the Soup—All for Their Fins?

文·張靜茹　圖·薛繼光

近來英國國家廣播公司播出一集有關鯊魚的影片。片中出現一艘日本漁船，硬生生割下剛捕獲、仍有知覺的鯊魚魚鰭，再把傷口累累、奄奄一息的鯊魚又拋回大海。

漁船為取得魚鰭而凌虐鯊魚的鏡頭，已成為西方媒體呼籲人們保護鯊魚時不可缺的證據。亞洲國家食用魚翅，也成為護鯊人士眼中的暴行，備受攻擊。

吃魚翅與保護鯊魚有何關係？魚翅消費為何會影響鯊魚族群？一向被視為人類殺手的鯊魚，也會被過度消耗而需要保育？擁有許多漁船的臺灣也捕捉鯊魚，漁民真的只把魚鰭帶回陸地？身為魚翅消費國，若對真相缺乏了解，面對自己的飲食習慣被當成保育箭靶，恐怕又要糊裡糊塗地不知如何反應了。

南方澳漁港裡，一艘艘緊挨著的漁船，輪流等待卸下漁獲。夾雜著吆喝的人聲，巨形鉤具由上空對準船艙隆隆而降，一條條需要二、三人抬動的鯊魚慢慢升起，由港口向陸地，緩緩移近。漁商引頸而望，交頭接耳，出艙的鯊魚過磅完成，喊過價錢，小鐵鉤又爭相往肥嫩的魚體上撏下，

Not long ago the British Broadcasting Corporation broadcast a film about sharks. In one scene, fishermen on a Japanese deep-sea fishing boat brutally cut the fins from a still-conscious freshly caught shark, then threw the dying creature back into the sea, its body covered in open wounds.

This shot of fishermen cruelly abusing a shark to get its fins is brought out as evidence in every Western media campaign for the protection of sharks. Conservationists see the Asian custom of eating shark fin as an act of violence, and have repeatedly condemned it.

What has eating shark fin to do with shark conservation? How does consuming shark fins affect shark populations? Is it possible for sharks, always seen as killers and enemies of man, to be over-consumed and in need of protection? Taiwan has a large fishing fleet; when its fishermen catch sharks, do they really only bring their fins back to land? As a country which consumes shark fin, if we are not aware of the true situation, we may once again unwittingly find that our culinary habits have become the target for attacks from Western conservationists, and not know how to respond.

In the fishing harbor at Nanfang Ao, a row of fishing boats lie close alongside each other, waiting their turn to unload their catches. Amid shouts and calls, enormous hooks are lowered

一尾尾死亡多時，卻仍大眼圓睜的鯊魚，紛紛被拖往港口旁的漁市。

工人手握半圓形、長形各式利刃，快手快腳，一刀刀往鯊魚背鰭、腹鰭、長長的尾鰭劃下，準確俐落。霎時，一片片魚鰭與肢體分離，血腥味不斷衝進鼻尖，血向著港口流了滿地。

失鰭的鯊魚，繼而被開腸清肚，短短功夫，一條條，整整齊齊被疊成了鯊魚塚。缺乏完整形體的鯊魚，被帆布蓋住，只露出半個頭部，利牙雖尖，眼睛塌陷，已不再令人畏懼，只等著夜晚貨車來載往臺北中央市場拍賣，結束上岸的旅程。

至於與魚體分離的鯊魚鰭，故事卻剛剛開始。

失翼的鯊魚

對人們而言，魚鰭往往最沒有利用價值，但鯊魚魚鰭，卻是鯊魚最值錢的部位，常常漁獲還未進港，魚鰭早已被魚翅工廠標走。

魚類被大分為硬、軟骨兩種，和大海裡成千上萬種硬骨魚兒不同的是，鯊魚骨骼全是軟骨，三百五十多種的鯊魚也幾乎就是地球上軟骨魚類的全部。軟骨在其他動物身上含量很少，鯊魚軟骨卻由軀幹延伸至魚鰭。只不過身體末端的魚鰭，膠質更豐富，鯊魚鰭也就成了人們眼中的美食。

臺大食品科技研究所教授張鴻民表示，中國人一向喜愛吃膠質食物，如豬蹄筋、雞腳、鴨掌，花樣繁多，鯊魚鰭會被利用並不奇怪，這是中國人的飲食習慣，就像其他國家也有自己的飲食文化一樣。

再由廢物利用的觀點來看，人們捕捉、利用鯊魚的同時也利用魚鰭，還可以說是一種節省資源的行為。

根據典籍記載，魚翅最早出現在中國，就是一道民間粗食。美食家唐魯孫曾為文指出，魚翅在中國食譜出現得很晚。清朝

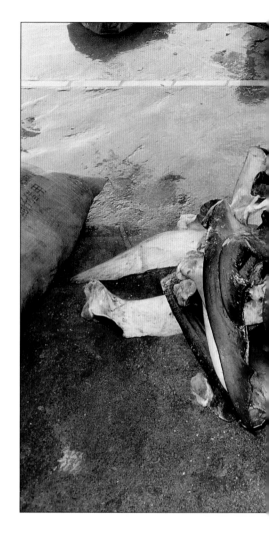

乾隆時期御膳房的菜單還沒有魚翅，慈禧當權後，「炒翅子」才開始入菜，當時絕無今日的大鮑翅、砂鍋魚翅等做工繁複的菜式。

廢物利用？

鯊魚鰭進入宮廷繞了一圈，尊貴起來，再回到民間，經過各家料理師父發揚光大

水鯊（巨峰齒鮫）魚鰭被視為上翅，魚肉價格不高。遠洋漁船考慮經濟效益，往往只帶回魚鰭。

The fins of the blue shark are seen as the best grade. Because the sharks' meat does not command a high price, for economic reasons deep-sea fishing vessels often only bring the fins back to land.

down into the boats' holds, and one after another sharks which would take two or three grown men to lift rise slowly upwards and swing unhurriedly across the quayside. The fish merchants look up at them, whisper into each other's ears, and when the sharks have been weighed, call out a price. Then small steel hooks are hurriedly brought down onto the fat and tender flesh of the sharks' bodies, and the sharks, dead but with their large eyes still staring wide, are dragged away to the fishmarket beside the quay.

With practiced hands the workers use straight or semicircular knives to quickly and cleanly slice away the sharks' dorsal fins, pelvic fins and long tail fins. The fins are soon separated from the sharks' bodies, and the stench of blood assails the nostrils as it covers the ground and runs towards the harbor.

隨著亞洲國家的經濟起飛，魚翅的消耗量大增。圖為迪化街魚翅專賣店。
As the economies of Asian countries have taken off, consumption of shark fin has greatly increased. The picture shows a shop on Taipei's Tihua Street which specializes in shark fin.

，變成了一道道美食。

港口漁市地上深色帶血的鯊魚鰭，在臺北康熙苑餐廳師傅黃德興眼中，處理起來就有著一門大學問。

鯊魚一共有六到八個魚鰭，不同魚種、部位的鰭因為厚薄度，被商人分成上、中、下翅三種等級，送往加工廠加工成乾燥的魚翅，因為需要陽光曝曬，南部東港、茄定與澎湖等漁村，常可見鯊魚鰭被鋪排在廣場上晾曬。

鯊魚皮上有粗刺的盾鱗，必須先在工廠磨去。曬乾的魚翅韌硬，要先煮、泡二日，自來水得不時向著沖浸，才能化剛為柔。煮前，還要去外皮、軟骨、脊刺，一般家庭很難自行處理。選魚翅也不容易，腹鰭一對，稱為划水，二個背鰭比較厚，是做排翅的原料，價格較昂貴，餐廳裡做什麼樣的菜，配哪一部分鰭，可都有講究。

「今天魚翅可以做出上百道菜來，」黃師傅說。餐館若要要噱頭也可以做個魚翅宴，不管厚膩的排翅，稠黏的散翅，或以全雞、鮑魚燜清湯的「雞鮑翅」都行。杯觥交錯中，餐廳服務生端上一盅盅紅燉魚翅，褐色黏稠的湯裡排襯著小半圓形的排翅，調羹一撥，四散開來，就湯送入口中，香濃滑潤。怎樣也無法讓人與血腥的割鰭鏡頭連想在一起。

好吃靠配角

去年，一位立法委員為示響應環保主張，以身作則，在立院呼籲同仁舉手支持不吃魚翅，結果會場與會人數雖多，卻鴉雀無聲、無人高抬貴手。除了委員與選民來往頻繁，吃魚翅機會較多外，魚翅好吃或許也是尚未弄清狀況的國會議員不願輕舉妄動的原因。

不過，魚翅味腴而鮮，其實和本身沒有多大關係，據說過去大陸有一位學梅派戲的京劇坤角陸素娟，她偶一登臺，必以梅蘭芳的承華社全體藝員為配角。她曾自比為魚翅，意思就是自己本身平常，全靠佐料撐場。

經過磨沙、曝曬、儲藏多時的魚翅，已泛淡無味，全賴他種鮮汁以襯其美，因此，吃魚翅最重要是與之同煮的食物，雞、

The finless shark carcases are then slit open, gutted and cleaned, and soon they are piled up in a neat stack. With their characteristic outline gone and their bodies covered by a tarpaulin which leaves only half their heads exposed, although the sharks' teeth are still sharp, their eyes are sunken and they are no longer frightening. There they will wait until night, when lorries arrive to take them for auction at Taipei's central market, ending their landward journey.

But for the fins which were cut from those bodies, the story has just begun.

Sharks without fins

Generally speaking, fishes' fins are the part of them which is of least use to mankind. But with sharks, the fins are the most valuable part. Even before the fishing boats reach harbor with their catch, the sharks' fins have usually long been bid for by processing companies.

Fish can be broadly divided into bony and cartilaginous species. Unlike the thousands of species of bony fish in the sea, sharks' skeletons are made up entirely of cartilage, and the 350-odd species of sharks account for almost all the cartilaginous fishes. Other animals' bodies contain only small amounts of cartilage, but in sharks it extends throughout their bodies, including their fins. But the fins, at the body's extremities, are even richer in gelatin, and this makes them a delicacy in people's eyes.

Professor Chang Hung-min of Taiwan University's Graduate Institute of Food Science and Technology says that the Chinese have always liked to eat gelatinous foods, such as pork tendons, chicken feet and duck feet to name but a few. There is nothing surprising about shark fins being used as food, for this fits in with Chinese gastronomic habits, just as other countries have their own culinary culture.

Furthermore, from the point of view of utilizing waste products, if people catch and use sharks, there is nothing wrong in also making use of their fins, and one can even say that it is a way of conserving resources.

According to ancient records, when shark fin first appeared in China it was just as a low-grade food among the common people. The gourmet Tang Lu-sun wrote that shark fin appears very late in Chinese recipe books. In the reign of the Qing emperor Qianlung (ruled 1736–1795), shark fin was not yet among the dishes named on the menus of the palace kitchens. It was only after the empress dowager Cixi came to power that "Fried Fin" began to appear on the royal dining table, and in those days it was given nothing like the complex preparation required for today's shark fin dishes such as Shark Fin with Abalone or Shark Fin Casserole.

But once shark fin had found its way into the imperial palace its status rose, and from then on chefs everywhere used their best efforts to turn it into a delicacy.

Waste recycling?

In the eyes of chef Huang Te-hsing of Taipei's Kang-Hsi Garden restaurant, there is a great art to the way the dark and bloody shark fins are processed after they leave the floor of the quayside fishmarket.

Sharks have six to eight fins, and after being removed from the shark's body these are sorted into three grades according to their thickness, the shark species and the fins' position. When the fins reach the processing factories, they must first be dried in the sun. In open spaces in southern fishing villages such as Tungkang and Chiating, and on Penghu, one can often see shark fins spread out on the ground to dry.

Sharks' skins are covered in tooth-like "denticles" (also called "placoid scales") with thick spines, which have to be ground off at the processing factory. Dried shark fins are hard and tough, and to soften them before use they must be boiled and soaked for two days, with the water left running constantly. Before boiling them one must remove the skin, cartilage and ridge spines. This preparation is not something most people would be willing or able to tackle at home. Selecting shark fins is no easy task either.

鯊魚屬軟骨魚類，魚鰭富含膠質，成為中國人的佳餚。但魚翅的消費，也成為鯊魚族群減少的原因之一。（基隆水產試驗所劉振鄉提供）Sharks are cartilaginous fish, and their gelatin-rich fins have become a favorite dish of the Chinese. But consumption of shark fin has also become one of the reasons for the decline in shark populations. (courtesy of Liu Chen-hsiang of Taiwan Fishery Research Institute, Keelung)

火腿、鮑魚、豬肉，許多鮮美食品來熬魚翅，魚翅想不好吃都難。到了今天，魚翅更被視為「現代八珍」之一，酒席、宴客為示真材實料、待客隆重，總少不掉它。

只是既非所有的魚類魚鰭都有「榮幸」成為八珍；鯊魚沒有其他魚類分擔風險，鯊魚肉過去又一直未被好好「開發」，也就出現鯊魚被活生生割掉魚鰭，魚體被擲回海洋的悲劇。

魚肉乏人問津

吃魚翅的人，大概很少想到：鯊魚肉哪裡去了？

鯊魚是非常原始的魚種，進化也很緩慢，身上排水系統不如硬骨魚類，就靠身上含量極高的尿素加強滲透壓，以防止海水進入體內，鯊魚的腥臭味也就比其他魚類濃烈；過去海裡資源又豐富，因此市場上鯊魚肉並不普及。

以臺灣為例，沿、近海漁船捕獲的鯊魚，大部分的魚肉都化整為零，打成魚漿、製成魚丸、甜不辣，人們很少直接煮食鯊魚肉。

遠洋漁船在海上時間長，空間又有限，消費不大、價格遠低於其他魚種的鯊魚肉常常就地被處理掉，只帶回魚鰭。

在南方澳港口，一艘遠洋漁船卸下一袋袋早在船上包裝好的魚鰭，凍硬的鰭上仍結著霜、冒著寒氣，「鯊魚呢？」「丟掉了啦！」漁民忙著以鐵鉤將冰凍糾結成團的魚鰭剝開，一邊說，因為是魚肉價格很低的水鯊（巨峰齒鮫），除了魚鰭、魚肚，其他部份太佔位置，就近丟回海裡了。

有一些遠洋漁船捕獲的鯊魚，學者將之稱為「混獲」，即鯊魚並非主要捕捉魚種，但鯊魚為了捕食其他小魚，就和海豚愛與魚群嬉戲一樣，常跟著進了魚網。對漁民而言，鯊魚已經上船，魚鰭不利用也是浪費。

活生生的斷鰭

早在本世紀初，魚翅隨著華人外移腳步，深入各洲，華商在各地廉價收購魚翅，再高價售出，各國漁民也了解鯊魚鰭能帶來高附加價值，「斷鰭」行為因此成了常態。「信任地球生態保護組織」臺灣負責

The two pelvic fins are thinner than the two dorsal fins, which are used to make fin steaks and are more expensive. But whatever the dish, selecting just the right fins to suit it is a fine art.

"Nowadays, there are hundreds of different dishes you can make with shark fin," says Huang Te-hsing. As a publicity stunt, a restaurant may even lay on a shark fin banquet, for which such dishes as thick and fatty fin steaks, viscous and sticky fin rays or "Chicken and Abalone Shark Fin"—shark fin in a clear broth made by slowly simmering a whole chicken with abalone—are all good candidates.

Everyone's glasses are raised and the waiters bring on bowl after bowl of Red-Simmered Shark Fin, or *pai chi*—small half-moon fin steaks in a thick, sticky brown soup. When one dips in the spoon, pushing the pieces of fin apart, and takes a mouthful of the full-flavored, silky-smooth soup, there is no way one would connect it with the gory scene of a shark being finned.

A strong supporting cast

Last year a member of the Legislative Yuan, to set an example in support of environmentalism, called on other legislators to show by raising their hands that they were willing to abstain from eating shark fin. But although the chamber was fairly full, a deathly hush fell and not one person raised a hand. In their frequent contacts with the electorate, legislators have many opportunities to eat shark fin, and its fine flavor is another reason why parliamentarians, unsure of the real situation, were not willing to give their support hastily.

But in fact, the sweet, fresh flavor of shark fin has little to do with the fins themselves. It is said that whenever the mainland Peking opera actress Lu Sujuan of the Mei Lanfang school made one of her rare stage appearances, she would be accompanied by all the artistes in Mei's troupe. She once likened herself to shark fin, meaning that she herself was quite ordinary, and owed her success entirely to the other "ingredients."

After being descaled, sun-dried and stored for a while, shark fin has little flavor of its own, and relies entirely on the sauce. This means the most important thing in a shark fin dish is what is cooked with it. When cooked together with such flavorsome foods as chicken, ham, abalone or pork, the shark fin couldn't taste bad if it tried. Today, shark fin is regarded as one of the "eight modern treasures," and is *de rigueur* at any dinner or banquet where the host wishes to impress his guests.

But because not all fishes' fins have the "honor" of being one of the "eight treasures," no other fish can help sharks spread their risk. In the past the market for shark meat was never well "developed," and this led to the tragedy of sharks having the fins cut from their living bodies and being thrown back into the sea.

No-one wants their meat

People who eat shark fin probably hardly ever wonder what happened to the rest of the shark.

Sharks are extremely primitive fish which have evolved very slowly, and their system for excreting water from their bodies is less efficient than that of bony fish. They rely on a very high concentration of urea throughout their bodies to raise osmotic pressure and so keep out seawater. Thus sharks have a much stronger fishy smell than other fish species, and in the past when marine resources were abundant, shark meat was not widely eaten.

In Taiwan, for example, most of the meat from sharks caught in its inshore and offshore waters is made into fishpaste, fishballs and tempura. People very rarely cook shark meat as such.

But deep-sea fishing boats spend long periods at sea and their hold space is limited. Thus with little demand for their meat and a price far below that of other fish species, sharks are usually dealt with on the spot and only their fins brought back.

At Nanfang Ao harbor, a deep-sea fishing boat is offloading sack after sack of shark fins

人張敬玉表示，今天大部份的漁業國家，多少都有只取鯊魚魚鰭的行為。

直到前幾年，一位澳洲記者乘飛機出海拍攝漁船失火新聞，意外發現在澳洲經濟海域內的日本漁船，活割鯊魚鰭，此情才被公諸於世，日本漁船也因此惡名昭彰。拒食魚翅的呼聲也隨之而起。

尤其隨著東亞國家的經濟成長，魚翅消費有增無減，也成為保育人士的口實。根據統計，僅香港一地，每年即消耗七百萬磅的魚翅。除了東南亞仍是魚翅最大消費地，臺灣、大陸的消費量，也讓人擔心。今天臺北街頭除了本土風味的魚翅羹、潮州魚翅等，香港新同樂魚翅餐廳、泰國魚翅也搶攻市場。雖然臺灣也捕捉、自製魚翅，魚翅卻需仰賴進口。

進口燕窩與魚翅的唐苑食品公司負責人陳茂隆表示，只要大陸流行的東西，就會供不應求而漲價，魚翅即是其一。如今鯊

which were bagged up on board while the boat was still out at sea. The deep-frozen fins are covered in frost, and a cold mist rises from them. "Where are the sharks?" "We threw them back!" replies a fisherman who is busily splitting apart the frozen fins with a hook. They were taken from blue sharks, whose meat commands a very low price, he explains. Except for the fins and maw, the rest would take up too much space and is returned to the sea there and then.

Some of the sharks caught by deep-sea fishing boats are actually incidental to their main catch. Sharks hunt smaller fish to eat, so that just like dolphins which love to play around shoals of fish, they are often caught in the nets along with them, as a "bycatch." For the fishermen, once the sharks are on board it seems a waste not to take their fins.

Live finning

As far back as the beginning of this century, in the wake of Chinese emigrants, shark fins

今天嗜吃魚翅的華人可以變出上百道的魚翅大餐來。
Today, Chinese who enjoy shark fin can get it prepared in a wide variety of ways.

found their way onto every continent. Chinese merchants bought shark fins cheaply in other countries and sold them at a premium. As fishermen of other nations learned that shark fins could fetch a handsome price, "finning" became a widespread practice. Keith Highley of the Taiwan office of the environmentalist organization Earthtrust, says that today, most countries with a fishing industry practice shark finning to some extent.

But this did not become widely known until a few years ago, when an Australian journalist flying over the sea to film a report of a fire on a fishing boat by chance discovered a Japanese fishing boat within Australia's 200-mile fishing limit cutting the fins from live sharks. Japanese fishermen got a very bad name, and calls for people to refuse to eat shark fin began to be heard.

Especially since Asian countries have been enjoying economic growth, consumption of shark fins has grown steadily, and this has provided ammunition for environmentalists. According to statistics, Hong Kong alone consumes seven million pounds of shark fin each year. Although Southeast Asia is still the largest consumer of shark fin, the quantities consumed in Taiwan and mainland China are also worrying. Today on the streets of Taipei, besides local-style dishes such as Shark Fin Soup or Chaozhou-Style Shark Fin, one also finds Hong Kong's Sun Tung Lok Shark Fin Restaurant and Thai shark fins vying for a share of the market. Although Taiwan catches sharks and processes their fins, it still has to import shark fin too.

Chen Mao-lung, owner of Tarng Yuan Foods Company, which imports swiftlet nests and shark fins, says that whenever something becomes fashionable in mainland China, demand is sure to outstrip supply and the price goes up. Shark fin is just such a commodity. Despite the large numbers of sharks being caught today, the price of shark fin continues to rise and there is even a demand for artificial shark fin to fill the gap in the market. Thus in the dry goods shops of Taipei's Tihua Street one can find so-called "vegetarian shark fin."

The pot calling the kettle black?

The Chinese bear no particular grudge against the shark, but shark fin's status in Chinese cooking has turned everything topsy-turvy: the by-product has become the main course and shark meat is now the waste product for which a use has to be found.

Keith Highley notes that in California, local residents have been encouraged to eat shark meat, in the hope that the local fishing fleet will land the sharks' meat as well as their fins and so make better use of this marine resource.

Fishermen's first consideration is economic, and returning poor-quality, low-value fish to the water has long been the practice among deep-sea fishing fleets the world over. This does not just affect sharks, but the problem is that with worldwide marine pollution and overfishing, fishermen themselves describe today's fisheries as only being good for fishing "three days on and two days off." "All kinds of fish are getting scarcer," they say, "and we can't catch enough however hard we try." An article which appeared in the *Washington Post* in March of this year reported that of 17 major fisheries around the world, fish stocks in 13 are severely depleted, while the other four continue to be overfished.

Quite apart from questions of morality, the fact that natural resources are dwindling fast means that practices such as finning can no longer be condoned. Thus many people believe that finning will only disappear if the consumption of shark fin is reduced, and countries where shark fin is not eaten have begun to lambast countries where it is. The verdict that "Asian countries' effect on shark numbers is the greatest" has come to be widely shared by Western magazines and scholars.

But the current situation with the shark is not the same as with the rhinoceros. If one says that

魚捕得雖多，魚翅照漲不誤，市場上還需要人工魚翅填充，賣南北貨的迪化街也出現所謂的素食魚翅。

五十步笑百步？

中國人雖然並非有意與鯊魚過意不去，但魚翅透過中國廚藝，反客為主，由鯊魚附加物搖身成為主食，魚肉反成為廢物利用的對象。

張敬玉就表示，美國加州曾經為此鼓勵居民食用鯊魚肉，目的是希望當地漁船將鯊魚肉也帶上岸，節省海洋資源。

漁船由經濟利益考量，把質差、價低的漁獲沉葬海底，原是全世界遠洋漁船都有的作法。問題是，由於世界性的海洋污染與濫捕，漁業界自己形容今天的漁業資源已是三天打漁，兩天曬網，「什麼魚都在減少，怎麼努力抓都抓不到。」今年三月美國華盛頓郵報一篇報導指出，全球十七個主要漁區，有十三個魚源嚴重枯竭，其他四個仍持續遭到濫捕。

除了行為「不夠道德」，如今大環境資源匱乏的走勢，也容不得斷鰭這樣的舉動。因此許多人認為，只有魚翅的消耗減少，割鰭的行為才可能消失，不吃魚翅的國家也就對吃魚翅這件事同仇敵愾起來。「亞洲國家對鯊魚影響最大」的說法，也幾乎成了西方雜誌、學者異口同聲的結論。

但和犀牛保育不同的是，如果臺灣是犀牛滅絕中「壓死駱駝的最後一根稻草」，針對鯊魚目前的情況，要指責「誰是主要的鯊魚終結者」，都只是五十步笑百步。

全方位的利用

因為今天鯊魚數量的減少，魚翅其實只是原因的一端。

美國一篇文章提到，美國餐廳裡的燒烤魚排，也是鯊魚的終結者。灰鯖鮫和長尾鯊因為肉質細膩、昂貴，在加州海岸幾乎被捕殺一空。根據南方澳漁會表示，臺灣的灰鯖鮫就出口到歐美國家。

近年來鯊魚肉的開發、利用逐漸成功，今天漁船大、設備好、捕漁技術進步，加上餐廳手藝提升，鯊魚開始在各國被物盡其用。臺灣亦然，近幾年和鯊魚有關的海產也陸續上市。

小吃店吃麵，可以點一盤煙燻後呈黃色澤的「鯊魚煙」；海鮮店裡炒個鯊魚肚；西餐廳點套魚排餐，鯊魚排的價格還不輸給豬排。臺灣漁船捕捉量很高的丫髻鮫，除了魚鰭被視為上翅，打出來的肉質，是最高級的貢丸、魚丸貨源。以鯊魚為論文的海洋大學博士莊守正表示，如今沿、近海捕獲的鯊魚被利用的很徹底。

重達三、四噸的豆腐鯊，過去魚肉乏人問津，如今情勢逆轉，除了像件裙擺的魚鰭被製成魚翅，成為魚翅店的擺飾，魚肉價格也大漲，被視為「鯊王」，莊守正表示，如今一尾豆腐鯊的價格往往超過一輛名貴轎車。且由市場需求看來，魚肉消耗還有更高峰。

戲台下的大白鯊

尤有甚者，十六年前美國好萊塢上演電影「大白鯊」後，戲裡被視為殺人魔的鯊魚，成了現實世界真正的受害者。因為人們爭相收藏牠那被喧染成本世紀最恐怖的下顎，在美國一付大白鯊下巴高達五千美金，重賞下必有勇夫，拿著槍械獵殺白鯊，成為西方潛水者的最愛，進而殃及各種鯊魚，骨架全都進了標本店。

除了娛樂性的獵鯊，近年來，人們更發現鯊魚是已知不會得癌症的動物之一，美、日投入無數心力研究，如今各種鯊魚軟骨相關藥品上市，連臺灣南方澳漁港鯊魚被殺刮剩下的骨頭，都被藥廠下了訂單。至於鯊魚皮皮包，在日本則要上千美金。

味道不易被人們接受的鯊魚，在本世紀

由豪宴上精緻的烹調到小攤上混雜其他作料的散翅，魚翅可以很「高級」，也可以平民化。
From the refined dishes at sumptuous banquets to the shark fin rays mixed with other ingredients at small snack stalls, shark fin can be very "high class," or food for the common man.

Taiwan is "the straw which breaks the camel's back" for the rhinoceros, trying to pin the blame for wiping out the shark on any one country is just a case of the pot calling the kettle black.

For in the decline in shark numbers today, shark fins in fact are only part of the problem.

All-round utilization

One American article asserts that the grilled fish steaks on sale in American restaurants also bear some of the responsibility for the shark's demise. Due to the high price of their fine, tender meat, the mako shark and the thresher shark have been fished almost out of existence along the California coast. According to the Nanfang Ao fishermen's association, Europe and America are actually importing mako shark meat from Taiwan.

In recent years the market for shark meat has

been successfully developed, and with today's large, well-equipped fishing vessels and advanced fishing techniques, and the increasing skill of restaurateurs, sharks have begun to be exploited to the full in countries around the world. Taiwan is no exception, and many new shark products have recently found their way onto the market.

When you eat noodles at a snack stall, you can order a side dish of glistening yellow smoked and salted shark meat; in a seafood restaurant you can enjoy stir-fired shark maw; and in a Western-style restaurant you can order a shark steak which won't cost you any less than a pork chop. Taiwan's fishing fleets catch large numbers of hammerhead sharks, which not only produce top-grade shark fin, but also provide meat which goes into the best fishballs and

西方醫學界發現，鯊魚軟骨有抗癌作用，雖然尚未被核可為藥劑，但過去被丟棄的鯊魚軟骨，如今也被收購一空。Western medical research has discovered that shark cartilage can combat cancer. Although no anti-cancer drugs developed from it have yet been approved for use, sharks' cartilaginous skeletons, which used to be thrown away, are now quickly bought up.

初因為魚肝油需求，曾有過浩劫。便宜的化學合成肝油解除了第一次的危機。但科技的進展也造成人們再度對鯊魚進行無可挽救的殺戮。

鯊魚？不了解！

根據紐西蘭估計，如今全球每年總共有一到二億隻鯊魚死於商業漁船之手，曾經來過臺灣的美國鯊魚學者格魯伯（Gruber）形容，若把這些鯊魚頭尾連接起來，足以繞地球五圈。

鯊魚的危機如烽煙四起。在美洲，哥斯大黎加海岸的丫髻鮫因為魚鰭昂貴遭大量捕捉；佛羅里達海岸的檸檬鮫被用做蝦餌，如今難尋芳蹤；澳洲沿岸的白鯊也逐漸減少；紐西蘭附近南太平洋海域，每年也都遭過度捕撈。

在世人共同的「合作」下，鯊魚消費大增，割鰭後丟掉魚體的情況減輕；但並非所有製造魚翅的鯊魚，魚肉都被消費者接受。提供魚肉的鯊魚，魚鰭也不全是大廚師眼中所謂的「上翅」，鯊魚被無端浪費的情形也依然存在。

但除了呼籲少吃魚翅，要確實保護鯊魚，仍必須由鯊魚的捕獲量去控制。

不過大海中魚兒的行蹤不易掌握，海洋資源的保護也比陸地更難推動。雖然國際上對鯊魚的研究已在陸續進行，鯊魚族群成下降趨勢也是不爭的事實，但屬於軟骨魚類的鯊魚在魚類中自成一門，種類繁多，每個海域都有分佈，過去人們畏於鯊魚的攻擊性，鯊魚又非鮪魚、旗魚等重要的世界性資源，研究極為缺乏。

遠見與近利

三百多種鯊魚的分布、產卵場、洄游路徑、族群量，面貌如何，科學家仍沒有完整的圖像。更進一步，目前商業捕捉、利用的鯊魚有多少種？市場上哪一些鯊魚族群減少是因為魚肉、魚翅兩者共同造成？哪一些是因為魚翅需求而發出警訊？魚翅市場上，針對不同魚種，分為白翅、黑翅，部位又有呂宋黃、尾鉤各種稱呼，對證到真實的鯊魚世界，又是那些種類，都需要更深入調查。

在無法掌握正確數據下，即使保育人士

gongwan (pork-and-fish balls). Chuang Shou-cheng, who wrote his doctoral thesis at National Taiwan Ocean University on the subject of sharks, says that today, the sharks caught in the waters around Taiwan are utilized very fully.

In the past, no-one wanted shark meat, but today things have changed. The whale shark, which can weigh up to three or four tons, provides huge skirt-like fins which after processing become centerpieces which shark fin shops can hardly bring themselves to part with. But now the price of whale shark meat has also risen greatly, and it is seen as the "king of sharks." According to Chuang Shou-cheng, today a single whale shark is worth more than a luxury car. And from current trends it would appear that demand for shark meat will reach even higher peaks.

The great white shark offscreen

Sixteen years ago the Hollywood film *Jaws* depicted the great white shark as a rapacious maneater. But since then, the great white shark has become the real victim offscreen. People are eager to collect its fearsome lower jaw, and in the USA a great white's jaw can fetch up to US$5000. Such rich rewards are naturally a powerful inducement, and to go shooting great white sharks has become a favorite pastime for Western divers. They also target other shark species, and the skeletons can be seen on sale in gift shops.

Recreational fishing has reduced shark numbers. Also, following the discovery some years ago that sharks never get cancer, the Americans and Japanese have invested a great deal of effort in research and today many medicinal products made from shark cartilage are on the market. Even the cartilaginous bones left over from the sharks cut up at Nanfang Ao harbor are all snapped up by pharmaceutical companies. Shark skin handbags sell for thousands of US dollars in Japan, and artificial skin made using chondroitin from shark cartilage has been used to treat burns patients.

The shark, with its flavor which is unappetizing to most people, faced disaster early this century because of the demand for fish liver oil. Cheap synthetic liver oil averted that first crisis, but the advance of science and technology have led to mankind's second unbridled onslaught on the shark.

A dearth of knowledge

According to estimates from New Zealand, 100 to 200 million sharks a year are now killed by commercial fishing fleets. American shark biologist Samuel Gruber, who has visited Taiwan, says that if these sharks were laid nose to tail, they would stretch five times round the world.

Such large-scale fishing has led to a crisis in shark populations everywhere. In the Americas, hammerhead sharks are fished in large numbers off the coast of Costa Rica for the high price of their fins; along the coast of Florida, lemon sharks are used to make shrimp bait and have now all but disappeared; along the coasts of Australia, the numbers of great white shark have also gradually declined; and in the South Pacific around New Zealand, overfishing occurs every year.

With the "cooperation" of people around the world, consumption of shark meat has increased greatly, and this has reduced the number of sharks thrown back after finning. But not all sharks with usable fins produce meat which is acceptable to consumers, and not all sharks which provide good meat also supply fins which are seen as the best quality by chefs. Thanks to this mismatch, gratuitous dumping of shark carcases continues to take place.

But apart from encouraging people to eat less shark fin, effective conservation of sharks must start with controls on the numbers caught.

However, it is not easy to keep track of the fish in the ocean, and conservation of marine resources is even harder to implement than conservation on land. International research into sharks is gradually proceeding, and the falling trend in shark populations is an undisputed fact. But the cartilaginous sharks form their own separate group

大聲呼籲，許多國家考量到漁業收入與漁民生計，鯊魚的保護仍只停留在少數國家自己的海域內。

「這是個遠見與近利的觀念問題，」張敬玉說，有關鯊魚的精確數據雖是未知，但如果有証據足以讓人懷疑鯊魚的數量在減少，就應該先採取一些行動了。因為有太多經驗證明，在人們完全了解野生動物後再加以管理，通常都太遲了。如此，最直接的受害者還是使用者與賴鯊魚維生的漁民。

珍饈羅列，食過即空

民初的知名作家魯迅在《徬徨》書中名為「祝福」的短篇小說裡，諷刺一位瞧不起封建時代人物的新青年，卻全心想著「福興樓的清燉魚翅，一元一大盤，價廉物美，現在不知增價了否？往日同遊的朋友，雖然已經雲散，然而魚翅是不可不吃的」，作者借主角心想魚翅，暗示知識份子的虛偽，為掩飾自己的怯懦，只好吃得油膩一點，朦住自己良心，不去想社會底層人的生活。

今天油膩膩的魚翅卻非常平民化，由上流到走卒，吃得起三、五千元一碗魚翅的人越來越多；臺灣夜市裡，也有一碗四十元的香菇魚翅羹，碗裡也見得到散翅飄浮。香港酒樓有所謂「碗仔翅」，煮好了整鍋的散翅，翅雖稀少，慰情聊勝。

富有的觀光客也能在東南亞享受到豐盛的大排翅，受中國人影響，日本人也吃魚翅，印尼人也以咖哩拌魚翅佐餐。

不論華、洋、或大宴、小吃，一碗碗香郁的魚翅羹湯，使鯊魚鰭由世界各個港口，廣泛深入許多國家與華人圈子。吃魚翅已經不是中國人的專利；也不須背負階級差異的壓力。但今天吃魚翅卻仍存在著道德問題，更要擔心的是，魚翅還能讓人吃多久？□

（原載民國83年10月光華雜誌）

鯊魚鰭被割掉後，鯊魚肉通常被打成魚漿、製成魚丸。
After the sharks' fins have been cut off, their meat is often made into fishpaste and fishballs.

among fish. Their many species are to be found in every ocean, but in the past, because of people's fear of sharks' aggressive temperament and because they were not seen as an important global resource like tuna or sailfish, research into them was extremely sparse.

Long-term benefit or short-term gain

Scientists still have no complete picture of the distribution, spawning grounds, migration routes or populations of the more than 300 species of shark. Furthermore, deeper investigation is required into many questions, such as how many shark species are currently commercially fished and exploited, which commercial shark species' populations are falling because of both shark meat and shark fin consumption and which purely due to demand for shark fins, and which real shark species' fins are actually referred to by such shark fin market terminology as "white fin," "black fin," "Luzon yellow" or "tailhook."

With no hard data available, despite conservationists' vigorous appeals, many countries give first consideration to the income of their fishing industries and the livelihoods of their fishermen, and efforts to conserve sharks have not gone beyond the 200-mile fishing limits of a small number of countries.

It's a problem of perceptions of long and short-term benefit," says Keith Highley. He argues that even though there is no precise data on shark numbers, if there are sufficient grounds for suspecting that sharks' numbers are declining, then action should be taken without delay. For experience has already shown too many times that if management of wild species is not begun until they are completely understood, it is usually too late. Then the people who suffer most directly are consumers and the fishermen who depend on the shark for their livelihoods.

An unnecessary luxury

In the early years of the Republic of China, the famous author Lu Xun, in a short story entitled "The Blessing," published in his anthology *Indecision*, satirized a modern youth who scorned the characters of the feudal age, yet longed for "Fuxing Lou Restaurant's shark fin simmered in clear broth, a dollar a serving, cheap and tasty—is it still so cheap? The friends we went there with in the old days have all gone their separate ways, but eating shark fin is something I just can't do without." Lu Xun used the main character's craving for shark fin to hint at the hypocrisy of intellectuals, who had to eat rich foods to disguise their own cowardice, so as to deceive their consciences and not think about the plight of people at the lower levels of society.

Nowadays, rich and oily shark fin has become very much a popular food. From the highest to the lowest levels of society, more and more people can afford to spend NT$3000–5000 on a bowl of shark fin. In Taiwan's night markets, one can even find shark fin and mushroom soup at NT$40 a bowl, and one really can see fin rays floating in the soup. Restaurants in Hong Kong serve "Fin Bowl"—a whole pot of soup cooked with a few fin rays. The soup is thin, but it's better than nothing.

Rich tourists in Southeast Asia can enjoy a hearty meal of large fin steaks; due to Chinese influence the Japanese are also eating shark fin, and the Indonesians have created a dish of curried shark fin.

Whether in China or the West, whether in a fancy restaurant or down-home eatery, bowl after bowl of fragrant shark fin soup bring large numbers of shark fins from harbors all over the world into many countries and Chinese communities. The Chinese no longer have a monopoly on eating shark fin, and it is no longer a symbol of social status. But for those who eat shark fin today, there is still a moral issue, and a question of even greater concern: how long will there still be shark fin to eat? □

(Chang Chin-ju/
photos by Hsueh Chi-kuang/
tr. by Robert Taylor/
first published in October 1994)

致命的「生產力」？
Slow and Steady Dooms the Race

文・張靜茹

千百種海鮮，鯊魚絕非被消耗最多的種類，為什麼鯊魚卻被學者認為是繼海洋哺乳動物鯨魚之後，最該保護的「海產」？難道其他魚類就沒有遭竭澤而漁的危機？

人們都知道，海洋魚類的繁殖策略，往往是一次產卵上百萬顆，如亞洲人愛吃的烏魚子，常被加工成對稱的腎形，一個腎形的魚莢裡，就含有一、兩百萬個魚卵。

可是屬於軟骨魚類的鯊魚，卻偏偏「反骨」到底，不與其他硬骨魚類遵循同一模式傳宗接代。

悲情豆腐鯊

鯊魚有胎生、卵生、卵胎生三種，但不論哪一種方式，生產數都很低。例如被南非、美國列為保護的大白鯊，每胎很少超過十一隻；臺灣漁船捕捉數量極高的水鯊與丫髻鮫，每回產子也都不超過一百尾。

但這些都還算是鯊魚中的高生產者。目前人類已知的鯊魚中，有二分之一以上每胎只生產兩隻幼鯊，其中虎鯊甚至每兩年才生產一次，以三十年壽命估算，等於一生繁殖不超過三十個子孫。與其他魚類更重要的差異是，鯊魚要十二歲以上，才有能力繁衍後代。這也使鯊魚無法成為家族龐大的生物。

海洋大學漁業科學系博士後研究員莊守正表示，鯊魚族群劇減的速度因此比其他魚種快，漁場常常在被漁船發現不久後，就被捕一空。

現今地球上最大型的魚類豆腐鯊就是一例，臺灣沿、近海是全世界豆腐鯊最大產地，自從漁民稱為「憨仔鯊」的豆腐鯊肉被開發為海鮮新星，不到十年，今天漁民已很難再抓到豆腐鯊。研究人員也只能望豆腐鯊標本興嘆。

「尚未研究就沒有了，」海洋大學副教授劉光明也說，豆腐鯊和鯨魚一樣，以浮游生物為主食，沒有攻擊人的不良紀錄。許多潛水者在海洋中巧遇西方稱為「鯨鯊」的豆腐鯊，還會與之嬉戲一番，「臺灣若要列出該保護的鯊魚名單，豆腐鯊應首推第一。」

救救鯊魚

學者認為，鯊魚的繁殖策略採取接近大型哺乳動物的菁英主義，和牠們在海洋食物鏈的位置有關。

大部分的鯊魚屬於掠捕食性，大魚吃小魚，是食物鏈中最高層的生物，因此數量原本就少，它扮演提升其他動物基因品質的功能，如此才得以維持生態品質與平衡。人類的魚網密集、過量地對準鯊魚，鯊魚就有替補不及而瀕臨絕種的危機。

如今美、澳動作迅速地保衛起自己的鯊魚資源，和鯊魚的再生產能力低有很大關係。「就這個原因，也足以讓臺灣對沿、近海一些鯊魚展開保護措施了，」則是臺灣漁業界與保育界人士的共同看法。　　□

（原載民國83年10月光華雜誌）

*O*f all the hundreds of edible sea creatures, sharks are by no means the ones consumed in the greatest quantities. So why is it that sharks are seen by scholars as the sea creatures most in need of protection after the whales? Aren't other fish species in just as much danger of being hunted to extinction?

Everyone knows that most sea fishes' reproductive strategy is to spawn millions of eggs at a time. For instance, people in Asia love to eat snakehead fish eggs, and snakehead roes are sold processed into kidney-shaped pairs. One roe contains one to two million eggs. But sharks, which count among the cartilaginous fish, do not follow the same reproductive pattern as the bony fish.

The tragic whale shark

Among the sharks, there are viviparous species (which give birth to live young), oviparous species (which lay eggs), and ovoviviparous species (in which the egg develops within the mother's body but remains separate from it). But whichever their method of reproduction, they all produce very small numbers of young. For instance, the great white shark, which has been listed as a protected species by South Africa and the USA, rarely produces more than 11 pups at a time, and the blue sharks and hammerhead sharks which are caught in huge numbers by Taiwanese fishing boats never produce more than 100 young at once.

But among sharks, these species count as the most prolific breeders. Of all the shark species known to man, more than half only produce two pups at a time. One of them, the tiger shark, only breeds once every two years, so that over its estimated lifespan of 30 years, it cannot produce more than 30 young. But an even more important difference from other fish species is that sharks take up to twelve years to become sexually mature. This is another reason why sharks cannot produce large numbers of offspring and their populations have been declining much more rapidly than other fish species. When new shark fishing grounds are discovered by the fishing fleets, they are usually fished out within a short time.

The whale shark—the largest fish species alive on our planet today—is an example. Taiwan's inshore and offshore waters were home to the world's largest stocks of whale sharks. But then whale shark meat was developed as a new fashionable seafood. Today, less than a decade later, fishermen are hard put to catch a single whale shark, and researchers too can only look at mounted specimens and sigh with regret.

"They hadn't been researched yet, and now they're gone," says Liu Kuang-ming, an associate professor at Ocean University. Just like whales, he says, whale sharks feed mainly on plankton, and have never been known to attack man. Many sea divers who happen on a whale shark will play with it for a while. "If Taiwan brings out a list of sharks which need protection, the whale shark should be at the top."

Save the sharks

Biologists believe that sharks' choice of a reproductive strategy similar to that of large mammals, of producing relatively few, well-developed offspring, is linked to their position in the marine food chain.

Most sharks are predators which eat smaller fish, and are at the top of their food chains, so that their numbers are limited anyway. Their role is to maintain the "genetic fitness" of their prey species, thus conserving ecological quality and balance. But mankind's nets have been cast too closely around the sharks, giving them no chance to recover and forcing them to brink of extinction.

The reason why America and Australia have now moved so quickly to protect their sharks has much to do with sharks' slow rate of reproduction. The view that this in itself is reason enough for Taiwan to implement conservation measures for certain shark species in local waters is shared by people in Taiwan's fishing industry and conservationist circles alike. □

(Chang Chin-ju/photos by Hsueh Chi-kuang/ tr. by Robert Taylor/first published in October 1994)

誰來吃燕窩？今天燕窩已日漸大眾化，不再只是官宦人家的食品。一些餐廳的燕窩消耗量是十年前的一、二十倍。（張良綱攝）
Who eats bird's nest? Swiftlet nest is now widely accessible and is no longer the preserve of high officials; many restaurants are today serving ten or twenty times as many nests as they did a decade ago. (photo by Vincent Chang)

燕窩——從餐桌走上談判桌

Eaten Out of House and Home— Swallowing Up the Swiftlet

文・張靜茹 圖・鄭元慶

　　今年四月，「華盛頓公約組織」出版了「燕窩在全球消費現況」的報告，指出「包括日本、美國、韓國、大陸與臺灣，全世界華人每年要吃掉一千多萬個燕窩。」

　　雖然臺灣並非燕窩最大的消費地，但華人世界對燕窩的消費，是否足以影響燕子的生存？若要燕窩能為人類永續利用，華人如何調整這一與食補文化息息相關的飲食習慣？燕窩真的

＊　＊　＊

In April of this year CITES published a report entitled "The Consumption of Swiftlet Nests Around the World." The report stated that each year Asians around the world—in Japan, North America, Korea, mainland China, Taiwan, and elsewhere—consume more than 10 million swiftlet nests per year.

Although Taiwan is by no means the largest consumer of bird's nests, there are many questions that should concern all Chinese both in Taiwan and abroad: Will the consumption of nests affect the survival of the swiftlet? If swiftlet nests are to be used in a sustainable

具有療效？這些問題，確實值得海內外華人進一步面對與關心，本刊因此製作了三篇有關燕窩的專題，希望所有華人共同思考。

最遲在今年底，一百廿多個國家組成的「華盛頓公約組織」（CITES），會正式提出將生產燕窩的金絲燕，列入瀕臨絕種動物名單中；但華人社會對燕窩的消費量，也正達到有史以來的最高峰，燕窩會成為引爆「生態保育與中國傳統食補文化」戰爭的新星嗎？

口水自己有，何必吃鳥的？

根據華盛頓公約組織的調查，目前每年進入市場的燕窩在一百八十噸左右。一個燕窩巢平均六克重，等於消費掉兩千六百五十多萬個燕窩。燕窩最大消費地是香港，其次是北美華人。近年來，臺灣與大陸的燕窩消費量則與其經濟力一般，急起直追。

根據海關統計，去年臺灣進口的燕窩也高達二、三噸。數字反映在現實生活，近來臺北街頭就出現了燕窩專賣店；不少「高級」、當然也高價的餐廳，爭相標榜珍貴的燕窩菜餚，招徠客人；電視上「因為珍貴，所以送給你」的罐裝燕窩廣告，更頻頻於中秋、春節強力送出秋波。

但另一方面，國際保育團體也呼籲華人少吃燕窩！臺灣因為走私犀牛角、象牙，正遭逢國內、外保育團體的交相指責，與國際經濟貿易制裁的威脅。風聲鶴唳中，「美化環境基金會」就在去年發起拒食燕窩活動。更有人看不慣臺灣人的誇富心態說，「燕窩不過是一種含有較高蛋白質的鳥類分泌物罷了，口水自己有，何必吃鳥的？」

難道燕子也步犀牛之後，面臨即將滅絕的危機？既然如此，為何又可以大量進口

fashion, how should Chinese adjust their culinary culture? Do the nests really have any medicinal value? Here we offer three articles related to this issue so that for Chinese everywhere the swiftlet nest may become food for thought, as well as belly.

By the end of this year at the latest, the Convention on International Trade in Endangered Species (CITES) will formally propose placing the swiftlet (genus *Collocalia*, family Apodidae), which produces the culinary delicacy "bird's nest" (often called "swallow's nest"), on the list of endangered species. Yet the consumption of swiftlets' nests in Chinese societies has reached an all-time high. Will swiftlets' nests be the next center of attention in the ongoing conflict between modern environmental protection and the traditional Chinese diet?

Why eat bird saliva!?

According to a CITES survey, about 180 tons of swiftlets' nests enter the market each year. If an average nest weighs six grams, that's equivalent to more than 26 million of them. People in Hong Kong consume the most, while Chinese in North America are second. In recent years, the consumption of swiftlets' nests has gone up sharply in Taiwan and mainland China as the two places have become increasingly wealthy.

According to customs statistics, last year Taiwan imported 2.3 tons of swiftlets' nests. This figure is reflected in day-to-day experience: Recently many shops have appeared in Taipei City which specialize in swiftlets' nests. Many "high-class" (and of course high-priced) restaurants compete with each other to attract customers with swiftlet-nest dishes. On television, there is an ad for canned bird's nest in which one of the characters says: "It's very precious and expensive, so I give it to you as a gift." The advertising is especially intensive around the Chinese New Year and Mid-Autumn Festival.

Meanwhile, however, international environmental groups are calling on Chinese to eat fewer swiftlets' nests. Already Taiwan is facing criticism and potential economic embargoes from domestic and international conservation groups because there is illegal smuggling of rhino horn and elephant ivory. Amidst all the sound and fury, last year the Beautiful Taiwan Foundation started a campaign to refuse to eat swiftlets' nests. In addition, there are already many people in Taiwan fed up with the exaggerated emphasis some people place on conspicuous consumption of expensive delicacies, and ask: "Bird's nest is just a relatively high-protein bird secretion. You've got the same thing in your saliva, so why steal from the birds?"

Is it possible that the swiftlet is following in the footsteps of the rhino and is on the edge of extinction? If this is the case, how can they be imported in such large volume? Eating a swiftlet's nest is not like getting ivory or rhino horn, which has to be taken off the dead animal, so why is it a conservation issue?

A serving of heartlessness

The most popular nests for eating are contributed by four varieties of swiftlets living in seaside cliffs and caves throughout Indonesia, Thailand, Malaysia, and Vietnam. Some scholars believe that other varieties of swiftlets make edible nests, but these are largely ignored, because they are too few in number.

Swiftlets in different places have their reproductive seasons at different times, but all of them, before giving birth to their young, make homes for their young in a very special way: They move their heads back and forth rapidly and expectorate streams of sticky, rubbery secretion on the rocks to build their nests. In this process, the adult birds neither sleep nor eat, and they only complete their work after moving their heads continuously tens of thousands of times.

If the nest is taken away, the adult swiftlet will persevere and build a second and even a third one. Because of the added expenditure of effort and calories, however, the female's productivity is lowered, and the number of eggs laid

will not compare to the number that would have been laid in the first nest. By the end, exhausted adult birds with inadequate nutrition can only use natural hollows in the cliff to make up haphazard nooks, and the eggs or the chicks often fall down the cliff and are smashed to bits.

No wonder sympathetic observers consider that each bowl of cold and sweet bird's-nest soup is one serving of heartlessness.

Why are Chinese so enamored of swiftlet saliva? In fact, though Chinese medicine goes back over 2000 years, it was only at the end of the Ming dynasty and the beginning of the Qing (the mid-17th century) that people began to widely come to the conclusion that the nests have nutritional value. At that time the four great tonic foods were said to be "ginseng, downy antlers, swiftlet nest, and cinnamon."

The solution to pollution?

The *Suiyuan Shidan* (a work on edible substances, dating from the Qing dynasty) records: "Swallow's nest is a valuable item, not to be used carelessly." In former times people did not consume nests the way we do today; even nobles and high officials did not eat them very often. During the Guangxu reign at the end of the Qing dynasty (which fell in 1911), the Empress Dowager Cixi dined on thirty different dishes for breakfast, of which seven included bird's nest. But the actual consumption by the imperial household was limited, and was indeed mostly intended to demonstrate status by having this dish that few others could afford.

As for the curative powers of swiftlet's nest, in the work *Bencao Fengyuan*, a compendium on medicine also dating from the Qing dynasty, swiftlet nest is listed as the most versatile of foods. Although the words "slightly sweet, nourishes the lungs, stops colds, is tonic and clears up the chest" are not very appetizing, they suggest that this food is very beneficial for the respiratory system. Also during the Qing dynasty swiftlet's nest came to be seen as a general-purpose health and beauty aid.

市場上燕窩可分為三種
，並有金絲燕咳血築巢
之說，事實上是由三種
不同的金絲燕所築成。
In the market, swiftlet
nests are divided into
three levels of quality,
including one allegedly
made with swiftlet
blood; in fact, the three
types are made by
three different varieties
of swiftlet.

？吃燕窩，又不是吃燕子，也不似象牙、犀角，得由大象、犀牛身上硬剝下來，爲何又觸犯生態保育？

無情湯

成爲人類席上珍饌的燕窩，主要由四種分佈於印尼、泰國、馬來西亞、越南等東南亞海岸岩壁與洞穴的金絲燕所貢獻。也有學者認爲，可食用的燕窩，來源不只這四種，但因爲數量少，較少被人提起。

分佈各處的金絲燕，每年繁殖季不同，但在育雛之前，成鳥都會如春蠶吐絲般來回不停擺動頭顱，吐出一道道如絲的膠性唾液黏在石壁上製巢，過程中，成燕不眠不食，小小的頭需連續擺動數萬次才能完成。

如果首次築成的燕窩被取走，成燕會奮而續築第二、三個巢。由於體力與熱能的過度消耗，此時母鳥的生產力，已無法與第一次築巢所產的卵數相比。營養不足的成鳥，只好利用斷崖上的天然凹洞，造出缺乏具體巢形的燕窩。如此一來，卵或幼雛常因此由岩壁摔下，粉身碎骨。

也難怪悲天憫人者會認爲，一碗碗的冰糖燕窩，就像一碗碗的無情湯。

中國人又爲何對燕子口水情有獨鍾？事實上，中藥雖有二千多年的歷史，但根據典籍記載，燕窩眞正成爲人人皆知，具有療效的滋養補品已是明末清初，當時「參、茸、燕、桂」被同列爲四大補品。

空氣污染，燕窩看俏

清朝隨園食單中記載「燕窩貴物，原不經用」，古人對燕窩的消費，不如今天。當時連達官貴人，亦不常食。宮廷則自乾嘉以來，御膳才幾乎每天上燕窩。燕窩燒鴨子、燕窩福壽湯，均是御筵常饌。光緒年間，慈禧的早膳三十幾樣菜中，用燕窩的就有七樣。但宮廷實際消費有限，食前

In the Qing dynasty classic *Dream of the Red Chamber*, heroine Lin Daiyu has a weak constitution, suffering from coughing and asthma. In Chapter 45 of the book, Xue Baochai comes to visit and suggests that, each day upon arising, Daiyu take a high-quality nest, add half a tael of rock-candy, and cook it into a broth. Though it takes some getting used to, it turns out to be more effective than medicine. When Jia Baoyu finds out that Daiyu eats swiftlet's nest daily, he tells his mother, and she sends her maid to deliver one each day. Bird's nest and ginseng are the two most frequently depicted tonic foods in *Dream of the Red Chamber*; though Daiyu consumes the most, others eat swiftlet nest as well, for health or for beauty.

Even today, some people still buy bird's nest to improve their respiratory organs or to enhance their beauty. The Huang Chang Sheng medicine shop on Tihua Street in Taipei reveals that among those who buy the nests are factory workers who inhale dust and particles all day. Also, given the current seriousness of air pollution, many children have respiratory problems. But there is not much one individual can do to change the air quality; how much easier it is to munch down a swiftlet's nest. Many parents spare no expense to buy birds' nests for their children.

Unable to cure Lin Daiyu

The problem is, can eating swiftlet saliva really improve one's constitution, make one more beautiful, or extend one's life?

The main ingredient in swiftlet's nest is protein, accounting for more than 90%. As far as bionutritionists are concerned, there are many sources of protein, so why do people have to eat bird's nest? Moreover, experts indicate that the protein in swiftlet nest is one which cannot be broken down by the human digestive system, so that it has no real nutritional value to speak of for human beings.

As for whether it has some medicinal value, Kong Yuncheung, a professor of biochemistry at

方丈大多只是擺排場。

至於燕窩的療效，清代《本草逢原》中提到，燕窩為食品中之最馴良者。所謂「甘淡平，大養肺陰，化痰止咳，補而能清」，意指味道雖然不很高明，但對呼吸器官很有幫助；此外，燕窩在清朝也被視為養顏美容的天然健康食品。

清代《紅樓夢》中的林黛玉體質嬌弱，素有咳嗽、氣喘之病，不勝大補。書中第四十五回寫薛寶釵前來探望黛玉，建議她每日早起，拿上等燕窩一兩、冰糖五錢，熬出粥來，吃慣了，比藥還靈。而賈寶玉知道黛玉天天要吃燕窩粥，也在賈母跟前透了風，果然鳳姐便派人每天送一兩燕窩來。燕窩與人參正是紅樓夢全力描寫最多的兩種補品，書中吃燕窩最多的是林黛玉，其次是王熙鳳，她們一個要補，一個為養顏。

即使到今天，仍有人為了改善呼吸器官、養顏買燕窩吃，迪化街黃長生藥材行就表示，購買燕窩者中有成天呼吸工廠粉塵的工人。如今空氣污染嚴重，許多小孩氣管不好，但空氣改善困難，吃燕窩容易，許多家長會不惜花高價買燕窩「孝子、孝女」一番。

治不了林黛玉

問題是，吃了燕子口水，果真能改善體質、養顏美容、延年益壽嗎？

燕窩的主要成分是蛋白質，含量佔百分之九十以上，在生藥學者眼中，蛋白質來源多的是，何必單挑燕窩食用？更有學者指出，燕窩中的蛋白質是一種人們消化器官無法分解的酵素，對人體無營養價值可言。

至於是否有特別藥理作用，香港中文大學生化系講座教授江潤祥曾提出驚人的發現，指出燕窩可能含有預防與治療愛滋病的物質。「但燕窩當中真正有效的成分，

也是很微量，且不易提取，只有更確實找出有效成分，進而合成，才可能對疾病產生明顯的作用。但要走到這一步還言之過早，」他說。

古籍上也記載，燕窩「病勢初淺者為宜，若陰火方盛，血逆上奔，雖用無濟，以其出柔無剛毅之力」。總而言之，就是吃燕窩與改善空氣一樣，緩不濟急。因此對只能偶爾「瀟灑吃一回」的人來說，吃燕窩恐怕更不划算，國內食療學者就不時呼籲：不如以中藥典籍中記載，與燕窩有相同療效，價格卻很大眾化的白木耳替代。

嘔心泣血？

燕窩對疾病的療效，不如人們誇張的那麼高，今天人們對燕窩本身的認知，其實也有許多誤解。

燕窩市場上，人們以燕窩顏色、含羽毛等雜質的程度來區分品質與貴賤。「內行人」認為金絲燕第一次所造的巢品質最佳，稱為「官燕」；第二次築巢因為口水不足，攙有雜質，俗稱毛燕，價格最賤；第三次築巢，因唾液盡失，只好嘔血完成，市場上遂認定血燕是燕窩中的極品。

根據生態學者的調查，官燕、毛燕與血燕實際上是不同金絲燕的巢，其中爪哇金絲燕巢是幾乎完全由唾液組成；灰腰金絲燕巢則含有百分之十左右的羽毛，而棕尾金絲燕築出的血燕窩，其實是因為築巢材料不同，加上生存環境含較高的氧化銅所致。中國人迷信越奇特越有補頭的心態，造成血燕價格被亂哄抬，甚至在產地創造了將白燕窩染紅的加工業，而真正嚐到燕窩甜頭的其實是商人。

血燕之說，也許是心存上天有好生之德者，希望如此能為燕子博取一些同情，也可能是人們想像自己辛苦經營的家，被三番兩次、連偷帶拆得無影無蹤時的反應。無論如何，嘔血之說，雖然純屬虛構，金

the Chinese University of Hongkong, has made a startling claim: He suggests that swiftlet's nest may include something which can prevent or cure AIDS. But he cautions: "The active ingredient in the nest is very minuscule, and it is difficult to extract. Only when the active ingredient is more clearly identified and synthesized will there be any possibility of having an impact on the disease. It is still too early to talk about this step."

Classic texts wrote of the nest: "It is useful in the early stages of an illness; but when symptoms worsen, it is of no use, because it is too gentle and lacks strength." In other words, eating swiftlet's nest can only be of gradual value, and has no short-term impact. Therefore, for people who can only eat a little food at a time, it is not very worthwhile to consume bird's nest. In fact, local nutritionists occasionally advise that it is not nearly as useful as eating inexpensive *Tremella fuciformis*, an edible fungus, which, according to traditional medical texts, has the same effect as bird's nest.

Made with blood?

Swiftlet nest doesn't have nearly the miraculous curative powers many claim for it, and in fact people today have many misunderstandings about it.

In the marketplace, people distinguish quality (and therefore price) by looking at the color, or the amount of feathers and other odd bits in the nest. Those allegedly in-the-know say that the first nests built by swiftlets are the highest quality, and they call these "official nests" (that is, of the quality that an imperial official would have eaten). A second kind of nest, which is widely believed to be the second nest built by a swiftlet and therefore supposedly has less saliva and more feathers and plant bits, is commonly called a "feather nest." It has the lowest price. There is a third type of nest, said to be the third nest built by a swiftlet. Some people say that because by that time the swiftlet has too little saliva, it must expectorate blood to complete the

nest, and in the marketplace this "blood nest" is seen as the highest form of swiftlet's nest.

But according to ecologists, in fact the official nests, feather nests and blood nests are made by three different types of swiftlet. Of these three, the nest of the *Collocalia fuciphaga* is made almost entirely with saliva. The nest of the *Collocalia maxima*, on the other hand, includes about 10% feathers. And the so-called blood nest, made by the *Collocalia vestita*, gets its unique appearance because it is made with different materials and because the environment in which it is found has a higher concentration of copper oxide. The Chinese superstition that the more unusual something is the more tonic it must be has driven up the price of "blood nests" beyond all reason; it has even led to the rise of an industry which dyes white nests red, and it is the businessmen who really end up having the sweetest deal.

Perhaps the story that these nests are made with blood derives from well-intentioned nature lovers, in hopes that they might win a little sympathy for the birds. Or maybe it's a reflection of how people would feel if their hand-built home had been stolen twice without a trace so that they had to build it yet a third time. Whatever the reason, though the blood nest is a complete fiction, the effort required for a swiftlet to build any nest is still prodigious.

Born of necessity

But why would the swiftlet choose to build its nest in such a masochistic way? In fact, most birds simply collect some materials from the surrounding area, and don't use saliva at all. But the swiftlet is a member of the Apodidae family of birds. There are more than 90 species of Apodidae around the world, and the special feature which unites them is that they all use saliva mixed with feathers and plant matter to build nests.

The swiftlet differs from the barn swallow of traditional Chinese poetry that one sees flying around carved pillars or people's homes. The

絲燕完成一個巢的艱困，仍不下於杜鵑泣血。

吐口水？吐苦水！

可是，金絲燕為何要選擇看來自虐的方式築巢？大部分的鳥類築巢都就地取材，並不利用唾液造窩。但全世界有九十幾種雨燕，牠們共同的特徵，則是以唾液混合絨羽、植物纖維造鳥巢，金絲燕在分類上就屬於雨燕科。

雨燕與中國古詩詞中穿梭於雕樑畫棟、珠簾繡戶的家燕、洋燕不同，家燕與人類親近，喜停棲地面撿唧泥團，飛回屋簷、樑上築巢。雨燕卻一生幾乎不落地，由襁褓之齡打開眼睛到能夠飛行，除了入巢休息、繁殖，就在廣大的空中遊戲、求偶、交配，捕食隨氣流而上的昆蟲。

雨燕終生以廣闊天際為家，為利於飛行，就在離地面上幾百公尺的岩壁上築巢，有些雨燕擁有類似蝙蝠、以聲音引導方向的本領，可以深入好幾英哩的黑暗洞穴中，繁衍後代。中華民國野鳥學會江明亮解釋，在資源不如陸地的天空，雨燕欲將巢黏附於絕壁高處，就以本身含有膠質的唾液，混合地面飄至空中的植物，或自身的羽毛黏結成巢。但散佈在東南亞群島海岸上的金絲燕，由於海邊隨風而上的自然素材缺乏，牠們也就比其他同科的鳥兒辛苦，必須分泌更多的口水。由於巢的口水成分比較「實在」，不幸登上中國人的補品寶典中。

雨燕與眾生繁多的后土保持距離，目的是以策安全。沒想到無論如何高來高去，金絲燕只因為口水吐得稍微多一點，就面臨生存的危機。

中國燕窩被吃光了

有人認為，中國原來也產燕窩，但是被老祖先嗑光了。明代出版的《閩小記》指

barn swallow is more at ease around human beings. It enjoys coming to the ground to scrounge for mud, then flies back up to the eaves or rafters of a house to build its nest. Swifts, on the other hand, almost never touch the ground for their entire lives. From the time they first open their eyes they know how to fly and, except for resting or reproducing in the nest, they spend all their time playing, courting, mating, and catching bugs for meals in the air.

Since swiftlets spend their lives airborne, they make their nests hundreds of feet above ground in cliff sides. Some swiftlets have sonar to guide them, like bats, and can fly several miles into dark caves to produce the next generation.

Chiang Ming-liang of the Wild Bird Society of the ROC explains that, living as they do high in the air, where there are no materials for nests, the swiftlets must build their nests on cliff sides, and thus use their own sticky saliva to bind together plant matter that has been blown up into the air by the wind, or some of their own feathers, to make a nest. But for the swiftlets living along the coasts and islands of Southeast Asia, because there are even fewer materials blown into the air from below, their job is even harder, and they must secrete even more saliva. It's because of the fact that the saliva content in the nests is so high that these birds have had the misfortune to have the Chinese see their nests as an especially tonic food.

The reason swiftlets keep their distance from life on the ground is for safety. Little could they know that no matter how high they go, this little extra bit of saliva would threaten their very existence.

Eaten out of house and home

Some people believe that China originally also had swiftlets' nests, but that these were completely consumed by previous generations. The text *Min Xiaoji* (*Notes on Fujian*) from the Ming dynasty describes the swiftlet's nest as a delicacy found on islands along the coast of

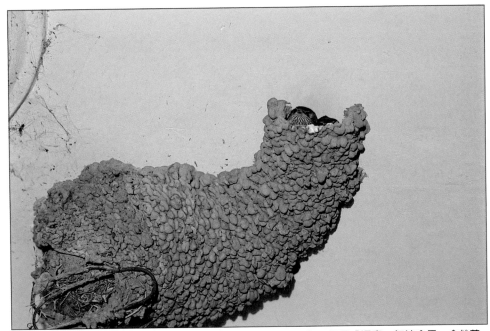

洋燕以泥團築巢於人類生活環境中，成為中國文人詩詞中的要角，但是「泥窩」無法食用；金絲燕吐涎於高崖絕壁處造窩，雖遙不可及，卻成為人類桌上的佳餚。

The Pacific swallow, which is frequently mentioned in traditional Chinese poetry, uses mud to build its nest in a human environment; their nests can't be eaten. The swiftlet, on the other hand, builds its nest with its own saliva far up on cliff sides. Though it is too far off for us to see, it has become a delicacy for human consumption.

Fujian and Guangdong provinces, collected by fishermen and sold inland. But today there are only a very few swiftlets along the Fujian-Guangdong coast. Professor Kong Yun-cheung relates that he saw swiftlets' nests in Zaoqing in Guangdong, and suggested to local officials that they should carefully protect them, and even wrote an article about it in a mainland publication. But upon returning for another visit he found they had all been taken away, and there was no trace of the swiftlets.

In fact, historically only a very limited number of people had the means to eat delicacies, and most ordinary people just stuffed their bellies with whatever they could find. Few people could, like Lin Daiyu, sit around every day taking bird's-nest soup. But things have changed with the rise of capitalism in the twentieth century, and more and more "average people" can afford to dine on swiftlet's nest.

Ten years ago, when the Sun Tung Lok Shark's Fin Restaurant of Hong Kong opened a branch in Taipei, it sold less than ten orders of bird's-nest soup per month. Today, with each cauldron of soup going for over US$35 a shot, "in just one day we sell many times more orders than we sold in a whole month back then," says Ho Ying Kam of Sun Tung Lok. "It's fast becoming a mass consumption product," says the Huang Chang Sheng medicine shop.

出，燕窩為閩、粵沿海諸島的特產，漁民採之運入中原出售。但今天閩、粵沿海的金絲燕已經寥寥無幾。江潤祥教授表示，他曾在廣東肇慶見過燕洞，還對當地提出應該好好保護的建議，並在大陸「動物學報」上為文發表。但他二度探訪時，卻發現燕窩早被一網打盡，金絲燕也已無影無蹤。

中國歷史中，有條件吃奇食異味的人有限，至於大多數的老百姓，也只是胡亂塞飽肚子。要像林黛玉動不動就喝燕窩湯，能有幾人？但到了資本主義風行的廿世紀，風水卻真有輪轉，確實有越來越多的「老百姓」吃得起燕窩。

十年前，香港新同樂餐廳在臺灣開幕時，一個月賣不到十盅冰糖燕窩，如今一盅九百元的冰糖燕窩「一天就比過去一個月賣的數量多好幾倍，」新同樂總廚師何應金說。「快成普及品了，」黃長生藥行也說，比起一餐飯動輒上萬，一斤上等燕窩賣四萬多元，每天煮一碗冰糖燕窩，可以吃將近三個月，因此大有人買，不怕沒生意。許多食品公司在這幾年就競相投入罐裝燕窩的開發。

繞樹三匝，無枝可棲

根據野生動植物交易調查組織的報告指出，一九三〇年代，東南亞的採燕工業不振，但是到了一九八〇年代末期，由於香港、臺灣、日本生活指數增高，燕窩需求也有戲劇性的增加。而各地搶購貨源，除造成價錢飛漲，更導致採收緊張，竭澤而漁的情況。曾花一年多時間在泰國虎崖燕洞拍攝採燕情形的法國攝影師艾立克，就常見到大量的幼雛、卵和燕窩同時被採收後，成堆拋棄於地面，且爬滿大快朵頤的蟑螂。

野生動植物交易調查組織的報告也指出，二十年來，泰國、緬甸與世界最大金絲

Compared to a group serving of bird's-nest soup at a restaurant, which can cost over NT$10,000 (about US$400), one *jin* of swiftlet's nest costs NT$40,000, which is enough to make a bowl of bird's-nest soup each day for three months. Therefore there are plenty of customers and no fear that business will dry up. Many food processing companies have been moved by the recent competition to invest in development of canned bird's-nest soup.

Supply on demand

According to a report by TRAFFIC International, which monitors trade in flora and fauna, the nest-collecting industry was not very large in Southeast Asia in the 1930s. But by the end of the 1980s the standard of living had become quite high in Hong Kong, Taiwan, and Japan, and demand for birds' nests soared. The struggle to get the product led not only to inflated prices, but also to intensification of destruction. Eric Valli, a French photographer who spent more than a year at Rimau (Tiger) Cave in Thailand recording the nest-collecting situation, frequently saw great numbers of chicks and eggs discarded like garbage in a pile, covered with crawling cockroaches.

The TRAFFIC report also points out that over the last twenty years, in Thailand, Burma, and Sarawak in Malaysia (the greatest swiftlet nest producing area in the world), the number of two types of swiftlet nests has dropped by about

40% due to excessive collection and theft.

This is not the only reason for the dramatic fall in the number of swiftlets. Mining in caves, destruction of the rain forests, and collection of guano have also disturbed the birds' habitat; all of these have been a blow to the existence of the swiftlet. "But undoubtedly, the greatest direct threat to the swiftlet is the gathering of nests," concludes the report.

Because swiftlet nests are mainly found in nations that are chronically short of foreign currency, it is difficult to control the scavenging of the nests. In Thailand, where the government has the right of ownership of all the nests, they are seen as an important export product, and businessmen are subcontracted to collect them.

7000 insects per day!

In 1989, the Malaysian government announced a complete ban on gathering of nests in Sarawak in hopes that the number of swiftlets would return to their former level. But demand for nests has continued to rise, and the price went from M$140 per kilo in 1987 to M$4000 in 1991, leading to constant poaching. Since efforts to protect the birds had little effect, the only thing was to lift the ban after three years.

燕產地——馬來西亞沙勝越，由於過度採收與偷獵，有兩種金絲燕已經減少百分之四十左右。

金絲燕銳減的原因其實不只一端，當地政府在石灰洞採礦、熱帶雨林遭砍伐，和收集鳥糞干擾了燕子作息等等理由，都對金絲燕的生存造成衝擊。「但毫無疑問的，採收鳥巢正是對金絲燕最大而直接的威脅，」評估報告指出。

由於燕洞多位在亟需外匯的國家，燕窩的收成並未被適當地控制。在泰國，燕窩更被掌控著所有權的政府，視為珍貴的外銷貨物，而放租給商人採集。

一九八九年，馬來西亞政府曾宣布全面禁止在沙勝越燕洞採集燕窩，希望金絲燕族群能夠恢復。但燕窩需求有增無減，價格更由一九八七年的每公斤一百四十馬幣漲至一九九一年的四千馬幣，禁採地區不斷遭到盜獵，護燕成效不佳，三年後，只好又開放採收。

一天吃七千隻蚊蟲

金絲燕在生物鏈的地位，絕不只是提供燕窩給人這一「較高級」的生物吃而已。鳥會成員、埔里國中老師謝景煌就說，金絲燕嘴型短而寬，是捕食昆蟲的高手，一天必須吃掉自己一半以上體重的昆蟲。若以一公克昆蟲約有一千四百隻計算，一隻十公克的燕子，等於一天吃掉近七千隻蚊蟲，一生吃掉的數量，更是天文數字，對平衡生態起很大的作用。金絲燕減少，代表的是蟲兒越多，殺蟲藥的使用量越高，當地的水文、生態整個都會受到影響。

「金絲燕的族群，要在現有缺乏管理的採收情況下繼續維持是不可能的，」世界自然基金會(WWF)因此在四月出版了最新的國際燕窩交易報告，準備在今年十一月，華盛頓國家公約組織於美國佛羅里達開會時，提出將金絲燕列入第二類瀕臨絕種野生動物名單，加以保護。此外，循著犀角與象牙的保護模式，也有保育團體醞釀要求富裕的消費國控制燕窩的進口數量。國內若干生態保育人士認為，燕窩並非犀角一般的藥品，若遭到指責，國人將沒有理由招架。

絕跡？或犀牛角第二？

但也有食品界人上認為，若由文化觀點來看，歐美環保人士動不動就祭出貿易抵制大旗，是不尊重各民族獨特的飲食習慣，「若是責怪中國人誇富的心態不當，可以接受，但若因此罵中國人殘忍、什麼都吃，是不公平的，」臺灣食益補行銷總監溫鴻銘說，如果金絲燕控制得當，沒有理由禁止人類吃燕窩。

事實上，WWF計劃將燕窩列為野生動物保護名錄的第二類，而非生存最危急的第一類，正是希望針對燕窩的採集，進行適度的管理，以達到永續利用。

針對燕窩，保育箭頭的主要指向是採集方式不當。因此有不少學者研究如何適當採集燕窩，並提出對策。但改變採集方式，採收量會減少，不見得會被需財孔急的產燕國家採納，推動起來困難重重。所以，WWF同時要求人們減少消費，讓採燕工業因需求減少而降溫，金絲燕才能有喘息的機會。

站在人道立場來看，中國老祖先也說，「鷦鷯巢於森林，不過一枝，偃鼠飲河，不過滿腹」。在今天，人人可以填飽肚子，甚至常常吃撐肚子，琳瑯滿目的食譜中，實在不差這一道燕窩。

否則，以今天人們對燕窩胃口大開的情形看來，只有二種結果：金絲燕絕跡，或者燕窩取代犀牛角，成為我們的夢魘。□

（原載民國83年9月光華雜誌）

The place of the swiftlet in the food chain is by no means to provide nests for consumption by a "higher" life form—human beings. Hsieh Ching-huang, a middle school teacher from Puli and a founder of the Wild Bird Society of the ROC, points out that the mouth of the swiftlet is short and broad, so it is an expert at scooping up insects; it must eat more than half its body weight in bugs every day. Calculated at a rate of 1400 insects per gram, a 10-gram swiftlet must eat 7000 insects a day; over the course of a lifetime, the figure becomes astronomical. This is very beneficial for maintaining the ecological balance. A decrease in the number of swiftlets means an increase in the number of insects, with a consequent need to increase pesticide use, leading to damage to the entire local environment.

"It will be impossible to maintain swiftlet flocks under the current unmanaged system of nest gathering," says the World Wide Fund for Nature (WWF). Recently it published the latest report on international trade in swiftlets' nests, and is preparing to propose at its meeting in Florida this November that the swiftlet be listed as a Class 2 endangered species and be protected.

Further, following along the same pattern as for rhino horns and elephant ivory, conservation organizations may ask the wealthier consuming nations to restrict imports. Environmentalists feel that swiftlets' nests are not typical medical products, and that it is impossible to justify importing them under any pretext.

The sequel to rhino horns?

However, some in the food industry argue that, from a cultural point of ™view, European and American conservationists are always ready to call for trade boycotts of others, but have no respect for the significance and origins of the culinary habits of other cultures. "If you want to criticize Chinese for putting too much emphasis on conspicuous consumption, that I could accept. But if for this reason you say that Chinese

are cruel and will eat anything they can get their hands on, that's not fair," says Humphrey Wen, marketing director for Cerebos (Taiwan) Ltd. If swiftlet nests are properly managed, there is no reason to ban people from eating them altogether.

In fact, WWF plans to list the swiftlet nest as a Class 2 protected item, and not as a Class 1 item (which is to say, one in urgent need of protection). They simply want to have appropriate management of nest collection in order to achieve the goal of sustainable use.

For swiftlet nests, the main focus of conservationists is on the inappropriate way in which the nests are gathered. Thus there are many scholars studying the best way to collect the nests, in order to propose alternative strategies. But any change in how the nests are collected that would reduce total intake is not likely to be accepted by the financially strapped nest producing countries, so there are many obstacles to promoting new policies. At the same time the WWF is asking people to reduce consumption so that the nest-gathering industry will slow down in response to the drop in demand. Only then will the swiftlet get a chance to catch its breath.

From a humanitarian point of view, previous generations of Chinese said, "Even the rat and wren take only what they need to fill their bellies." Today, people have no trouble filling their stomachs and in fact often eat too much. Is it really necessary to keep this dish on our already varied menus?

Otherwise, given the enormous current appetite for these nests, there can only be two possible outcomes: The swiftlet will disappear, or the bird's nest will replace the rhino horn as a new nightmare for Taiwan's efforts to show others that its people, too, are environmentally responsible. □

(Chang Chin-ju/
photos by Chen Yuan-ching/
tr. by Phil Newell/
first published in September 1994)

危險邊緣
On the Brink

文·張靜茹

金絲燕族群能否延續，必須仰賴一套合理的採集方法，但以往金絲燕的採集並不像今天這樣毫無章法。為什麼時光往前走，人們處理自然資源的方式卻逆向而行？

民國七十九年，法國攝影師艾立克花了一年多的時間，在泰國西南沿海一個名叫虎洞的巨大海洞中，拍攝泰國當地住民採集燕窩的情形，並發表在國家地理雜誌上。採燕人如何從絕壁上取得燕窩，才廣為人知。

以生命換取燕窩

由於金絲燕在離地面上百公尺的岩壁上築巢，採燕可說是極高難度的工作。採燕者必須深入伸手不見五指的洞中，不借助器械，口叼火把，一手攀著以青竹和爬藤編成、如蛛網的天梯，一手以工具掏取燕窩。

馬來西亞一個燕洞中，三年內曾摔死八個人。高難度的採燕技術，往往是父傳子的家傳絕學，也因此，許多家族常常出現斷臂缺腳的成員。

陰森潮溼的空氣、滿洞飛舞的金絲燕、啼泣的燕聲，加上懸崖絕壁上意外事件頻傳，傳統的採燕人認為，黑暗巨大的燕洞是神靈的財產，必須先經神明允許才能進入，否則會觸怒洞神，遭到不測。

因此，傳統採燕人每年在採收之前，必須先行祭洞儀式，殺一條水牛當做奉獻，

The swiftlet colonies' survival depends on a sustainable method of nest harvesting. But in the past the nests were never harvested as indiscriminately as today. Why is it that as time marches forward, the way people treat natural resources regresses?

In 1990, the French photographer Eric Valli spent over a year at a gigantic sea cave called Rimau ("Tiger") Cave on the southwestern coast of Thailand, photographing how the local minority people gather swiftlets' nests. When his pictures were published in *National Geographic* magazine, many people saw for the first time how the nest gatherers pluck the nests from the sheer cliffs.

A price in human lives

Because swiftlets build their nests on rock faces hundreds of feet from the ground, harvesting them is extraordinarily difficult work. The nest gatherers must go deep into the pitch-dark caves, where, with no machines to help them, they get light only by gripping torches in their mouths. They hold themselves fast with one hand to weblike trellises of bamboo lashed together with vines, while with a special tool in their other hand they chisel the nests from the rock.

In one swiftlet cave in Malaysia, eight people have fallen to their deaths in the space of three years. The difficult technique of nest harvesting is usually passed down from father to son as a family secret, and many families have several members with arms or legs missing.

The oppressive, damp air thick with wheeling, twittering swiftlets, and the many accidents on the sheer cliffs, led traditional nest hunters to believe that the huge black caves were the property of spirits. If one did not gain the cave spirits' permission before entering, one would anger them and put oneself in peril.

Thus before beginning their harvest each year the traditional nest gatherers would first make a ceremonial sacrifice to the cave, killing a water buffalo which they offered in return for harvesting this natural resource.

Last chance?

Because of their respect for nature, the traditional nest gatherers would not strip the caves clean. According to records made by the biologist Medway in 1958, nest gatherers in Sarawak made harvests twice yearly, in November and February, and they left the third nests for the swiftlets to hatch their eggs and raise their young. In his report, Medway noted that although the harvesting season differed from area to area, all the local people applied the same principles.

Is it because the advance of science and technology has destroyed people's belief in cave spirits that some of the nest gatherers have succumbed to temptation, or is it because of the rising price of birds' nests? In the second half of the 20th century, their respect for nature has faded. In Sabah, Sarawak and many other places, the traditional way of harvesting has disappeared. The old ways left the swiftlets the chance to survive, but today's harvest continues uninterrupted all year, and has caused a marked decline in the birds' numbers.

Eric Valli observes that there are two kinds of nest hunters today: those of the old school who still sacrifice a buffalo to the cave spirits each year before beginning their harvest, and the

吃燕窩的人，可知金絲燕築巢與採燕者的艱辛？採燕人必須攀著竹梯，上到高達四百呎的絕壁上採燕窩。
（臺灣食益補公司提供）
Do those who eat nests know the arduous work the birds and the collectors go through? Nest-hunters have to trust their lives to slender vines as they scale sheer cliffs as high as 400 feet. (courtesy of Cerebos Taiwan Ltd.)

younger generation who generally believe that a successful harvest and safe return depend entirely on their own skill. There are also nest hunters who use hydraulic lifts instead of scaling the old bamboo trellises, making nest harvesting much safer and much easier.

On many small Southeast Asian islands, the cliffs are still festooned with frameworks of

作爲換取自然資源的代價。

給金絲燕留一線生機

由於對自然的敬畏，傳統的採燕人不致對燕趕盡殺絕。根據動物學者密德威在一九五八年的紀錄，採燕人在沙勝越，每年分別在十一月與二月收集兩次，第三巢則留存著好讓燕子孵育幼雛。他在報告中指出，雖然每個地方採收季節不同，當地住民卻有相同的採收原則。

不知是科技的發展使人們不再相信有洞神，或燕窩價格飆漲，讓採燕人禁不住誘惑？人們對自然的敬畏，在二十世紀下半期，有了改變。如今在沙巴、沙勝越和許多地方，傳統的採收法則已毀掉；過去的採收，還爲金絲燕留一線生機，今天卻整年不停的採收燕窩，明顯地使金絲燕族群減少。

艾立克指出，今天的採燕人分爲兩種：老一代的採收人每年在採收前，仍會殺一條牛祭洞神；年輕一代卻普遍認爲採收的成功與全身而退，靠的是自己的功夫。今天更有人以液壓式升降梯代替過去的竹陣，採收燕窩時更安全，也更容易。

在東南亞許多小島的懸崖上，如今佈滿進入燕窩洞穴的竹架，但就像被採空的礦場般，竹架已腐、洞穴已廢，鳥兒也不知所終。

心存感激

大陸作家莫言曾寫過一篇關於採燕的文章。文中提到金絲燕吐涎築巢，是大自然中少有的奇觀，嗜食燕窩者既不知金絲燕的辛苦，更不知採燕人的艱辛，所以絲毫感覺不到燕窩的珍貴。故事主角因爲家人從事採燕工作，當她長大後，用針挑出燕窩裡的雜質時，眼前便會出現驚心動魄的採燕畫面。因此她希望吃燕窩的人懷著無限的敬惜之情來烹製每一個燕窩，因爲這物背後隱藏著許多燕的和人的心酸血淚。

今天，透過攝影與新聞媒體，更多人了解金絲燕築巢與採燕者的艱辛；但有別於過去，今天自信滿滿的年輕採燕者當然不會在乎人們的感激。至於數量越來越少的金絲燕，當然就更不需要了。　　□

（原載民國83年9月光華雜誌）

✳　　✳　　✳

bamboo which lead into the swiftlet caves, but just like abandoned mineshafts, the bamboo is rotten, the caves are empty and the birds are gone.

A sense of gratitude

Mainland Chinese author Mo Yan once wrote a story about nest gathering. In it he describes how the swiftlets' way of building their nests with saliva is one of the wonders of the natural world, but the rich and powerful who eat the nests know nothing of the swiftlets' labors, and still less of those of the nest gatherers, so that they have no sense of the nests' value. The family of the girl who is the story's main character are nest gatherers, and after she grows up, whenever she is cleaning dirt off swiftlets' nests with a needle, the terrifying scene of the nest harvest appears before her eyes. She hopes that people who cook and eat the nests will do so with a sense of infinite respect, for each of them bears the anguish, blood and tears of both swiftlets and humans.

Today, thanks to photography and the news media, more people understand the efforts of the swiftlets and toil of the nest gatherers. But unlike the past, today's self-confident young harvesters care little about people's gratitude, and still less about the swiftlets themselves, whose numbers are continuously dwindling.　　□

(Chang Chin-ju/
tr. by Robert Taylor/
first published in September 1994)

讓燕窩成為科學化藥材

Science-Based Swiftlet Medicines—
The Nest Generation

文・張靜茹 採訪整理

研究燕窩的香港中文大學生化系講座教授江潤祥，雖提出燕窩中某種成分可能預防與治療愛滋病的說法，但他卻反對人們吃燕窩。他認為目前的研究，離真正找出治病有效成分還有一段距離，本刊仍請他現身說法，談談燕窩的科學研究。

我為什麼研究燕窩？因為今天西藥的研究原則，其實與中藥的道理日漸接近。我很希望透過燕窩，明白中藥作用的原理。

中藥是中國人經過長久使用發現的精華，一定有某一程度療效才能流傳下來。只是它缺乏科學分析，才被神秘化，原因就是不清楚它所含的有效成分。

中醫雖然不會製造科學化藥品，但藥材治療的根據，卻與目前西方第四代、也是最新的藥品蛋白醣(Proteoglycan)的原則相同：藥材不直接殺死細菌，而是調理身體的抗病能力，所謂固本培元、扶正袪邪，增加身體免疫力。與西方現代正在發展的治療道理毫無二致。

研究膠質成熱門

所謂蛋白醣，就是含蛋白的醣份，它對人體的幫助是促進同一種細胞的互相「認識」，這樣有何作用呢？舉例來說，今天人類的頭號殺手——惡性腫瘤的形成，是因為相同的細胞不記得自己是同類而分離

Kong Yuncheung, a professor of biochemistry at the Chinese University of Hong Kong, has been studying swiftlet nests using modern science. Although he has speculated that an active ingredient in the nests may be helpful in treating AIDS, he is strongly opposed to the casual eating of the nests. He cautions that there is still quite a distance between current research and finding the active medicinal component in the nests. Sinorama has asked him to speak about his research.

Why do I study swiftlet nests? Because today the principles of Western pharmacology are increasingly close to the principles behind Chinese medicine. I hope to understand the principles of Chinese medicine through studying the swiftlet's nest.

Chinese medicine has crystallized from many discoveries made by the Chinese people over a long period of time. It could only have been passed along if it indeed had a certain degree of effectiveness. It's just that because it hasn't been tested scientifically, it has been mystified; it is still not clear what the active ingredients in many Chinese medicines are.

Although Chinese medicine cannot produce synthetic drugs, the basis of the curative powers of Chinese medicines is similar to the principles underlying the fourth generation of Western medicines, which will use proteoglycans. Traditional Chinese medications do not directly destroy germs, but adjust the body's own immu-

，隨著血管遊走，破壞由同一細胞組成的器官，而蛋白酶最大的功能正是可以固定同一種類的細胞。

人體本身有很多蛋白酶，它在膠質中的含量也非常高，因此研究膠質，在西方是最新的課題。含膠質高的藥品在中藥材裡非常多，甚至中國人喜好的食物，如西方人少吃的海參、臺灣的當歸豬腳、廣東的雞爪煮花生、星馬的肉骨茶，去掉油，都是膠質豐富的食物。

而燕窩中的成分也以蛋白酶為主。我們懷疑燕窩的有效成分可能就是蛋白酶，但目前尚無法確定。可是我們卻能肯定實驗室中的燕窩抽提物，能促進淋巴細胞分裂。人體本身有兩種免疫能力，其中之一就是靠淋巴細胞將癌細胞去掉。我們實驗室是首先發現鳥類身上有促進淋巴組織細胞分裂作用者。

尋找代用品

雖然西方研究蛋白酶並不是從中藥發現，但如果將中國人對膠質的使用，進行科學化的研究，說不定能由中藥發現和提存出對世人有重大貢獻的藥品。

若真有那一天，那就更不應該將金絲燕趕盡殺絕。今天大部分人吃冰糖燕窩其實

香港中文大學講座教授江潤祥（左）研究燕窩的科學成分，最終目的是希望找出它的代用品。（中國飲食文化基金會提供）
Kong Yuncheong, a professor at the Chinese University of Hong Kong (left), uses scientific methods to study the ingredients in swiftlet nests, hoping in the end to discover a substitute product for them. (photo courtesy of the Foundation of Chinese Dietary Culture)

今越南開放，我看當地金絲燕也會很快就沒有了。

香港是燕窩最大的消費與轉口地，我雖是「世界野生動植物保護資源協會」的顧問，但無法參與此地有關燕窩政策的制訂；我只能做研究，研究明白了，找代用品也就容易了。

是吃口感，跟治病完全無關。如今燕窩市場大好，加上金絲燕銳減，價格因而飆高。雨燕的分佈很廣，許多地方如菲律賓、甚至東非都有人將類似食用燕窩的他種燕窩採來，要我鑑定品質，為他們開個價，好出口。過去越南會安、歸仁燕窩被市場視為最高級的「貢燕」，如

能否成為藥品？

在中藥材裡，燕窩的使用較晚。也許我們可以從它身上看到中國藥材如何由自然食品演變到清朝後的補品，未來再提升至藥品的有趣歷程，就像一部中國藥學史。但前提當然得讓金絲燕生存下來，否則就像犀角粉，如何成為解熱劑的過程，可能隨著犀牛的絕種而無跡可尋；也喪失了它成為科學化藥劑，讓世人長久、廣泛使用的可能。　　　□

（原載民國83年9月光華雜誌）

nity, according to the ancient principle of "consolidating the body's own defense functions and eliminating toxins." This philosophy is exactly the same as the preventive approach currently being emphasized in Western medicine.

Researchers turn to gelatin

Proteoglycan is a huge molecule of polysaccharide which includes a protein moiety. It encourages similar cells to "recognize" each other. Why is that good? Take the following example: The main killer of people today, cancer, occurs because similar cells forget that they are similar, and split up (metastasis). They travel through the circulatory system, and invade other organs or clog up blood vessels. One important function of proteoglycans is to encourage similar cells to stay together.

The human body contains a great deal of proteoglycan, and it can be found in large amounts in gelatinous substances. Proteoglycan has become a focus of recent research in the West. But there are also many traditional Chinese medicines which contain a very high concentration of proteoglycan. Indeed many foods that the Chinese enjoy but Westerners dislike, such as sea cucumber, pigs' trotters in Tang Kuei broth, or chicken feet stewed with peanuts, are excellent sources of proteoglycan.

Proteoglycans are the main ingredient in swiftlet's nest. We suspect that the active ingredient in the nests is indeed proteoglycan, but right now we can't be sure. However, we can confirm that in the laboratory swiftlet nest extract can promote lymph cell division. The human body has two types of immunity, and one of these is the ability of lymph cells to eliminate cancer cells. Our lab was the first to discover a bird product that can promote division of lymph cells in culture.

Searching for a substitute

Although Western research into proteoglycans did not derive from discoveries in Chinese medicine, if we scientifically study the uses of gelatinous medicines by the Chinese, we may be able to discover and extract a group of proteoglycan medicines that would be a great contribution to all mankind.

Thus there is even more reason not to destroy swiftlet nests. Today most people consume bird's-nest soup for the epicurean sensation, and not for its medicinal value. There is a huge market for swiftlet nests, and the number of swiftlets has sharply declined, so that prices have skyrocketed. The Apodidae (of which the swiftlet is one genus) are widely distributed. I have had people from many places, like the Philippines and even East Africa, bring me other types of bird's nests faintly similar to the swiftlet nests that are now consumed; they want me to confirm their quality and set a price for them so they can export them. In the past, swiftlet nests from Vietnam were seen as the highest quality on the market. Today, Vietnam is opening up, and I bet that the swiftlets there will quickly disappear.

Hong Kong is the largest consumer and transshipper of swiftlet nests. Although I am an advisor to the International Union for Conservation of Nature and Natural Resources (UCN), I cannot influence local policy concerning the importation of swiftlet nests. I can only do research, and if the research leads to understanding of the active ingredient, then substitute products will be easy to come up with.

Can it be made into medicine?

Swiftlet nest is a relative latecomer among Chinese medicines. That makes it easier for us to follow how it evolved into being seen as a tonic food during the Qing dynasty. And in the future it may be elevated to the status of a scientific medication. But the precondition for that is to ensure the survival of the swiftlet. Otherwise, there will be no way to ascertain the curative powers of their nests, as may happen for rhino horn powder if that animal is exterminated. This will end any chance of developing drugs from them which could benefit all mankind. □

***(edited by Chang Chin-ju/tr. by Phil Newell/
first published in September 1994)***

葫蘆裡賣什麼藥？——龜板

From Panaceas to Pollutants—
Turtle Shells' Checkered History

文 · 張靜茹　圖 · 張良綱

人類利用龜鱉動物的歷史長遠，對龜族生態的認識卻有限，除已命
（邱瑞金攝）
Red-eared turtles are the most commonly seen foreign species in Taiwan
Some 400 species have already been recorded, but new ones are being

名的四百種烏龜，今天仍不斷記錄到新種。圖為今天台灣水域最容易見到的外來種巴西龜。

Though man has a long history of using turtles and tortoises, we still know little about their ecologies. discovered all the time. (photo by Diago Chiu)

馬來龜雖非保育類，但出現尚未長大的馬來龜龜板，可能代表了烏龜族群已遭濫捕、過度利用。
Damonia subtijuga is not a protected species of turtle, but the trade in shells of its young may suggest that it is already being overhunted and overused.

　　近來台北街頭出現不少標榜可治聲啞喉炎、補肝益氣的「龜苓膏」專賣店。龜苓膏原本是兩廣的地方性食品；在香港，它正如台灣街道上的仙草攤一般，酷熱天，坐下來吃上一碗，清涼又消暑。一位在迪化街採購的小姐就說她非常喜歡吃龜苓膏，因為和仙草一樣，可以養顏美容。

　　含有龜板成分的龜苓膏除跨海前來台灣，如今也遠渡重洋到新加坡、美國各地，頗有成為華人圈共同食品的雄心大志，不過你可知道，吃龜苓膏也可能吃出問題？

　　繼犀角、虎骨、熊膽之後，牽涉到保育類動物的中藥材「龜板」，近來也受到保育人士的關心。但過去眾人關注保育類動物產製品的焦點是「有否走私、用量多少」，至於龜板，主管生態保育的農委會與保育團體、甚至中藥商本身，最急於知道的卻是「它到底是哪一種烏龜的殼？」

你賣的是哪一種龜殼？

　　四月初，一荷蘭商人由台灣進口的中藥，因為含有龜板成分，遭荷蘭警方取締、沒收，販賣商還因此被起訴。

　　但和犀角、虎骨情況不同的是，前兩者的來源犀牛、老虎，種類少，且都面臨絕種、已列入保育；目前已知的龜類卻有十

Recently the streets of Taipei have been festooned with signs posted by the sellers of guiling *paste, touting its success in treating hoarse and sore throats as well as its salubrious effects on the liver. The paste, made from turtle shell, was originally a food used in Guangdong and Guangxi. In Hong Kong it is sold at stands like those that sell* xiancao *herbal jelly in Taiwan. On a hot day, sitting down and drinking a refreshing bowl of it is a good way to cool down. A woman buying some on Tihua Street in Taipei says she likes it because it does wonders for her skin, just like* xiancao *jelly.*

The paste has traveled still farther from home, and now can be found in Singapore and all over the United States. It seems to be harboring an ambition to become a standard in Chinese cuisine everywhere. Yet are there problems associated with eating guiling *paste?*

Turtle shell has recently joined rhino horn, tiger bone, and bear gall as an ingredient whose use in traditional Chinese medicine has come to the attention of conservationists. Whereas for those other animal products the focus has been on smuggling and the total amount being consumed, for the shells of chelonians (turtles, tortoises and terrapins), the Council of Agriculture (the ROC agency in charge of ecological and conservation measures), conservation groups and even makers and dealers of Chinese medicines are most concerned with determining which species bore the shells being traded.

Which turtle's shell?

In early April traditional Chinese medicine containing turtle shell was shipped from Taiwan by a Dutch dealer. In Holland it was confiscated by the police, and criminal charges were brought against the importer.

The circumstances, however, differ markedly from the trade in rhino horns and tiger bones, for whereas there are only a few species of rhinos and tigers and all are endangered and thus listed as protected animals, so far 12 families and

nearly 400 species of chelonians have been discovered. Protected species account for only a tenth of them, and there is nothing illegal about making medicine from the remaining 90 percent.

Yet Chinese practitioners of Chinese medicine have traditionally classified turtles and tortoises into five or six general types based on considerations of locale and medicinal effect. The groupings vary greatly from those of Western zoology. Makers and dealers of Chinese medicines may even market the shells of all assortment of species as just plain "turtle shell." These firms simply do not know if some of the shells were taken from protected species.

Today, with growing international consciousness about the importance of protecting animals, nations are no less concerned with protecting themselves. Holland simply wants to be absolutely clear about which shells are being sold within its borders, and so, without regard to the circumstances, it just went ahead and confiscated the goods in question, leaving the Dutch importer and the Chinese exporter, the Mingtung Chinese Medical Company, to call for help in all quarters.

117 medicinal ingredients from turtle shell

Though offering immediate results, Western medicines often have bad side effects, whereas traditional Chinese medicines are usually safe and mild. With the growing popularity of natural medicines and health food, Chinese traditional prescriptions have gradually been gaining popularity in the West. In recent years, Taiwan has been promoting so-called "scientific Chinese medicine," with clear labeling and strict testing. The days of secret formulas are past, and exports to Europe and America are growing year by year. The assistant general manager of Mingtung, a Mr. Chang, points out that overseas Chinese account for only about half of the Western demand. When he went to Europe to lecture about Chinese medicine, many caucasian physical therapists and other medical professionals attended his classes. In Germany and Switzerland

緬甸陸龜
Burmese star tortoise

烏龜
Chincmys rccvcsii

粗頸龜
Siebenrockiella crassicollis

各式龜板，有來自保育龜、
非保育龜，辨識起來，讓研究
人員大傷腦筋。圖中緬甸陸龜為保育
類。（張賢哲提供）

There are so many species of turtles and tortoises—both protected and unprotected—and each has its unique shell. Telling them apart causes researchers big headaches. The Burmese star tortoise and *Geoemyda grandis* are protected, whereas the *Cyclemys dentata* and *Cuora amboinensis* are not. (courtesy of Chang Hsien-cheh)

安步閉殼龜
Cuora amboinensis

二科、將近四百種，其中列爲保育的種類只有十分之一，因此以其他十分之九的烏龜作爲藥材並不違法。

不過中藥商只依產地、療效，將龜板大分爲赤米龜、蘇板等五、六種，與生物學上對烏龜的命名出入極大，有藥商甚至將各式各樣的龜板統稱爲烏龜殼，對自己葫蘆裡賣的藥，是否涉及珍貴的保育類，也丈二金剛，摸不著頭腦。

國際上對牽涉到保育類動物的利用，如今可說風聲鶴唳，人人自危，荷蘭就非要弄清楚自己國度裡賣的到底是哪一種龜殼，因此不管三七二十一，先沒收再說，讓荷商與台灣出口商「明通中藥公司」急著四處求救。

一百一十七種龜板藥方

由於西藥藥到病除的效力，也引起人體許多的副作用，而中藥療效緩和、安全，加上自然療法、健康食物風行，如今中藥材逐漸「東風西漸」。台灣近年來推廣所謂科學中藥，要求藥材標示清楚、嚴格檢驗，不再像過去以祕方自居，因此每年出口歐、美的數量不斷增加。明通中藥公司張姓副總經理表示，今天外銷的中藥材，有一半左右的消費者並非華人，他至歐洲講解中藥的使用，前來上課的許多是洋面孔的年輕理療師、復健師，德國、瑞典也都已核可中藥爲正統藥材。

但若無法爲龜板正名，荷蘭龜板事件，可能給才打開的歐洲中藥市場蒙上陰影，國內二十幾家出口中藥商，連帶都會受到影響。若因此國際要求禁用龜板，不只中藥商損失慘重，許多消費者也會受波及，因爲龜板是現下中藥裡使用最廣的動物藥材。

根據中國醫藥學院教授張賢哲統計，目前涉及保育類動物的中藥材有十三種，包括象皮、水獺肝與已禁用的犀角，醫藥界

some Chinese medicines have already been certified.

But the Dutch turtle shell incident, by showing dealers' inability to distinguish between species, may have cast a dark shadow across the market for traditional Chinese medicines in Europe that will affect all of the twenty-some Taiwanese exporters. And if calls for a ban on the use of chelonian parts follow, the traders won't be the only ones who are hurt. Consumers too will be hit, because turtle shell is one of the most common ingredients in traditional Chinese prescriptions.

According to Chang Hsien-cheh, a professor at China Medical College, there are 13 components of Chinese medicines traditionally taken from protected animal species. For quite some time now, the industry has virtually ceased using many of them—including elephant skin, otter liver and rhino horn, for which trade has already been banned. Other ingredients, such as bear gall, antelope horn, and musk are prescribed more frequently, but none so often as turtle shell. According to records of the Board of Foreign Trade, the amount of turtle shell being imported into Taiwan exceeds 200,000 kilos or even 300,000 kilos per annum. When you consider that a sun-dried shell weighs only a few ounces, this means that more than a million shells come through ROC customs each year.

There is a long history of turtle shells being used in Chinese medicine. *Shen Nong's Herbal Classic*—the oldest text about traditional Chinese medicines, written more than 2000 years ago—clearly lists the properties and main medical uses of turtle and tortoise shells. Good for the kidneys, chelonian shell is largely used for treating sore feet and hips, strengthening the bones and muscles and treating long-term diarrhea. Today Chinese herbalists also prescribe it for treating pancreas infections and tumors. When reading ancient medical texts, Chang Hsien-cheh discovered that there were more than 117 common prescriptions containing che-

除了甲殼可製藥材，烏龜面臨生存危機的原因還有許多。台灣原生的柴棺龜因為棲息的濕地遭開發，族群日漸衰弱。（陳添喜攝）

Apart from use of their shells in medicine, there are a number of reasons why turtle and tortoise populations are in a state of crisis. Taiwan's native *Clemmys mutica* is on the decline as its wetland habitat is destroyed. (photo by Chen Tien-hsi)

已幾乎不用了，其中熊膽、羚羊角、麝香等用量雖仍普遍，但都不如龜板多。在國貿局海關進出口記錄上，近年來台灣每年進口龜板量將近十萬公斤，一個曬乾的龜板不過幾兩重，等於每年有四、五十萬隻烏龜被去殼製成藥材。

龜板在中藥使用的歷史淵遠流長，二千多年前我國最古老的藥物文獻《神農本草經》，已清楚記載其性味與主治病症。龜板主要治療腰腳酸痛，還有補心腎、強筋骨與止久痢的功能，今天中醫師也拿它來治療胰臟炎、腫瘤。張賢哲整理中藥典發現，和龜板有關的常用藥方有一百一十七個。至於龜苓膏，只是龜板在治療之外延

double-immortal" jellies which are widely sold and commonly prescribed to treat osteoporosis. Today more and more people are falling victim to disorders involving the spine and nervous system. According to Lin Cheng-wu, the owner of Seng Yuang, a vendor of traditional medicines, they are the biggest consumers of turtle shell.

When exam season rolls around, the parents of many students go to herbal pharmacies to buy the traditional prescription called "Confucius' pillow." Liao Swun-fu, the third generation of his family to run the Huang Chang-sheng Pharmacy, points out that turtle shell has long been used together with pilose antler, "dragon bones" (fossil bones now sometimes claimed to be dinosaur bones) and milkwort in this popular prescription said to increase memory and spur the acquisition of wisdom.

In Chinese medicine, the liver and tendons are thought to have a special relationship, as are the kidneys and the bones. Being good for the tendons and bones, turtle and tortoise shells are hence also thought to be good for the kidneys. Far-fetched explanations are often made about how traditional prescriptions affect the kidneys and increase male sex drive. Huang explains that turtle shell's effects shouldn't be so narrowly defined. Rather it should be regarded as increasing general vitality, just as developing skills in *waidan* kung fu can develop one's *qi*. And so whether one is young or old, male or female, suffers from a sore back, nagging sore throat, or weak blood and *qi*, there is an appropriate prescription containing turtle shell. In traditional Chinese pharmacies, turtle shell is mixed with hemlock parsley, Sichuan lovage root and human hair in "Buddha's hand soup," a common prescription said to help ease childbirth. Sometimes claims are even made that turtle shell can cure infertility in women.

Twenty years ago clinical experiments carried out in the West determined that chelonian shell does indeed stimulate the nerves in the lumbar vertebrae, and, by loosening the pelvis,

lonian shell. And *guiling* paste, which is regarded as a food rather than a medicine, is not even one of them.

Three in one

Chelonian shell, so unyielding on the outside, is a great repository of medicinal substances within. Combined with pilose antlers, it is found in the "four treasure" and "turtle and deer

伸出的一種食品，藥典上並不存在。

三效合一？

看來堅硬的龜板，裡層含豐富動物膠質，龜板與鹿茸、各式植物藥合熬的「龜鹿二仙膠」、「四珍膠」，民間到處有售，是中醫師最常推薦給骨質疏鬆症病患使用的藥方。今天罹患脊椎神經、腰椎神經毛病的病患日增，生元藥材公司老闆林承斌說，消費龜板最多的正是這類病人。

每逢考季，很多家有考生的父母會到中藥店抓「孔聖枕中方」，在顧客川流不息、已歷三代的迪化街黃長生中藥行裡，老闆廖孫福表示，龜板與鹿茸、龍骨、菖蒲、遠志合用，可以增強記憶、開智慧，是很受歡迎的藥方。

中醫學認為肝與筋、腎與骨彼此相關，補筋骨的龜板也有養腎功能。許多中藥常遭人穿鑿附會，被繪聲繪影有所謂強腎、壯陽之效。黃姓中藥師解釋，所謂補腎，並非狹義的增強性能力，而是補元氣，就像練外丹功是練氣一樣，因此不分腰痠背痛、久咳、氣血養虛，無論男、女、老、少，有各種針對不同年齡、症狀的龜板藥方。在中藥店裡，龜板調配川芎、當歸、頭髮的處方「佛手湯」，有助產婦順產，也是常被購買的藥方；民間甚至傳說龜板膠可以治不孕症。

二十多年前，西方曾針對龜板進行臨床實驗，發現它確實有刺激腰椎神經，鬆弛骨盆腔，幫助產婦順利生產的功能。日本在一九六七年針對龜板成分分析指出，龜板煉製的龜膠，軟骨素硫酸特別豐富，可以增強人體免疫機能。

雖然中醫藥界有必要全面、廣泛針對龜板療效加以臨床記錄，做更科學的研究，但龜板若缺乏療效，在民族發展歷程中早被淘汰了，中研院文哲所籌備處研究員李豐楙認為，中醫、藥是經驗科學，有不可不信之處。

由於龜板兼具食品、保健、治療的三重效能，因此除台灣，大陸、香港、日本、韓國，甚至歐美華人社區的龜板使用數量長期居高不下。亞洲國家使用龜板對烏龜族群的影響到底如何，遂也成為保育組織急於了解的事。

猜猜我是誰

除了南極，人們統稱的烏龜，分布在全球各地，被大分為海龜、淡水龜、陸龜。在台灣，對誤入魚網的海龜，常被用來放生，玳瑁則被大量精製成眼鏡架、各種飾品，過去也有少部分龜肉被製成肉乾。但由於海龜種類、數量少，來源不穩定，加上熬膠量大不如陸龜與淡水龜，今天又都具保育龜身分，因此一般中藥商並不以海龜為藥材來源。

此外，雖然台灣本身有五種淡水龜，由於人工成本高昂與傳統使用習慣，藥商都由大陸與東南亞印尼、緬甸、越南等地進口取自陸龜與淡水龜的龜甲。但在動物保育不成氣候的時代，龜板有療效比較重要，至於確實是取自哪一種烏龜，並非中藥商所關心的重點。

另一方面，過去生態學上對烏龜的研究有限，至今大陸、東南亞等開發中國家，還不斷記錄到新種烏龜。目前只有優游於各大洋、體型碩大的七種海龜，如玳瑁、革龜在各地的動向受到較多關注，加上有五種瀕臨絕種，海龜已全數被列入保育。其餘眾多龜族，除華盛頓公約列出的十多種瀕臨絕種陸龜，如分布地侷限於島嶼的馬達加斯加輻射龜，加拉巴哥群島的象龜之外，絕大多數烏龜的生活習性與族群現況，乏人關心，能辨識各種烏龜的人更微乎其微。

因此別說進出口商有眼不識泰山，無法以貌取龜，對海關、保育官員、警察等法

does help with childbirth. In 1967 a Japanese analysis of the chemical components of turtle shell found that the abundant chondroitinsulfuric acid distilled from it strengthens the immune system.

Many more clinical records need to be kept about the medicinal effects of turtle and tortoise shell in traditional Chinese medicine before prescriptions will have an ample scientific basis. Yet if chelonian shell really had no medicinal effects, people never would have used it for so long, holds Li Feng-mao, a researcher at the Academia Sinica's Institute of Chinese Literature and Philosophy. Chinese medicine and its prescriptions are the products of empirical science, and many of the claims made about them stand up to scrutiny.

Because chelonian shell is used in foods, tonics and curatives, demand for it has been steadily rising in mainland China, Hong Kong, Japan and Korea, and even overseas Chinese communities in Europe and America. Now conservation groups are urgently trying to understand how Asian consumption is affecting turtle and tortoise populations.

Guess whose shell I am?

Chelonians, including marine and freshwater turtles as well as land-lubbing tortoises, can be found everywhere but Antarctica. In Taiwan, the sea turtles that get caught in fishermen's nets are often set free as a Buddhist gesture of goodwill toward other living beings. The hawksbill turtle

宰食烏龜，是中、外共有的傳統，龜卵至今仍是許多民族眼中的美食。（陳添喜攝）

There is a tradition of killing and eating chelonians both in China and elsewhere, and many people still regard turtle eggs as a great delicacy. (photo by Chen Tien-hsi)

has been used for tortoiseshell in spectacle frames and clothing accessories, and in the past a small number were used to make dried meat. But because the few species of sea turtles are all protected and their small populations would make for an unstable supply, and because the amount of gelatin in them is far below what is found in freshwater turtles and tortoises, few manufacturers use sea turtles as a source for traditional Chinese medicine.

And although Taiwan itself has five species of freshwater turtles, due to the high cost of labor here, medicine dealers import all of their tortoise and freshwater turtle shells from mainland China and the Southeast Asian countries of Indonesia, Burma and Vietnam. With environmental conservation yet to have come of age in these places, the medicinal effects of turtle shells are the focus of dealers' concern there, and they have little understanding about which shells come from which species.

Furthermore, relatively little environmental research has been carried out on chelonians. In the developing countries of Southeast Asia, new species are still being discovered. Currently the only species receiving much attention are seven large species of sea turtles that roam the world's oceans, including the hawksbill and the leatherback. Five are classed as endangered. For the remaining species of turtles and tortoises, apart from a dozen or more that have limited ranges,

令把關者，甚至大部分國內外動物學者，要慧眼識保育龜，都是一大考驗。目前到底有多少種龜板涉及保育類，各國也提不出實際數據。就連有一百多個會員國、資源最豐富的國際保育組織「華盛頓公約組織」，都只能由收集「亞洲有多少種烏龜、被利用的情形如何」等基本資料，來展開保育亞洲龜族的第一步。

百分之五是保育類？

去年七月農委會委託張賢哲開始為龜板尋找「主人」——調查台灣使用的龜板到底是哪些烏龜貢獻的甲殼。張賢哲針對三十家左右進口商合法申請的龜板，一貨櫃一貨櫃清點，也只能辨識出百分之六十的種類。其中確實攙雜有保育龜龜甲，比例約在百分之五左右，包括有孔雀龜、緬甸陸龜、大地龜。但其他百分之四十，是否涉及保育類，仍待進一步了解。

合法進口的龜板中有保育類，在中興大學動物系副教授吳聲海看來，並不令人驚訝，問題仍在人們缺乏鑑別烏龜的能力。尤其對進出口龜板國家，無法鑑定保育類物種，加上顧慮龜板市場龐大，牽涉人數眾多，更不可能依法實際執行沒收保育類龜板、懲罰進口商、禁止保育類產製品進出口的工作，出現保育類龜板也就不足為奇了。

烏龜是極其古老的動物，靠著盔甲，適者生存，從兩億年前存活至今，因此傳統上地方性捕捉食用，並未對烏龜族群造成太大衝擊。在中醫藥界看來，中藥使用龜板千百年，從未出現貨源不足的問題。張賢哲就說，中醫藥界沒有人研究過龜板替代品的可行性，因為沒有必要。然而今天烏龜為何又面臨前所未有的生存危機？

根據美國史密森博物館在一九八九年出版的《地球上的龜鱉動物》一書指出，除了都市化國家烏龜常成千上百的死在高速

such as the giant turtles of the Galapagos islands and the radiated tortoise of Madagascar, which CITES, the Convention on International Trade in Endangered Species, list as protected, few people know or care much about the living habits or populations of most turtle species, and fewer still can distinguish between them.

Indeed, it's not just the importers and export-

ers who have problems telling them apart. The people who should be keeping watch, customs and environmental personnel and police—as well as even the vast majority of zoologists both here and abroad—also find it a daunting task. And no nation has reliable figures on what percentage of traded chelonian shells are from protected species. Even an international environmental organization like CITES, with more than 100 member nations and ample resources, has only taken its first steps toward protecting Asian turtle species by collecting basic information about how many species of Asian chelonians exist and how they are being used.

Five percent are protected species?

In July of last year the Council of Agriculture

公路上；過度採集，是造成烏龜族群全面出現警訊的主因，尤其肉用與寵物市場的貿易量大增，大、小龜族成為人們的佳餚、寵物，無法完成延續後代的任務。

好吃又好養

一九九三年世界田徑錦標賽上，來自瀋陽的「馬家軍」，摘下三面金牌，女子三千公尺更囊括前三名，該隊以龜湯、鱉血等中藥調理團員體力的訓練方式也一傳十、十傳百，據說馬家軍一個個生龍活虎、臉蛋紅撲撲，可以承受大量訓練，卻沒有一些運動隊伍常見的過度疲勞、運動傷害等現象，就歸功於食補得當。

馬家軍的魅力卻給國際生態保育工作帶來不少困擾，如今東南亞與東亞媒體廣泛出現運動員食用龜血來促進競賽能力的新聞。

人類食用烏龜其實不分中外、古今，十六、七世紀，印度洋沿岸島嶼如馬達加斯加、科摩羅島上的許多巨型陸龜，就是西方水手最珍貴的食物，因為牠們能在船艙內幾星期不死，在熱帶地方，船離開港口好幾星期，水手仍能吃到新鮮的龜肉。到十九世紀末，印度洋上的許多巨龜因此幾乎絕跡。至今海龜與龜卵仍是中南美洲許多地區重要的蛋白質來源。

在亞洲，除了龜板，龜血、龜肉、甚至龜尿對人體都能產生作用。中國在戰國時代《山海經》已有吃龜的記載，漢代留下的石刻庖廚圖裡，灶上掛有烏龜，當時劉向的《別錄》中也記載，以龜肉做羹湯，

中醫藥師常推薦筋骨疾病患者服用龜板膠。龜板使用量可觀，已成國際關注的議題。

Practitioners of traditional Chinese medicine often recommend taking the gelatin from turtle shells as a remedy for problems with the muscles and tendons. The tremendous volume of the turtle shell trade has become a focus of international attention.

appointed Chang Hsien-cheh to conduct a survey to determine exactly which species' shells were being sold in Taiwan. Taking the 30 firms that legally import turtle and tortoise shells, Chang looked through one container after another, and could only determine the species of 60% of them. About 5% were protected species, including the Burmese eyed turtle, the Burmese star tortoise, and the *Geomyda grandis*. What portion of the remaining 40% was protected is anyone's guess.

Wu Sheng-hai, an associate professor of zoology at Chunghsing University, isn't surprised the imported shells included those of protected species. The problem is that turtle shells look more or less alike. For importing countries, an inability to tell them apart, combined with the great size of the trade and the large number of people involved, make it virtually impossible to carry out legally based seizures of protected species' shells and punish the offending importers or to implement a general ban on the import and export of products made from protected species. Hence, it is hardly surprising to find that some shells belong to protected species.

Turtles are ancient animals. Relying on their protective shell, they've survived by just waddling along for 200 million years. They've shown true Darwinian fitness. Traditional local fishing hasn't made much of an impact on turtle species, and traditional Chinese medicine has been using turtle shell for thousands of years without ever a shortage of supply. Chang says that people in the field have never even bothered to research the possibility of turtle shells being replaced with other ingredients. So how is it that today turtles are facing a threat of a sort that has neven been seen before?

According to *Turtles of the World*, which was published by the Smithsonian Institution in 1989, excessive culling, along with highway construction in developed countries, is a main reason turtle and tortoise populations are now facing a general crisis. In particular, the trade in turtles as meat and pets is booming as never before. With tortoises and turtles of large and small species alike being adopted as pets or turned into culinary delicacies, there's no way for these chelonians to fulfill their duty of passing on their genetic legacy.

Good meat, good pets

At the 1993 World Track and Field Championships, "Ma's Army" of Shenyang came away with three golds, and all three medals for the women's 3000 meters. Suddenly there was a lot of talk about the turtle soup and soft-shelled turtle blood that coach Ma was feeding his runners. These were supposedly giving them the energy of tigers and healthy, glowing complexions, as well as enabling them to withstand very heavy training without succumbing to injuries like other runners.

The glamour connected with the club caused great difficulties for international conservation efforts. Today there are still frequent media reports in East and Southeast Asia about how athletes have increased their competitive abilities by drinking turtle blood.

In fact people have used turtles East and West, past and present. In the 16th and 17th centuries, on such Indian Ocean islands as Madagascar and the Comoros, there were several species of giant turtles regarded as particularly valuable by Western sailors because they could live in a ship's hold for weeks on end. In the tropics a boat could thus could sail for long stretches without coming to port and still have fresh meat. By the end of the 19th century, most species of giant Indian Ocean turtles were near extinction. Today marine turtles and turtle eggs are an important source of protein for many peoples in Central and South America.

Apart from shells, Asians also consume the blood, meat and even the urine of chelonians. The Warring States Era's *Classic of Mountains and Sea*s records that people ate turtles and tortoises. A Han dynasty stone carving of kitchen life shows a turtle on the stove. And *Detached*

大補。今天大陸東南沿海餐廳提供的烏龜大餐，紅燒烏龜、清燉龜湯、龜羊湯，菜色繁多，還不時有保育類的緬甸陸龜上桌供食客大塊朵頤。

台灣雖有食用與龜同類的「鱉」的風氣，卻沒有普遍的食龜熱潮，只有沿海如屏東縣恆春漁民，偶有機會吃海龍王送來的海龜，稱為菜龜。但養龜當寵物的流行風近年來卻吹進國內，台灣也成為寵物市場一個非常活躍的環節。前幾年流行養巴西龜，今天星龜、地圖龜等許多保育龜在水族館普遍可見，水族箱裡漂亮的保育類東亞箱龜可以賣到三、四千元，根據「野生物貿易調查委員會」的調查指出，國內水族館業者可以電話訂到兩百多種烏龜。

在國貿局海關進出口記錄上，龜板還有進口貨號可查出進口數量，但作為寵物或放生的烏龜活體，則混雜在熱帶魚等水族類中入關，國內消費數量多寡根本無跡可循。

何處覓金龜

比起食用龜肉與寵物風，龜板原本可視為廢物利用。野生物貿易調查委員會在東南亞的調查報告就提到，除回教國家，其他地區吃龜肉風氣很盛。因此若能在良好控制下，利用合法肉用市場遺留下的龜板，無可厚非；可惜目前龜板的進出口管道不明，食用龜肉與龜板利用也尚無法良好配合。亞洲國家經濟條件飛升，龜板的交易日益商業化、國際化，也給龜族帶來壓力。

今天除龜苓膏市場開拓觸角日廣，餐廳也買進龜板作藥膳材料。甚至有藥廠將龜板製成速食包，熱開水沖泡即可飲用，不須再煎煮熬燉，煞費功夫。

中醫傳統上並不喜歡以烏龜這樣的靈獸當藥材，遠在漢朝，張仲景在《千金要方》書中就針對中醫師開藥方，提出「夫殺

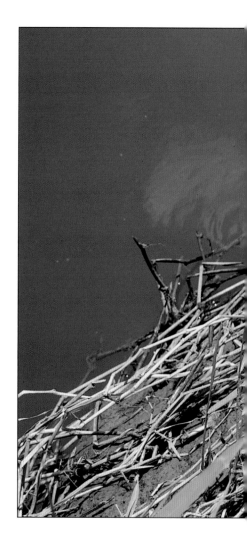

Accounts, by the Han dynasty scholar Liu Xiang, describes a turtle meat soup that is claimed to be extremely nourishing. Today seaside restaurants in southeast mainland China all offer turtle dishes on their menus: soy-braised turtle, clear turtle soup, turtle and mutton soup—a colorful assortment of dishes. And sometimes diners are even known to feast on protected elongated tor-

在野外生存的烏龜，幸運避開人類怪手，身上卻開始累積人類製造的污染物質。龜族未來的命運如何？

Lucky to have escaped man's bulldozers, turtles in the wild now serve as one of the best measures of pollutant accumulations. What does the future hold for chelonian populations?

toises.

Although soft-shelled turtles were once popular with Taiwanese gourmands, the meat of other turtles has never been eaten much in Taiwan. Now only a few fishermen in such places as Hengchun in Pingtung County eat the turtles driven into their nets by the Dragon King (the Chinese Poseidon). But the fad for raising turtles as pets has indeed come to Taiwan, which has become a lively link in the pet trade. A few years back it was popular to raise red-eared turtles here. Today star turtles, map turtles and other protected species can commonly be seen in public aquariums. The beautiful East Asian box turtle that is often seen in home aquariums can go for as much as NT$3-4,000. According to the

生求生，去生更遠」的說法，意思就是不應為了救一條生命，卻犧牲其他生命。歷代中藥書上也記載，最具療效的龜板是「敗龜板」，意指自然死亡的烏龜，黃長生中藥行老闆廖孫福表示，相傳敗龜板才能吸收足夠的大自然真氣，但其實兼有護生的意義，只是「今天使用數量太多，哪裡還有敗龜板可用？」

許多藥材商認為，由大陸進口的小型金龜是品質最好的上等貨，「現在很少看到金龜板，我們用量太大了，」生元董事長林承斌表示，貨源多才會被利用來作為藥材，但大陸吃的很凶，野外能採集到的量越來越少，許多種龜板都缺貨，連當地都不夠用，如今大陸龜板一斤賣到一千多元台幣，是印尼貨的十倍價錢。

雖然大陸、台灣都有人嘗試養殖烏龜營生，但並非每一種烏龜都能適應人工環境

，張賢哲曾建議藥商以人工繁殖最成功的巴西龜作為藥材來源，但巴西龜來自美洲，與傳統中藥使用習慣不同，療效也有待臨床實驗，尚難被市場接受。

烏龜中其實還包含了軟甲的鱉，中藥商也利用鱉甲做藥材，但在許多利用鱉肉的國家，都有養殖場供貨，不須由野外捕捉。「東南亞龜鱉動物調查」報告就指出，「無可懷疑，龜的國際貿易量遠遠超過鱉。」

動物學者的事？

各國對龜鱉類動物的利用不斷增加，要等人類把龜族的生態弄清楚，提出合理利用、保護辦法，猶如遠水救不了近火。野生物貿易調查委員會的初步調查就指出，越南的二十三種陸龜及海龜，面臨近來盛行的龜類產製品販售活動，有瀕臨絕種之

師大生物系博士班研究生陳添喜認為，非保育類龜族的生存情形需要更深入瞭解。圖為他在基隆河岸記錄台灣原生斑龜的生長情形。
Chen Tien-hsi, a doctoral student in the department of zoology at Taiwan Normal University, believes that the survival prospects for unprotected species need further study. The photo shows Chen on the banks of the Keelung River doing research on the green-headed turtle, a species native to Taiwan.

results of the TRAFFIC survey, consumers in Taiwan can order more than 200 species of turtles over the phone from dealers who sell to people stocking their home aquariums.

Using Board of Trade and customs records, it is possible to figure out how many turtle and tortoise shells were imported if you have the import shipment numbers. But living turtles, imported to be sold as pets or released in Buddhist ceremonies, are brought in big tanks that they often share with numerous species of tropical fish. There's simply no way to determine domestic consumption.

The disappearing Reeve's turtle

Unlike eating turtle meat and keeping turtles as pets, using the shells can be regarded as simply making use of something that would otherwise go to waste. TRAFFIC's report on Southeast Asia notes that turtles are eaten throughout the region with the exception of Islamic countries. Hence, with proper regulations the shells could be taken from what the turtle meat industry discards. Doing so shouldn't be controversial. Unfortunately, there isn't much known about current channels for importing and exporting turtle shells, and there still isn't any good way of integrating the turtle meat and turtle shell markets. Yet as the economies of Asian countries boom, the trade in chelonian shells is growing more commercial and international, and pressure on turtle and tortoise populations is intensifying.

Today, besides the booming market for *guiling* paste, restaurants are also buying chelonian shell as a healthy ingredient to use in cooking. The traditional medicine industry has even come up with instant turtle shell packs, which you can take home and throw into boiling water, eliminating all the preparation and stewing.

Traditionally Chinese have not liked to use divine beasts, of which the turtle is one, as sources of medicine. In *Qianjin Yaofang*, the Han dynasty doctor Zhang Chong-jing said, "Killing one life to provide for another is far

from the spirit of life." And in the books on Chinese medicine through history, the turtle shells regarded as most effective were the ones of turtles that died of natural causes. Liao Swun-fu of the Huang Chang-sheng Herbal Pharmacy explains that only they were believed to have absorbed enough life energy. It was a concept that served to protect life. "But now that the amount being used is so great, how can you find enough shells of turtles that died of natural causes?"

Many herbal medicine dealers say that shells of Reeve's turtle from Mainland China are best. "Now you rarely see Reeve's turtles because they're being overculled," says Lin Cheng-wu, who owns the Seng Yuang Herbal Pharmacy. When there was sufficient supply, their shells became a common ingredient in traditional herbal prescriptions, but now mainland China has developed a voracious appetite for these turtles, and the numbers that can be taken in the wild are growing ever smaller. For the shells of many turtle species there is a shortage of supply, even in their place of origin. Now shells from mainland China fetch more than NT$1000 a pound, ten times the price of shells from Indonesia.

Although attempts to breed and raise turtles in captivity have been made both in Taiwan and the mainland, not every species of turtle can adapt to these artificial environments. Chang Hsien-cheh suggests that the herbal medicine industry use the red-eared turtle, which has been artificially bred most successfully. Yet since this turtle comes from South America, traditional herbalists aren't used to working with its shell, and its medical effects are awaiting further clinical study. It's having a hard time getting accepted.

There is also a market for the shells of soft-shelled turtles, which are likewise used to make medicines. But these turtles are bred and raised in captivity in many countries where they are eaten, and there is no need to catch them in the wild. The TRAFFIC survey pointed out,

虞。

國際上對龜板的使用，也開始出現積極動作。歐洲國家如荷蘭，就採取嚴格標準，要求藥商提出龜種證明，否則出現龜板二字的藥材，一概沒收。無風不起浪，今年三月，我國駐瑞士代表也特別傳回華盛頓公約秘書處的通告，要求各國停止自坦桑尼亞輸入薄背陸龜與豹紋陸龜活體與產製品。「世界自然保育聯盟」更建議在保育名錄上增列多種陸龜。

張賢哲表示，如今連開發中國家如泰國，受不了國際保育組織的緊迫盯人，已下令禁止出口部份非保育類烏龜。更何況近年民生富裕的台灣，常是國際第一波批評的對象。

「西方對動物中藥的攻擊，或如荷蘭的過度反應，無法解決問題，」每年花上千元、熬一塊「龜鹿二仙膠」孝敬父親、以保健老人家筋骨的張賢哲表示：「除非也禁止人們吃龜肉。」但是今天中藥商對藥材的分類確實也需因應國際情勢加以調適，過去藥商對自己藥材的產地、種類往往漫不經心，提不出證明。「人們總認為進一步認識烏龜是動物學家的事，」張賢哲說。

就因為烏龜與面臨全面性滅絕的犀牛、老虎情況不同，許多中藥商仍未察覺龜板的問題已逐日浮出檯面，仍強調龜板不是保育類動物產製品。

研究淡水龜的師大生物系博士班研究生陳添喜表示，目前台灣牽涉保育類龜板的比例可能不多，但既是保育類，已是小族群，小量採集對牠們也足以構成大害。因此政府與中藥商，有必要採取行動，避免進口保育類龜板。

非保育類的保育

張賢哲希望能透過中藥商主動提供龜板，逐步建立各種烏龜的外觀、特徵，將保育龜類印刷成彩色圖鑑，扭轉人們對中藥商的成見，中藥商也可以據此要求賣方不再提供保育類產製品，海關則有能力過濾進口的龜板。農委會也提供計畫，請中國醫藥學院進行各種龜類的 DNA 研究，希望無法由外表判識的龜板，可以由 DNA 來辨認。展開各種動作，都是希望未來能對龜板的進口做良好把關。

野生物貿易調查委員會台北辦公室也表示，「進行調查並不表示會禁用龜板，而是希望能提供良好的管理方法，」進行台灣地區烏龜利用現況調查的台北野生物貿易調查委員會專案負責人盧道杰說，正如華盛頓公約組織原本無意要求消費國禁用犀角、虎骨，而是希望政府能有一套明確的管理政策，清楚告知業者，並投入人力確實執法，對非法者施以壓力，給合法業者留下做生意空間。

對於保育人士，則如師大生物系教授呂光洋所說，如果能將國內動物藥材仔細清查，確定來源，斷絕受保育的種類，而中醫、藥公會能自我管理，由國貿局統一進口，藥材上蓋有合法印章，有一套完整的規則避免走私，他就不會反對非保育類動物有限度的被作為中藥材。

不過，針對人們尚無法掌握的烏龜族群，研究海龜的陳添喜也擔心，很多人認為非保育類烏龜族群，仍可以適度利用，「但估算出全世界有多少烏龜，然後進行所謂合理利用，可能是無意義的。」他解釋，例如許多人認為綠蠵龜數量不少，不應列入保育，但對每年回澎湖望安產卵的綠蠵龜而言，如果牠消失了，望安就永遠不會再有這一本土物種，其他國度的綠蠵龜，也都與望安無任何臍帶關係了。

今天東南亞、大陸採集的龜板，為求成本低廉與採收方便，往往都在一地大量採收，造成同一族群一夕間消失。大家焦點都在保育類，「不表示非保育類就沒有生

"Without a doubt, trade in hard-shelled turtles far exceeds that of soft-shelled turtles."

A matter for zoologists?

With demand for turtles and their products growing worldwide, there isn't enough time to wait for humanity as a whole to get clear about chelonian ecologies and adopt protection measures and reasonable-use policies. TRAFFIC's preliminary study points out that in light of the recent rise in demand, 23 species of turtles and tortoises in Vietnam are endangered.

Recently, aggressive measures have been taken in regard to the international use of turtle shells. European countries such as Holland have adopted strict standards, asking companies to provide proof of species. Otherwise, products containing chelonian shell are immediately confiscated. In March of this year ROC representatives in Switzerland received a letter from the Secretariat of CITES, requesting a worldwide ban on the import of two species from Tanzania: the leopard tortoise and *Malacochersus tornieri.* The International Union for Conservation of Nature and Natural Resources has also asked that many tortoises be added to the protected list.

Chang Hsien-che points out that even Thailand, a developing country less able to meet the demands of environmental organizations, has banned the export of several turtle species that are not yet protected internationally. Prosperous Taiwan, a frequent first target for the criticisms of international environmental organizations, should be expected to do more.

"Western attacks on animal-based traditional medicines and the excessive reaction taken by Holland will not solve the problem," says Chang Hsien-cheh, who spends more than NT$1000 a year buying "turtle-deer double immortal gelatin" to keep his father's bones and tendons in good shape. "Not unless they also prohibit people from eating turtle meat." But today firms dealing in traditional Chinese medicines must adjust the actual ingredients of their medicines in response to international events. In the past these firms didn't show much concern for the species or the place of origin, and they lacked proof for any claims they might make. "They have typically believed that a deeper understanding was a matter for zoologists," Chang says.

The turtle trade is fundamentally different from the rhino horn and tiger bone trade, where the animals face total extinction. Many dealers of traditional Chinese medicines have not even sensed that there is a problem, and they insist that turtle shell is not a product made from endangered species.

Chen Tien-hsi, who is working toward a doctorate in zoology at Taiwan Normal University and is an expert on fresh water turtles, says that though the proportion of shells from protected species being consumed in Taiwan is small, for species with small populations, even light culling can do great damage, and so government and industry together must come up with measures that prevent the import of protected species.

Protecting the unprotected

Chang Hsien-cheh hopes that dealers will provide shells so that he can collect information on the appearance and special characteristics of each species of turtle and then provide printed color illustrations showing the protected species to the importers. This could change public perceptions of these traders, who could then demand that their suppliers not ship these protected species. Only then would customs be able to filter imports of turtle shells. The Council of Agriculture has also provided funds to China Medical College to carry out DNA analysis on every kind of turtle, with the hope that turtles whose species could not be determined by an examination of their appearance could be identified through DNA testing. Hence various different measures can be taken to prevent imports of protected species.

The Taipei office of TRAFFIC also points out that "the survey by no means called for a ban on the use of turtle shell, but rather held out the

存的問題，」陳添喜看過藥商進口的龜板許多是取自幼龜，代表牠們根本沒機會長大、繁衍就被殺掉了，「小馬來龜板就很多，」他說。

龜板上的污染史

看來，能解決現有「保育龜」的問題，也無法保證未來龜板就不會有缺貨危機。但在學生態的陳添喜眼中，龜板作為中藥，其實還有更大的危機需要面對。

由於龜類所需求的生存條件不高，除有些種類，如印度星龜對溫度要求嚴苛，常被養一、二年後就死亡外，許多烏龜就像卡通片中的「忍者龜」，能居住在專門匯集大都會污物的城市下水道內，生命異常強韌。台北市河川污染最嚴重的中山北路圓山基隆河段，就可以見到不少台灣原生的斑龜，連生物學者呂光洋都覺得難以想像。

烏龜耐汙力強，大量殺蟲劑與除草劑累積在其脂肪、龜甲上，陳添喜指出，今天烏龜已成最好的環境污染指標，環境學界正積極調查龜甲含重金屬的情況。正如龜甲為中國人留下長久的甲骨文字，如今它們也在累積人類的污染歷史，屆時，龜苓膏還能令人垂涎欲滴嗎？　　□

（原載民國85年6月光華雜誌）

註：農委會已出版張賢哲教授所著「龜板鑑識參考圖冊」，需要者請洽農委會保育科。

初民社會，人類對烏龜造型的解讀與今天大不相同。宜蘭外海水氣氳氲間的龜山島，有如神龜穿海而出。（邱瑞金攝）

The way people read the turtle's appearance in primitive society was very different from how people see them today. Turtle Mountain Island, shrouded in mist, looks like a turtle swimming across the sea. (photo by Diago Chiu)

hope that there could be better measures of control." Lu Dao-jye, who carried out the survey on current Taiwanese consumption of turtles, says that just as CITES didn't originally intend to call for a ban on the use of rhino horns and tiger bones by consuming countries, it now hopes that governments can develop clear control policies, inform industry, and deploy manpower to forcefully carry out these measures, putting pressure on those who break the law and leaving legal vendors room to operate.

Lu Kuang-yang, a professor of zoology at Taiwan Normal, holds views on this issue that may reflect those of many conservationists. He has said that he would not object to non-threatened species being used to a limited degree in Chinese medicine if a complete system were instituted guaranteeing that protected species were not being used. A detailed survey of animal products used in traditional medicines in Taiwan should be carried out so that the source of each is determined, and then the Chinese medicine industry could administer the process itself, with the Board of Trade handling all imports and issuing stamps certifying the legality of all components.

Nevertheless, Chen and many others fear that there still may be overuse of those non-protected turtle populations which people don't yet fully understand. "Calculating reasonable use for turtle species by simply estimating its worldwide population is meaningless." By way of example, he explains that since there is a sizable population of *Mydas japonica*, they aren't a protected species. But if the group of them that returns every year to lay their eggs on the beach at Wangan in Penghu is wiped out, Penghu still will have lost one of its native species.

In mainland China and Southeast Asia, the turtle industry stresses low cost and convenience, and consequently turtles are often overculled at certain locations, causing populations to disappear overnight. Everyone's focus has been on protected species, "but this doesn't mean that unprotected species don't face their own survival crises," says Chen, who notes that many of the of turtle shells imported to Taiwan are taken from immature turtles—meaning that turtles are being killed before they have the chance to propagate. "Many of the *Damonia subtrijuga* shells are of young turtles."

The history of pollution in turtle shells

There's no guarantee that solving the problems of protected turtles and tortoises now will prevent future shortages of chelonian shells. But as Chen, a student of ecology, explains, the traditional Chinese medicine industry is going to face an even greater crisis regarding the use of turtle shells.

Because chelonians aren't picky about their living conditions, with the exception of a few species such as the Indian star tortoise which has strict temperature requirements and often dies a year or two after being brought into captivity, most species of turtles resemble mutant ninja turtles and adapt quite well to sewers, which are designed to carry away urban pollutants. Turtles are tough. Along the stretch of the Keelung river near Chungshan North Road and the Grand Hotel, one of the most polluted stretches of river in Taipei, the great number of native green-headed turtles that can be seen make even a zoologist like Lu marvel.

Yet large quantities of pesticides and herbicides can accumulate in their fat and shells. Chen says that turtle shells are now among the best of ecological measures, with environmental scientists analyzing them to make records about heavy metal pollution. Just as chelonian shells hold the oldest traces of written language in China, now they hold a history of human pollution. In this light, how much longer will people have an appetite for *guiling* paste? □

(Chang Chin-ju/photos by Vincent Chang/ tr. by Jonathan Barnard/first published June 1996)

從「乞龜」到「槓龜」
——中國的玄武文化

Worshipped and Cursed—
The Turtle's Place in Chinese Culture

文·張靜茹　圖·鄭元慶

龜步雖緩，但氣定神閒，深藏不露，是中國人眼中隱者的形象，而非英雄氣短之輩。
While the turtle may be slow, its steady, unhurried composure gives it a placid character that Chinese compare to hermit sages. It's not the kind of beast that runs out of energy just when it needs it most.

除了身上的甲殼好用，今天烏龜更普遍被大江南北各地中國人用來罵人，但身躋「國罵」主角的烏龜，也是中國四靈動物之一，與龍、鳳、麒麟，同具崇高地位，甚至「配享太廟」，讓人供奉。烏龜怎會由靈獸翻身成為王八？

去年底台灣北海岸的一場放生大會裡，許多淡水性的斑龜被當成海龜放生，幾乎全數嗚呼哀哉，倖存的烏龜，「關懷生命協會」曾為牠們找尋善心人士認養，卻接到命相先生電話詢問，可否「認領」已升天的烏龜，因為他需要以龜殼來為人占卜、算命。

對這種「廢物利用」，以保育為宗旨、希望導正今天人們過度剝削自然的關懷生命協會，也只好加以拒絕。事實上，由於許多卜卦者忌殺龜，今天都以銅龜為人算命了。

不過，讓人好奇的是，自己命運都無法掌握的烏龜，如何能掌握人的命運？

「紅龜」也槓龜

當台灣許多人沈迷於大家樂、六合彩，散盡家財、鋌而走險，不少無辜的傳統糕餅商也遭受牽連，過去廟裡拜拜、家有婚慶壽旦喜事，人們爭相訂製麵龜、紅龜，如今眾多信徒擔心簽賭會慘遭「槓龜」，管它新例未設，舊例不滅，賭徒避龜唯恐不及，與龜沾親帶故的各式糕餅，據說生意大減。

除了賭徒怕吃麵龜會槓龜，今天人們開口罵人最常用的也就是「王八蛋、龜孫」，拖泥帶水、不乾不脆的人在台語中則被形容為「龜毛」。有民俗學者認為，烏龜在現代中國人意識中成為貶抑之詞，是因為一逢風吹草動，牠老哥就縮頭縮腦，詐死般不敢動彈。

*M*ore even than using its shell for medicine, Chinese people's favorite use of the turtle is for cursing each other. The turtle plays the leading role in many Chinese derogatory expressions. Yet it is also regarded as one of four divine animals, taking an august place alongside the dragon, the phoenix and the chimera. Turtles are even worshipped in temples. How have turtles managed to crawl the gamut from exaltation to degradation?

At a Buddhist ceremony of mercy on Taiwan's northern coast at the end of last year, quite a few freshwater green-headed turtles were mistaken for sea turtles and set free. Most died. For the survivors, the Life Conservationist Association went looking for kind-hearted people to adopt them. During their search, they got a call from a fortune teller who said he wanted to adopt some of the turtles that had already ascended to heaven instead, so that he could use their shells as instruments of divination.

Even though the request was "for making use of something that would otherwise be wasted," it was refused by this environmental group, which hopes to halt the over-exploitation of natural resources. In fact, many fortune tellers have prohibitions against killing turtles and use brass stand-ins.

Still, there's something here that tickles people's curiosity: How is that turtles, which seem to have no control over their own lives, have control over human destiny?

Worshipped and cursed

As *dajiale* and *liuhecai* (local versions of the numbers game) have grown in popularity and Taiwanese have shown a willingness to risk all they own playing them, traditional cake shops, though quite innocent of any impropriety themselves, have seen their own fortunes fall. In the good old days, people would run to the baker's to buy flour turtles to use as offerings at temple festivals or big family events like weddings or major birthdays. But now because of a Taiwan-

龍、鳳、龜、麟四靈動物，看來只有烏龜是活生生的生物，其實中國人意象中的靈龜與真龜已相去千里，圖為模擬自神話中「龍頭、龜甲」造型的玉器。
Among the four divine animals—the turtle, the dragon, the phoenix and the chimera—only the turtle is a real flesh-and-blood creature. In fact, Chinese depictions of the "divine turtle" often vary considerably from its biological counterpart. The photo shows a dragon-headed turtle carved out of jade

　　元曲《單鞭奪槊》就形容唐太宗之子李元吉：如今只學烏龜法，得縮頭時且縮頭。元代更把任妻外遇的懦弱丈夫比喻爲縮頭烏龜，烏龜因此成爲曖昧不明，暗示男人戴綠帽子的象徵。

　　但是，如果人類是在一步步認識自然的過程中，逐漸完成對文明的創造，回過頭來看看還未發明許多明諷暗刺罵人用語的初民社會，人們在烏龜身上卻看到了與今天完全不同的天地。

上法天，下法地

　　在只有自然物可用的洪荒時代，人們驚喜的發現了堅硬不易破損的龜甲，又從其身上看到了天地的造型。中國古人認爲天圓地方，還爲此創造出許多象徵天地的器物。自然物的烏龜，生來就背甲上隆像天，腹甲下平似地，駁衍像山，四趾運轉，恰是一幅天地四時不息的圖像。

　　對自然萬物才踩出摸索、試探步伐的人類，一個烏龜身體，正如一個蘊含天地基本秩序的小宇宙，這樣的理解，烏龜遂被認爲可上通天、下達地，更被用來執行見存亡、明吉凶的卜巫儀式。

　　當甲骨文出土後，四千年前河南殷商帝王的生活也隱約浮現甲骨文學者眼前。每日清晨，太史、太卜準備好烏龜腹甲、碳爐，帝王醒來第一件事即前來問卜，所問

194

ese expression that means "losing your shirt" but translates literally as "knocking turtles," gamblers steer clear of anything to do with chelonians, and consequently business for turtle cakes is way down.

Apart from gamblers' fears that eating a flour turtle will turn their luck sour, turtles have many other bad connotations in modern Chinese society. In fact, when people curse each other these days, the first thing to come out is often "turtle egg" or "grandson of a turtle," which serve as cuss words for all occasions. More narrow in meaning is "turtle hair," which describes a hedger or waffler unwilling to stick his neck out for anything, and indeed some ethnologists conjecture that the turtle's cowardly habit of pulling in its head and playing dead at the slightest whiff of trouble is at the root of its devaluation in the minds of modern Chinese.

The Yuan dynasty song "*Dan Bian Duo Su*" mocks Li Yuanji, son of the Tang emperor Taizong, for copying the turtle's method and shirking from danger. During the Yuan, weak and cowardly husbands who allowed their wives to have affairs were described as turtles with their heads pulled in. As a result, the turtle (and the tortoise too, since the Chinese don't distinguish between them) became bound up with insinuations of cuckholdry.

But if humanity has gradually come to an understanding of nature as it has built its own creation of civilization, then let's turn around to look at the early years of civilization, before there were many curse words or sarcastic expressions. Back then people had an entirely different view of the turtle.

Heaven and earth

In primitive times, when only natural objects were available, people were happy to discover hard and durable turtle shells, in which they saw the shape of the universe. From a belief that the sky was round and the world was flat, they would create many objects representing heaven and earth. Yet here was the tortoise, a creation of nature that carried its round shell over the ground, like heaven, and had a flat bottom, like earth. With a profile resembling a mountain and the turning motion of its four toes, it seemed to be a depiction of heaven and earth changing constantly through the seasons.

When humanity was still groping toward an understanding of nature and its myriad beasts, the body of the turtle seemed to encapsulate the order of the universe. Seen in this light, turtles became a link between heaven and earth, and were frequently used in divining ceremonies.

After the archeological remains of the Shang oracle bones and turtle shells were unearthed, scholars began to understand something of the life of Shang monarchs 4000 years ago. Early each morning, the court historian and court diviner would prepare a turtle shell and fire a charcoal stove. Upon rising, the king would immediately go to have a divination. Whether he asked about the weather, or military matters or hunting, the court diviner would take a burning stick and move it over the shell, which, when exposed to the heat, would crack into shapes that the diviner would interpret for the king. (It would often crack in the shape of a " ⼘," which became the Chinese character meaning divination.) The interpretations, which were also recorded on the shell, would give direction to the nation's policies. This went on every day throughout the rule of 12 kings, and the custom was practiced as late as the Han dynasty.

The *I-Ching* describes tortoise divination as the best method for making sense of the events of this world. Since the turtle was a godly beast by nature, sages would act in accordance with what was revealed on its shell, which would tell whether luck would be good or bad, whether action should be taken or not.

Sages weren't the only ones to use tortoise shells for divination. Ancient statesmen and military strategists would consult them, too. And some time in the course of the 4000-year history of Chinese divination, common folk picked

之事，從天候、戰事、到獵獲，不論大小。卜官則以火棒對著龜甲燒著，龜甲遇熱後現出「卜」字般的紋路，據說此為「卜」字的來源。執事者再視其紋路、為君王解釋吉凶，作為施政、行事方針，並在龜板上加以記錄，殷商十二個帝王日日如此，直到漢代也還存在這樣的風俗。

中國的卜卦祖典《易經》上記載，能解釋天下萬象者，莫大過著龜，烏龜是天生神物，聖人必須依其身上顯現的規則進退，遵照其身上顯現的天地變化、吉凶行事作息。

不只聖人抱龜南面，龜卜影響古代政治；四千年前的占卜，隨著物換星移，也換上另一個形式流落民間。至今台灣隨處可見的算命攤上，常有個沈甸甸的碗，裡頭擺著完好的龜甲、銅錢，對前途、生命迷

* * *

them up. To this day, at fortune-telling stands all across Taiwan, you can see heavy bowls containing tortoise shells and bronze coins. A passerby who wants to know his fate sits down, and the fortune teller shakes the coins in the shell before reading the customer's future.

The tortoise is also known as the "xuanwu," which means "black soldier." *The Book of Rites* explains that turtles and tortoises have armor-like exteriors (hence "soldier"), and they are dark in color (hence "black").

The Chinese have always sought stability and order, and they make a big deal about how their residences and tombs are oriented. "With a dragon on the left and tiger on the right to ward off bad luck and with a rose finch and a black soldier to regulate the Yin and Yang," it was believed, "children and grandchildren will surround you and your ancestors will be happy and prosperous."

The turtle, dragon, tiger and rose finch each govern one direction. In traditional Chinese cosmology, space was divided into four directions,

延平郡王祠的九座龜
趺，展現了古人心中
的烏龜，具有超強的
負重能力。

The turtle tablets of
Yenping's Chunwang
Temple show that in
the view of the ancient
Chinese, turtles could
bear extremely heavy
loads.

惘的過客坐下，算命術士揀起銅錢、丟入龜殼，搖搖晃晃，開始爲人指點迷津。

朱雀玄武調陰陽

烏龜又被稱爲玄武，《禮記》曲禮解釋，龜有甲，能禦侮，故曰武，加上體黑，故曰玄，因此取名玄武。中國人向來希冀穩定、有秩序的世界，住宅、墓葬均講方位，所謂「左龍右虎辟不祥，朱雀玄武調陰陽，子孫備具居中央，長保二親樂富昌」。

龜能與龍、虎、朱雀各霸一方，因爲在眞實的大宇宙裡，古人曾將空間分爲四方，每個方位各有七個星宿，北方七宿連結起來，輪廓像龜，因此龜成爲北方的代表。宇宙則由金、木、水、火、土等五行元素構成，龜常生活水中，是爲水族，成爲水的象徵。

今年三月，宜蘭三星鄉鄉民周仁凰路過長埤湖附近，發現一棵大樹樹根晃動，走近卻見一隻烏龜被虯龍盤結的樹根捆繞，動彈不得，他拿工具將樹根又挖、又剪，才將烏龜取出，這隻被樹根壓住多時的烏龜，背殼已變形，救龜的周仁凰說，過去聽說烏龜可長命百歲，且不需吃東西，這回他終於相信了。

米、麵做的乞龜已落伍了？今天打造「金龜」才神氣，只不過按照古例，乞龜必須分食，金龜，捨得分嗎？
Are turtles made from rice and flour out of date? At temple fairs only gold turtles seem to impress people these days. The problem is that turtles presented as offerings are supposed to be divided up and eaten afterwards. How will they divvy up the gold?

each of which had seven stars. Because the seven northern stars formed the outline of a turtle, the turtle came to represent the north. The universe was thought to be built of five basic elements: metal, wood, water, fire and earth. Since the turtle lives in water, it also came to represent the element of water.

In March of this year, Chou Jen-huang, a resident of Sanhsing Rural Township in Ilan County, was out walking when he saw something moving the roots of a big tree in the vicinity of Changpi Lake. Upon closer examination, he discovered that a turtle was caught up in the tree's roots and couldn't break loose. Chou used some tools to hack and pry at the roots, allowing him to pull free the turtle, which had been trapped so long that its shell had already changed shape. Chou recalls hearing that turtles could live for 100 years without food. But it wasn't until he saw this turtle's oddly shaped shell that he really believed it.

All turtles and tortoises move with slow, carefree gaits. They eat and drink little, have inoffensive personalities, don't harm other beasts and never lose their composures. As a consequence, it's easy to understand why a lifetime of 300-500 years was thought well within a turtle's grasp. The divine turtle, "peacefully living a hermit-like existence for thousands of years in a spring's waters" has much the flavor of a Taoist immortal who has removed himself from the troubles of the world. Indeed, teachers of *qi gong* breathing techniques always want their students to model themselves on the turtle. And in popular kung-fu novels, heroes escape danger using "turtle breathing" to play dead.

Mountain moving power

To Chinese, who have long tried to find the secret of eternal youth, turtles seemed to possess an enviable and god-like resistance to aging, and so they came to symbolize longevity. People would pray and make offerings to them for long lives. To someone passing a birthday, they would say: "May the turtle and crane extend your life." Then there was its appearance symbolic of heaven and earth, its powers of augury, and its inside-out body (with the bone on the outside and meat on the inside). Taken together, these qualities caused the Chinese to attach great spiritual significance to the turtle, and they are at the root of the many myths and traditions regarding it. In a nutshell, the turtle had an elegant appearance and spiritual significance, which caused the ancients to chose it as a companion of the dragon, the phoenix and chimera in the ranks of China's most godly of animals.

It was believed that when the emperor was moral, divine turtles would appear as signs of his high virtue. When he ruled benevolently and paid proper respect to his forebears, dragons in the heavens and turtles on earth would carry signs of good fortune. Monsters would disappear and lucky clouds would blow in. Yu the Great paid little attention to the luxury of his palace, putting all his energy into regulating the waterways. Busy during those years, he passed the palace gate three times but never even entered, and as a result the owled turtle was moved by his diligence and told him the secret of how to stop the floods.

The eastern fairy mountains, in a distant fog, were a paradise in the ancient Chinese imagination, a place where gods and immortals lived. Those mountains were said to be carried on the back of a strong-shelled turtle, which would rise and sink on the ocean waves, causing the mountains to be visible for only fleeting glimpses. The god of the sea was also said to ride on a turtle's back. One dragon was said to have nine sons, each of whom had his own special talent. One, a turtle named Baxia, could carry heavy loads. Turtle tablets, which were stone tablets with bottoms that looked like turtles, appeared in the Han and Tang dynasties. The stone tortoises under their shells would strain their necks upward, with big eyes and open mouths. Their four feet gripped the ground, as their shells bore their heavy loads. On the tablets would be recorded

龜步和緩，悠閒自在，加上吃喝不多，性情溫和，不傷他物，下氣上通，老神在在，因此被認為活上個三、五百年輕而易舉，所謂靈龜「靜養千年壽，重泉自隱居，」頗有道家道骨仙風、無為而治的風範。教人氣功的師父，總要徒兒們以龜為師。武俠小說人物面臨危急使出「龜息大法」，敵人無法傷及分毫，於是絕處逢生，躲過一劫。

力拔山兮氣蓋世

對古來不斷追求長生不死、羽化登仙的中國人而言，烏龜既能長生不老，自有其神聖之處，值得嚮往，烏龜遂成為長壽象徵，民間奉之以祈延年益壽，祝賀人「龜鶴延年」。加上造型符合天地之象，可以「通天達地」；外骨內肉，與大多數生靈反其道而長，都給了中國人靈感，成為許多神話、風俗的基本起源，最後「龜之為物，文采靈異，古人取之以配龍鳳麒麟」，烏龜終於躋身為中國重要靈獸。傳說當人君有德，會有神龜出為瑞應。德澤之世，天子敬天孝親，更有天龍負圖，地龜出書，妖孽消滅，景雲出遊。卑宮室，盡力乎溝洫的大禹，治水三過其家門不入，因此得到鴞龜傳授退除水患的祕訣。

東方仙山在遙遠的雲裡霧裡，是中國人心目中理想國度的模型、神仙居所，據說它由堅甲力背的靈龜負載著，才能浮浮沈沈於凡人無法探及的茫茫大海。靈龜更成為海神御駕之物。龍生九子，各有本領，其中一子「霸下」，能負重，漢、唐時代，就出現了上碑、下龜的龜趺造型，石龜由甲殼下揚起頸子，巨目咧口，四足撐地，力托千斤，碑上則記載功績聖德，今天台南延平郡王祠還有九座龜趺，成為遊客爭相拍照的風景。

自然神的玄武最後更被人格化，演化為仗寶劍、著黑衣，腳踩龜、蛇，武士形象

great moral achievements. The Yanping Chun Wang Temple in Tainan has nine turtle tablets, by which visitors line up to have their photos taken.

Eventually the "black soldier" of nature was anthropomorphized into the black-clad warrior God of the Northern Heavens, who carries a sword and stands on turtles and snakes. Legend has it that before the God of the Northern Heavens died, he cut open his own body and took out his stomach and intestines. His intestines became a snake and his stomach became a turtle. Erroneously, butchers adopted him as their patron saint, and Taiwan now has many temples devoted to him.

Chelonian geomancy

The image of the turtle as a spiritual beast became deeply implanted in people's minds. One ancient text warns its readers not to act rashly when catching turtles and always to carry out the proper ceremony to worship them first. There are also many legends among the people about how those who killed turtles eventually met with misfortune as their just desserts. Common Buddhist restraints against the killing of animals evolved into the Buddhist ceremony of releasing turtles, and in modern Chinese society there are probably more people who release turtles than who eat them.

Having an unusual appearance and symbolizing good fortune and long life, when the turtle left the rarefied air of myth to seek an earthy life among the people, its cultural significance grew only richer. The truth is that the turtle served to make life more convenient for our ancestors. Besides writing on turtle shells, people also used them as a trading currency in the era before the Qin dynasty.

The archeological remains of the Hemudu culture in Zhejiang show that 5800 years ago people there wore ornaments made from turtle shell just as people today wear gold or jade jewelry. Back then they placed a high value on turtle shell. Later, turtle shapes were often carved into

有辟邪神力的八卦
，據說造型源自烏
龜身上的圖案。

The eight diagrams,
which work as a
charm against evil,
are said to have
been based on the
lines on a turtle's
shell.

的玄天上帝。相傳玄天上帝死前剝開自己身體，取出腸、胃，腸化成蛇，胃變成龜，最後被附會成爲今天屠夫祭祀的對象，台灣也處處可見玄天上帝廟。

八卦、墓葬，有樣學樣

靈龜形象深植人心，中國古書《酉陽雜俎》裡記載，捕龜者，不能輕舉妄動，必需先行祭拜儀式而後才得以取之；民間也有許多殺龜、吃龜最終慘遭惡報的傳說，普遍的佛道信仰，對宰殺動物也具有約束力，最後更形成放龜文化，今天中國社會裡的放龜人，比起吃龜者就多很多。

造型特殊，具有祈福、祥瑞、長壽象徵的靈龜，由神話落實到民間生活，更加豐富。事實上，堅甲硬殼的烏龜，是幫助人類祖先生活更便利的用具。除了中國四千年前的文字，藉由烏龜軀殼流傳至今。秦朝以前，龜甲也曾被用做貨幣交易。

大陸浙江出土的五千八百年前河姆渡文化墓葬，人類腰間已掛著龜甲，就像今天人們身上穿金戴玉一般，當時人對龜甲也有所倚托、器重。漢代丞相、諸侯、大將所用的金印、印鈕也常出現龜形。唐代起，中國人的墓葬已砌成龜狀，中國社會重要的護身符八卦，更依樣畫葫蘆自龜背上線條樸拙有力的圖案。

漢、唐時代，人們爭相以龜字入名，各式龜名，不可勝數，除知名的唐朝樂師李龜年，做詩老嫗能解的白居易也將自己鍾愛的姪兒取名龜郎，日本受中國影響，至今也有姓龜田、名龜太郎者。

乞龜變「金龜」

由於龜的閩南語發音與「久」同音，淡水龜、陸龜腳趾又正好前五後四，相加爲九，烏龜天長地久的寓意，更孕育了閩南沿海的乞龜文化。

乞龜，是以紅麴和米或麵粉製成烏龜模

the gold chops used by ministers and lords during the Han dynasty. By the Tang dynasty, tombs were being made in the shape of turtles. The symbol of the eight diagrams, commonly used among Chinese as a charm, was derived from the strong and simple lines found on turtle shells.

During the Han and Tang dynasties, people thought up all sorts of ways of putting "gui," the Chinese character for turtle, into their own names. Besides the famous Tang dynasty musician Li Gui-nian, Bai Ju-yi, whose poetry could be understood even by old women, named his beloved nephew Gui-lang. The Japanese followed suit, and today the character appears in Japanese surnames and given names.

Flour turtles turn to gold turtles

Because in the southern Fujianese dialect, the word for turtle is a homonym for the number nine and for the word meaning long in time, and because freshwater turtles and tortoises have five toes on their front feet and four on their back feet, adding up to nine, turtles were thought to have lived as long as the world existed. From this arose the tradition of praying to turtles on the coasts of southern Fujian and Taiwan (where the dialect is also spoken).

"Qi gui" refers to making dough turtles out of red yeast and flour to serve as offerings to the gods. For temple fairs, people made offerings of turtles to gods, and when their prayers were answered they would make new offerings to show their gratitude. The entire village or a few households on a rotating basis would pay for making these turtles. In times of rich harvest and peace, a dough turtle to which villagers pray can range in weight from 300-600 kilograms. After the ceremony, each household takes a portion of it home to eat. It is split up so that everyone can enjoy the turtle's prosperity and good fortune, and so that all can follow the turtle to the territory of longevity and enjoy peace at home. It is said that when a master teaches novices the art of making flour turtles, he exhorts them not to put

樣，每逢廟會，人們會組織「大龜會」，求大龜、還大龜，由全村，或幾戶人家一起輪流出錢合製。五穀豐登、太平盛世，民間所求的乞龜，重者常可達五六百斤、甚至千斤。祭祀後的乞龜，由每戶人家切成小塊分食，如此人都分享到神龜的福氣、吉祥，與神龜同登壽域，家宅平安。據說初學製麵龜的學徒，老師傅第一件事一定特別叮嚀他別多或少做了腳趾頭，免得得罪顧客。

順應工商社會潮流，近來還出現以罐頭、錢幣、或黃金打造的乞龜。今年元宵節，澎湖天后宮信徒，就打造一隻將近八十兩重的金龜，輸人不輸陣，明年的爐主已信誓旦旦表明他將訂製九十兩重的金龜。

中研院民族所第一任所長凌純聲在其「中國古代龜祭文化」論文中指出，今天台灣的紅龜文化，來自閩南沿海，對早期先民，口腹需求最為首要，人在世愛吃龜肉，死後亦然，活龜遂成為與三牲、五牲等量齊觀的祭祀品，台灣早年也用活龜祭祀，儀式完成後將之放走，但後來活龜不易取得，才出現麵龜等各種替代品。

除乞龜風俗，台灣自福德正神以上都可以龜粿祭之，一年二百多天的神誕，供案擺滿各式牲禮、紅龜粿供品。在台灣人的生命禮俗中，由出生、滿月到作壽、死亡，也都與紅龜發生密切關聯，年屆花甲，親友會送紅龜六十二個，年過古稀得送七十二個，盼老壽星福壽雙全。

神話先出，儀式在後

由神話到民俗儀式，玄武文化繽紛多樣。中研院文哲所研究員李豐楙指出，玄武文化的形成，有其脈絡，最初是遠古人類透過對自然物的觀察，出現神聖的思維，例如濱海民族觀察到海龜浮形於海，才產生海龜從大海中負載河圖洛書而出的神話，烏龜背負神聖物品的傳統形成之後，再

too few or too many toes on their feet, or otherwise risk incurring the customers' wrath.

As society has become industrialized and commercialized, *qi gui* turtles have appeared made out of cans, coins or gold. This year during the lantern festival, devotees of Penghu's Tienhoukung Temple made a gold turtle that was nearly 80 taels. Not to be outdone, the director of activities for next year has said that he will put together a gold turtle of 90 taels.

In a paper entitled "Turtle Worshipping in Ancient China," Ling Chun-sheng, the first director of the Institute of Ethnology of the Academia Sinica, wrote that Taiwan's dough turtle tradition comes from the southern Fujian coast. For early Han settlers in Taiwan, putting food on the table was most important. Since people enjoyed eating turtle meat in the here and now, they figured it shouldn't be any different in the hereafter. Turtles joined oxen, sheep and pigs as one of the animals most commonly used as offerings in ceremonies honoring ancestors. At first living turtles were used in these ceremonies. After the ceremonies they would be released. But later, when it became hard to find living turtles, turtles made from flour and all kinds of other substances began to be used in their place.

Red dough turtles can be offered to all gods from the local earth god on up. With more than 200 days a year on which gods' birthdays fall, the altars are always jammed with sacrificial offerings and gifts of red turtle cake. Red turtles are tied up with all the days traditionally considered important in the life of Taiwanese: from birth, to reaching a full month of age, to major birthdays, to death. When people reach 60 years of age, relatives and friends give them 62 red turtles, and when they turn 70, they get 72.

First the legend, then the ceremony

From the stuff of myth to the stuff of folk customs, China's turtle culture is colorful and diverse, Li Feng-mao, a fellow at the Institute of Chinese Literature and Philosophy, points out

that the forms of Chinese turtle culture can in fact be traced back to ancient people's observations about nature. For instance, people living along coasts observed that sea turtles floated on the sea, and from this arose the myth about turtles on the sea carrying mystic signs and markings. Once legends about turtles carrying spiritual objects were established, it was just a short hop to cultural activities like making turtle tablets and offering dough turtles.

It is difficult now to establish a time-table for the process in which turtles were mythologized,

龜甲堅硬，自古即是人類的生活利器。烏龜軀殼更為中國人留下了四千年前的文字。（中研院史語所提供）

Turtle shells are hard and have long been used by people in their daily lives. The undershells of turtles' bellies were used to record writing 4000 years ago. (courtesy of the Academia Sinica's Institute of History and Philology)

被具象化為龜趺文物、乞龜儀式等民俗活動。

靈龜被神聖化的過程，今天很難詳細排列出時間表，但由古代帝王實行龜卜，到民間廣以龜甲算命，各種烏龜有關的神話、信仰、儀式，彼此有淵源，有承續性，都是中國靈龜文化的一環。「基本上也都是烏龜本身具有的特性，再被人類進一步解釋出意義、或誇大而成，」李豐楙說。

但烏龜真實的特性又是如何？現實環境中真有「千年王八萬年龜」？

誰怕誰？烏龜怕鐵槌

烏龜，與鱉同屬於龜鱉目，除了鱉甲為肉質較柔軟，兩者外型與內部結構大同小異，今天生物學者認為烏龜是由二億五千萬年前石炭紀後期杯龍類恐龍演化而來。在二億年前恐龍主宰地球時代，牠們與蜥蜴、變色龍、蛇類、鱷魚等爬蟲類已經存在，也是第一個適應陸地上乾燥生活的動物，在魚類與鳥類、哺乳動物間扮演過渡性角色。

與恐龍同屬爬蟲類的烏龜，為何沒有跟著恐龍消失？不管什麼原因造成恐龍的滅絕，現存爬蟲類由於具有適應環境的利器，因此逃過毀滅恐龍的災變。烏龜自誕生地球，對自身的保護就已有了極大的突破，讓背部鱗片結成堅固的硬塊，底部也用骨頭支撐，身體封閉宛如穿上牢不可破的盔甲，遇到危險，就將頭與四肢縮進甲中。台灣原生的黃緣閉殼龜（又稱食蛇龜），在面臨危急時，上下甲還可以全部關閉，不留絲毫縫隙。

動物學者認為，烏龜的安全構造，比任何高等脊椎動物都進步，可以度過各種外來環境壓力，因此烏龜出現至今，外型並未作太大改變，是演化極慢的物種。但相較於後生晚輩、具有創造工具能力的人類，在許多方面，烏龜還是「略遜一籌」。

but from their use by ancient kings to their use by modern fortune tellers, there are connections and continuity between all the various legends relating to turtles, with each being one link in the chain of divine turtle culture. "At a basic level, each show some characteristics of the actual turtle, with meanings that have been explained or expanded upon by humanity," Li says.

But what are the actual characteristics of a turtle? In nature do turtles actually "live for hundreds and thousands of years"?

The turtle and the dinosaur

Though the soft-shelled turtle has a soft, leathery shell, all chelonians (turtles, tortoises and terrapins) show little variation in their basic structure. Zoologists believe that today's chelonians have evolved from a kind of dinosaur that lived during the Carboniferous Period. They and other reptiles such as lizards, chameleons, snakes, and alligators were among the first animals to adapt to life on dry land. Through them, life has made the transition from fish to mammal.

Why didn't turtles die out like dinosaurs? Regardless of what led to the dinosaurs' demise, today's reptiles have been able to avoid the same fate by making advantageous adaptations to the environment. Turtles and tortoises represent a major breakthrough in self-defense: their scales have evolved into a hard shell over their backs, and bone supports their undershells, leaving their bodies encased in strong, unbreakable armor. When they come across danger, their head and legs pull back into their shells. When Taiwan's native turtle *Cuoro flavo-marninata* is faced with danger, its pulls so snugly inside itself that not even a small crack is available for predators to pry at.

Zoologists believe that chelonians have a more advanced protective structure than is found in any higher vertebrate, which has allowed them to survive threats of all kinds. In fact, up to the present, their exteriors haven't changed to any remarkable degree. Turtles and tortoises have displayed remarkably slow evolution. But in comparison to later-arriving, tool-using humans, they come up short in many respects.

In the Qing dynasty work *Completed Collection of Graphs and Writings of Ancient and Modern Times*, it is recorded that the ancients were known to use turtles as the legs of their beds, but no turtle shell could really have borne this form of abuse. The veterinarian Chi Wei-lien once had to set a cast for a pet turtle whose master had accidentally smashed its shell. And the shells of turtles that die in the wild disintegrate through exposure to the wind and the rain.

Although there are records of turtles that have lived past 100 years, today zoologists can look at rings in a turtle's shell much like the rings in a tree, to determine that most chelonians live only 20 or 30 years. True, some sea turtles can live 50 or 60 years, but in any case their lifetimes are far shorter than people had imagined.

Waddling out of prehistory

The British sinologist Joseph Needham, in his book *Science and Civilization in China,* points out that the worship of animals, besides being related to mistaken observations about the actual animals in nature, also reflects choices people made about identification. So-called folk beliefs were all originally selected and filtered from people's experiences. Some stem from a principle of analogy. For instance, since turtles have lower pulse and breathing rates than humans—and in fact some chelonians do live longer than most people—there arose a belief in the immortality of turtles. And so it has happened that folk beliefs differ from today's scientific understanding of turtles. But when the turtle has symbolic importance, the facts about actual turtles become no longer important. "Belief is belief, and some beliefs may be scientific. But folk beliefs aren't science, and don't need to turn into science," says Li Feng-mao.

Among the four spiritual beasts—the dragon, the phoenix, the turtle and the chimera—the turtle is the only actual animal. Yet the truth is

《古今圖書集成》中，曾有古人利用烏龜做床腳的記載，但龜板哪眞能讓人如此折騰？獸醫師祈偉廉就曾醫治過被主人不小心摔成外傷，必須重新接骨的烏龜。死於野外的烏龜，一身龜殼經過日曬雨淋，也會順著格子式的紋路摧枯拉朽，四下離散。

雖然人類記錄的烏龜，壽命有長達百歲以上者，今天動物學者由烏龜腹甲上類似樹木年輪的生長環估算，烏龜平均壽命不過二、三十歲，海龜雖可活到五、六十歲，仍遠遜於人們想像的數字。

混沌中走出秩序

以著作《中國之科學與文明》聞名的英國學者李約瑟曾指出，靈物崇拜除了與錯誤的生物觀察有關，選擇性的認同也是原因。所謂民俗信仰，本來就是經過人們的經驗選擇、過濾，其中也有類比原則，例如發現烏龜心臟跳動比人慢，呼吸次數比人少，確實又有些烏龜活得比人長壽，因此出現烏龜可以祈壽的信仰，如此民俗信仰就和生物實際的生態有了出入。但作爲人們的象徵物時，眞實的烏龜是如何已不重要，「信仰是信仰，其中也許有部份是科學，但民俗信仰不是科學，也不需要成爲科學，」李豐楙說。

在龍鳳龜麟四靈動物中，龜看來是唯一現實裡活生生的生物，其實龍、鳳、麒麟也都是採取自眞實動物外型，再加入想像而成。烏龜外貌雖已足夠讓人發揮想像，但在不同時代、神話中，還是出現龍頭龜身、或如《山海經》裡鳥首虺尾的旋龜等各種造型迴異的神龜。

人對世界的認知由分類開始，今天人類的知識是經過幾千年對萬物加以分類後累積而成，古人不似今人有科學儀器、先進技術，神話可以說是先民觀察宇宙萬象後整理、分類而成。例如爲何烏龜代表北方

that the other three were all based on real animals and then expanded upon with a little extra imagination. While the outward appearance of turtles is enough itself to excite people's imaginations, in the legends of some eras, it also appeared as an animal with a dragon's head and turtle's body. In *The Book of Mountains and Seas*, there appears a mythical turtle with a bird's head and snake's tail which looks quite different from its biological counterpart.

People started understanding the world by making categories, and today's zoological system of knowledge has accumulated from thousands of years of people putting animals into categories. The ancients didn't have modern science and technology. Myths can be described as being the result of our predecessors' attempts to sort out what they had experienced of beasts in their lives. Why does the turtle represent north and belong to the element of water? Because the north is frigid and full of water, and turtles live in the water. "The ancients used myths to explain their geographical environment, building their conception of the universe," says Li Fengmao. Myth was how humans created order out of confusion. It represents serious work in the development of humanity, and it is also a crystallization of the early wisdom gained from cultural development. Hence, one shouldn't look at the culture of divine beasts as being something absurd or weird.

Symbol of the people

Relics of ancient culture are most meaningful today in how they reveal a people's symbols. In particular, the culture of divine animals combines activities from both the old and new stone ages. These weren't created in an instant and weren't created by individuals: they represent cultural assets of the Chinese people. Culture is multifaceted, and different peoples have different cultural psychologies and different ways of explaining things.

In the West, early Christians didn't like turtles, and they viewed them as symbolizing

「放龜獲報」的傳說自古流行，中國人也特別偏愛放生烏龜。

Showing mercy by releasing turtles (and thereby being blessed with good fortune in return) has been a popular activity since ancient times. Of all animals, turtles are the ones the Chinese most like to set free.

evil forces during war. In Greece, turtles were once believed to be citizens of hell. But like the Chinese, Indians have a legend that "the world is supported by four elephants standing on a giant turtle." After hearing a Western scientist clearly give a scientific explanation for the formation of the world, one old Indian woman said that he was wholly mistaken, that the world was being supported by a giant turtle. When the scientist asked what was under the turtle, she said, "Of course there is an endless pile of turtles, one on top of another."

Different cultures may have similar views about certain things, but no culture has completely the same views about the symbolic import of turtles as the Chinese, because the turtle

、在五行中屬水？因為北方冰冷、寒凍，充滿水，而海龜產於水中，「古人是以神話的方式，來對地理環境進行解釋，建構他們對宇宙的概念、認知，」李豐楙指出，神話是人類試圖由混沌中走出秩序的表現，是人類發展中的嚴肅工作，也是一個民族文化發展初期的智慧結晶，因此不可視靈獸文化為荒誕怪異。

民族符號

今天看古代文化遺跡，民族符號的意義大於科學，尤其靈獸文化綜合了由舊石器、新石器時代開始的人類活動，不是一時間形成，也不是個人發明，而是民族共同的意識，所有中國人共同創造而成，也是中國人的文化財產。站在文化多元角度來看，民族不同，文化心理、對事物的解構也不同。

在西方，早期基督徒就不喜烏龜，形容牠們是戰爭中的邪惡力量，希臘國度曾認為烏龜是居住在地獄的子民。但和中國一樣的，印度也對烏龜的背殼有類似「地球是由四隻大象踩在巨大海龜上支撐著」的傳說。曾有西方科學家頭頭是道的解釋地球如何形成時，卻有老太太說他完全錯了，她說地球是由一隻大龜承載著，科學家問那烏龜之下呢？「當然還有一隻隻烏龜不斷疊著。」

不同文化對同一東西可能有所雷同，但沒有一個文化對烏龜的象徵，會與中國完全相似，因為它已經過眾多中國人不斷重新詮釋，融進中國文化中。例如佛家提倡放生觀念，並沒有分別心，中國人卻特別喜愛放生烏龜，它的意義不只是放生，而是放生進入中國文化脈絡後，民眾加入自己的認知，放生烏龜可以祈求長壽，功德觀念雖已滲入了功利色彩，但也顯示文化幾乎不可能原封不動移植。

神龜翻身

正如文化是多元的，一種東西也會有許多屬性，百種人總會附加百種意義。雖然靈龜文化至今盛行，但是烏龜聲譽在宋代也每下愈況。王八，據說是「忘」了四維八德，罵人無恥；也有人認為是因為百家姓裡王排第八，鱉的背甲上則有類似王字的圖案。但為何王八成了罵人經典？人類學者何聯奎認為，這是物極必反的結果。過去人們喜建巨大的龜趺，歌功頌德，宋朝市民階層興起後，烏龜就被世俗街坊、市民階級拿來諷刺帝王將相。清朝王士禎在《池北偶談》中曾說，漢、唐、宋以來，取龜字命名者，不可勝記，到了明朝，卻成為忌諱，殊不可解。

閩南人更是生動利用烏龜打比喻的高手。因為烏龜在五行中屬水，代表錢財，「遇水則發」嘛，因此「槓龜」——打翻烏龜，就被用來形容錢財飛了，也成為近年來賭風盛行的台灣最熱門的用語。

李豐楙指出，同樣的東西在不同脈絡裡會有不同解讀，是很正常、自然的事。尤其民俗文化具有很強的承續性，一種信仰一旦進入制度，成為文化認知，成為共識，就不容易消失。但人們也會區別附加在烏龜身上的不同屬性，每個取向會被放在不同的情形下使用，不易混淆。口罵人龜孫者，照吃麵龜求壽不誤；長久來閩南沿海共有的乞龜文化，也不會因為賭徒怕槓龜，就毀於一旦。不過，不論是何種屬性，今天中國人心中的烏龜，都與活生生的烏龜有了差距。對真實生活中的烏龜，正如淡水龜被當成海龜放生，命運可不是牠們自己可以掌握的。

天靈靈，地靈靈，不知以龜甲占卜烏龜之命，靈不靈？　□

（原載民國85年6月光華雜誌）

has gone through repeated interpretations in China, seeping deep into Chinese culture. For example, when Buddhism promoted the concept of showing mercy to animals by setting them free, it was meant to be applied indiscriminately, but when the idea came to China, the Chinese applied it especially to turtles. Of course in China it means more than just showing mercy to animals. After this concept entered Chinese culture, the people put their own understanding into it, and releasing turtles became something that is done to earn favor with the gods. The idea of good works being their own reward turned into something tinted with hoped-for personal gain. This transformation also illustrates how cultural concepts are not passed along intact.

Upending the mythical turtle

In reality, just as culture is multifaceted, so is just about everything else, and 100 people are likely to interpret the same thing 100 ways. Although spiritual turtle culture still flourishes today, the turtle's reputation had already fallen in the Song dynasty. The Chinese characters "wang ba" (king eight) are said to mean turtle because lines on the back of a turtle shell resemble the character "wang," which is the eighth of the 100 Chinese surnames. But how is it that "wang ba" became a curse word? The anthropologist He Lien-kuei believes that this an example of the pendulum swinging, of things reversing direction when they reach an extreme.

In former times people would build huge turtle tablets to honor people's achievements. Yet in the Song dynasty, after the lot of the common people improved, they would use the word "turtle" to make sarcastic references about the nobles. In the Qing dynasty book *Chihbei Outan*, Wang Shizhen says that during the Han, Tang and Song dynasties many people used the character for turtle (*gui*), in their names. But by the Ming dynasty, no one was using it. Its disappearance was hard to figure.

The southern Fujianese are masters of mak-ing examples out of turtles. It is said that the turtle belongs to the element of water, and that water represents money (because of the expression that runs "one will hit it rich when meeting water"). And so "knocking the turtle over" is used to describe money running out, and has been a very common expression among Taiwan's gamblers in recent years.

Li Feng-mao points out that things take on new meanings in new situations. This is normal and natural. In particular, folk culture has a strong continuity to it: When a kind of belief enters the system and becomes collectively acknowledged, it is hard to eliminate. But people find it easy to distinguish between the turtles' various seemingly contradictory qualities, and there's no fear of confusion. The same person who curses someone as a grandson of a turtle will also eat turtle cakes for good luck. For a long time now dough turtles have been offered to the gods in temples along the coasts of Southern Fujian and Taiwan. And this custom won't disappear overnight just because of gamblers' fear of knocking the turtle over.

But all of these cultural turtles, created as they were in the minds of the Chinese, are well removed from the actual reptile. For an actual living turtle, say a freshwater turtle "mercifully" released into the sea, life doesn't seem entirely like something that they control.

Abracadabra shallakazam. . . . Would a turtle shell reading accurately forecast the fate of the turtle?

(Chang Chin-ju/
photos by Cheng Yuan-ching/
tr. by Jonathan Barnard/
first published June 1996)

繼犀角、虎骨之後
，衛生署決定再暫
時禁用多種與保育
類野生動物相關的
藥材。中醫師今後
該何去何從？
After the rhino horn
and tiger bone
incidents, the
Department of
Health decided to
implement another
temporary ban on
several medicines
that are taken from
endangered
animals. What steps
should Chinese
medical doctors take
next?

不能用的都不用——中藥的下一步

After the Ban—Where Does Chinese Medicine Go from Here?

文・張靜茹　圖・郭惠芳

*A*fter the controversy over rhino horns and tiger bones resulted in US trade sanctions against Taiwan under the Pelly Amendment, the ROC Department of Health, aiming to prevent future disputes of this nature, asked the Chinese medical community to refrain from using another 13 medicinal ingredients taken from animals, including the gall secretions of bears, tortoiseshell and elephant skin.

Will traditional Chinese medicine be a victim of the US trade sanctions under the Pelly Amendment? How will the growing number of prohibitions on the use of animal medicines hurt traditional Chinese medicine, which stretches back thousands of years and is still highly regarded by many Chinese? How is the traditional Chinese medical community confronting a new 20th century subject: ecological conservation? Is the culture of traditional Chinese medicine really an ecological executioner?

"Will you die if you don't eat rhino horn?" Beginning two years ago, foreign conservation groups started attacking Taiwan as a "rhino terminator," and then in April of this year Taiwan became the first country against which the United States implemented trade sanctions for ecological reasons. The Chinese medical community has become a favorite public punching bag. As a doctor of Chinese medicine, Huang Ming-teh has had to face these issues.

True, the community has been getting pressured and some people have been whining that "people's lives are not regarded as important as rhinos' and tigers'," but how do doctors of Chinese medicine think banning animal ingredients will actually affect their ability to heal? Huang's surprising response: "It's no big deal. Losing a few animal ingredients won't have much of an impact on Chinese medicine's ability to treat illness."

Aspirin or dolichos root soup

The most straight-forward reason is "animal-

在美國「培利」法案針對台灣的制裁成立後，爲了避免再引起爭議，行政院衛生署繼犀角、虎骨之後，又列出熊膽、龜板、象皮等十三種藥材，籲請中醫、藥界暫停使用。

中醫、藥界會變成美國對我實施培利報復法案的「受害者」嗎？

越來越多的動物藥材遭禁用，對已經有千年歷史、到今天仍受廣大華人

213

青睞的中醫、藥，會有什麼樣的傷害？中醫藥界又如何面對二十世紀的新課題——生態保育？傳統中醫文化真是生態保育的劊子手嗎？

「不吃犀角會死嗎？」從前年國外保育團體以「犀牛終結者」攻擊臺灣，到今年四月臺灣成為美國第一個以保育不力為由，實施貿易報復的國家，中醫藥、界一直成為眾矢之的，中醫師黃明德就曾被這樣問。

雖然有許多人氣憤不平說「人命簡直不如犀牛、老虎」、中醫藥受到打壓……，但問中醫師禁用動物藥材在治療上會有什麼不利的影響？中醫師卻都平和地反應，「不會啦，少掉一些動物藥材，對中醫治病不會有什麼影響。」

你有阿斯匹靈，我有葛根湯

最直接的原因是：中藥裡動物藥材其實只佔少部分。臺北醫學院生藥研究所副教授張憲昌說，歷代本草中的藥材，植物一直佔有百分之九十以上；而且中藥材太豐富了，大部份也都可以找到療效相近的藥材替代。

以「培利法案」主角犀角為例，許多人好心建議說，一粒退燒藥阿斯匹靈不到十元，何必用犀角退熱？在中醫師看來，這個建議很「外行」。因為若只是退熱，中藥本身替代品很多，比如一味葛根湯，也只需要新臺幣十五元，沒有中醫師會只為了給病人退熱，開一帖五千元的犀角。

更重要的是，犀角、虎骨這些稀有動物身上的稀有藥材，中醫師也幾乎在「自我禁用」了。「傷害當然不大，」黃明德笑著說，要不是EIA（環境調查學會）攻擊臺灣，犀角身價哪會漲那麼高。根據中國醫藥學院附設醫院的紀錄，在禁用犀角前四年，這所全臺灣最大的中醫院有將近一百

萬人門診，使用的犀角只有○‧一公斤。以此推算，臺灣若真如保育人士說的有十噸犀角存量，恐怕幾輩子都用不完，真正的中藥商又何必懷著資金冒險走私、囤積犀角？

「當藥用的材料，來源一定要豐富、便宜，不可能太稀有、貴重，又不是在收藏古董，」古道堂中醫院醫師李仲亮說，犀角早已升等為貴重藥材，中醫自然少用。

方劑治病，不差一味

中藥材取自自然界，受限於地理分布等原因，數量來源不似由工廠生產、製造的西藥穩定。過去自然也有藥材面臨貨源不穩定的窘況，但神農嚐百草，經過二、三千年，總會出現量多、療效相近的藥材；當有效果更好的藥出現，早先的藥，也自然會被取代。

中國藥典上可查的方子有八萬個之多，但較常用的也不過幾百種，多的是名存實亡；衛生署新開出的十三種禁用藥材名單中，水獺肝、象皮、熊膽等，在中醫心中，或因療效差、或來源少，早就屬藥單上的「稀有動物」了。

何況「一個好的中醫師，其實不在乎多一種藥材，少一種藥材，」黃明德解釋，中醫治病觀念與西醫不同，不是每個人患同一種病，都給同一種藥。中醫視人為「全人」，「你長雞眼、痔瘡，他不會只醫你雞眼、痔瘡，」李仲亮說，以今天的字眼來說，就是他認為你「身上整個免疫系統已出毛病」。因此中藥也很少只以單方殺一種病菌，而是以方劑（複方）治療，藥材有君、臣、佐、使之分，醫師依著患者虛、寒、實、熱不同的體質、病情來增減藥量、靈活配藥。

比如與犀角同被EIA做為攻擊我國主力的虎骨，過去常被用來與其它十三種藥材共同泡製「木瓜虎骨酒」，是強筋骨、緩和

為了防止犀牛瀕臨絕種，大部份中醫師與中藥商均支持政府暫時禁止使用犀牛角。圖為去年南非犀牛人來台籌募款項，中藥公會也參與活動。(張良綱攝)
In order to prevent the rhino from going extinct, many doctors of Chinese medicine and pharmacies selling traditional medicines have supported the government's temporary ban against selling rhino horn. The photo shows Chinese medicine pharmacists participating in a fund-raising activity for rhino researchers from South Africa. (photo by Vincent Chang)

based ingredients make up a very small part of what is used in Chinese medicine," says Chang Hsien-chang, an associate professor of pharmacognosy at Taipei Medical College. Throughout history, plants have made up over 90 percent of the components of Chinese medicine. With the vast number of ingredients left after the ban, it's not difficult to find replacements to produce the same effect.

Take the rhino horns that played the leading role in the recent Pelly Amendment drama. If one aspirin costs NT$10, people have asked with the best of intentions, why is it necessary to use rhino horns to reduce a fever? And indeed to doctors of Chinese medicine, such a prescription

betrays ignorance. Among its many traditional substitutes is dolichos soup (about NT$15 a bowl). No Chinese medical doctor would prescribe a patient an NT$5000 dose of rhino horn just to relieve a fever.

For rare animal medicinal ingredients such as rhino horn and tiger bones, Chinese medical doctors have virtually instituted their own ban. "The ban doesn't do much damage," says Huang smiling. Originally there was little business for rhino horn in Taiwan, and if the UK's Environmental Investigation Agency hadn't attacked Taiwan, the price never would have risen so high. According to records of the China Medical College hospital, the nearly 1 million patient vis-

不論犀牛的瀕臨絕種是因過去西方在非洲大肆打獵，或者中國人長久以來以犀角為藥材，今天只有世人攜手救犀牛，犀牛才有生存之機，下一代也不會只能憑玩具想像犀牛的模樣。（張良綱攝）
No matter whether rhinos are facing extinction because of over-hunting by Westerners in Africa or because they have long been used as an ingredient in Chinese medicines, unless people around the world work to save the rhino, it won't have a chance at surviving, and the next generation will only see its likeness in stuffed animals. (photo by Vincent Chang)

下肢酸痛很好的用藥。但在木瓜虎骨酒裡，虎骨的作用主要是膠質多，有很多物品可以代替，因此只要保留川牛膝、天麻、五加皮、川續斷等植物藥，去掉虎骨，療效依然不減。

「好的中醫不會執著於古方，」李仲亮說，只要禁用的藥材不是以單方治病，就不會有太大的問題，而中藥裡，單方藥佔不到百分之五，「沒有人會抱著犀角，沒事就刮點犀粉來吃的。」

食、療同源，醫、藥分家？

雖然中醫師面對中藥未來，表現得氣定神閒，但中藥商卻沒有如此輕鬆。傳統醫療由於發展出「食療同源」的觀念，中醫、藥因此分成兩個系統，民間自己在日常生活使用中藥時，就不局限在中醫界的說法，而有「吃形補形」等其他民族傳統藥學也都存在的應用之道。

因此一些和今天保育類動物相關的產品，比如雨傘節、虎鞭、熊膽這一些醫界不用、少用或認為不是每個人都適合吃的藥材，在民間生活中，數量也許日漸減少，但確實還存在。

尤其中藥房目的是賣藥，是商業行為，動物藥材又常是貴重藥材，利潤較高，中藥商也可能為了商業利益，對購藥者強調稀有、貴重藥材的療效。

its to this hospital of Chinese medicine in the four years leading up to the ban resulted in the prescription of just 100 grams of rhino horn. If Taiwan has the ten tons of rhino horns that the EIA claims, it would take several generations before the supply would be used up. How could bona fide Chinese medical businesses be hoarding rhino horn to make a profit?

"A medical ingredient must be abundant and cheap. It can't be too rare or expensive," says Li Chung-liang of the Kutaotang Hospital of Chinese Medicine. "It's not like collecting antiques." Since rhino horn has long been an expensive ingredient, it has naturally been sparingly used in Chinese medicine.

Swatting a fly with a hammer

The ingredients for Chinese medicine are taken from the natural world, and are limited by such factors as geographical spread. Unlike the supply of Western medicine, which is determined by factory production, the supply for Chinese medicine is not stable. Supply problems for ingredients used in Chinese medicine are nothing new, but over several thousand years, numerous plants have been found to have similar effects to those in short store. Herbs determined to be more effective would simply replace the earlier ones used in the same prescription.

There are more than 80,000 prescriptions listed in Chinese medicine reference books, but only several hundred are commonly used. Many of the remaining exist in name only. Among the 13 prohibited ingredients in the list recently released by the Department of Health, otter liver, elephant skin, and bear gall secretion have been rarely prescribed for a long time now.

"A good practitioner of Chinese medicine isn't much concerned about there being one less or one more medicine," Huang Ming-teh explains. The concepts behind Chinese medicine are very different from those of Western medicine, and for two people with the same ailment, doctors of Chinese medicine often prescribe different medicines. Chinese medicine looks at the entire person. "If you have corns and hemorrhoids, a Chinese medical doctor won't just treat your corns and hemorrhoids," says Li Chongliang. Instead he will—using today's terminology—determine that your whole immune system is having problems.

Not irreplaceable

Thus Chinese medicinal ingredients are rarely employed by themselves in singular attacks on a germ or ailment. Instead ingredients in prescriptions play one of four different roles: "monarch, minister, assistant or guide." Based on the particulars of the illness and on whether the patient's constitution is characterized by "insufficiency or excess, heat or cold," the doctor will adjust the prescription.

Take tiger bone, which like rhino horn has been the cause of fervent attacks against Taiwan by EIA. It used to be commonly combined with 13 other ingredients in "papaya tiger bone brew." The brew was good for strengthening the tendons and bones and reducing muscle soreness in the lower body. But in Chinese medicine, where tiger bones are used for their high quantities of gelatin, many different substances can replace them. Such plants as cyathula root, acanthopanax bark, and teasel root can all stand in for tiger bones without reducing the brew's effectiveness.

"A good doctor of Chinese medicine won't insist on the classic prescription," says Li Chung-liang. As long as the prohibited ingredient isn't taken by itself, its loss shouldn't cause much of a problem. And in Chinese medicine, less than 5 percent of medicines are prescribed alone. "No one would stock up on rhino horn and eat it a little bit at a time for no particular purpose."

You get what you eat?

While doctors of Chinese medicine are calm about the future, the owners of traditional drug stores are not nearly so at ease. Traditional Chinese medicine promotes the theory that "food and curing have the same source," but from here

加上中藥常被迫做醫療體系裡的「收尾」工作，臺北市中藥公會理事長鄧芳男就表示，病人常是西醫治不好了，才來找中醫。為取信病人，中藥自然發展出一些珍奇藥材來治絕症，比如集合麝香、熊膽、牛黃、琥珀、珍珠等五種藥材的「五寶散」，就被用來治癌症，價格高昂。如果麝香、熊膽被禁，對生意當然有影響。

但許多中醫也指出，中藥店裡所謂的貴重藥材，特別是稀有藥材，百分之九十其實都是冒牌貨。

羊骨與虎骨同在，牛角與犀角並存

中國醫藥學院教授張賢哲表示，尚未禁用虎骨以前，若以DNA來化驗，都市的中藥房裡，真正的虎骨，恐怕百分之五都不到，鄉下則幾乎沒有。熊膽則百分之八十是牛膽、豬膽張冠李戴，在犀角事件鬧的最厲害時，也傳出許多犀角粉其實是水牛角研磨成的。

雖然許多人認為中藥商是「掛著羊頭賣狗肉」，但張賢哲表示，這種「沖貨」文化，由來已久，這也是中藥材在原有正品缺乏，自然就會出現其他藥品補替而致。許多沖貨也都經過臨床證實，確定有部分相似、相近的療效。

比如西藥未進入中國前，古代社會就多以水牛角來替代貴重的犀角退燒，在大陸，經過成分分析與臨床紀錄，更已將水牛角列入藥典中。

張賢哲解釋，中藥處方上的藥名，常常只是藥的代號，實際則包括了相類似的藥材。例如衛生署考慮禁用「豹骨」，但中藥裡並無豹骨這一藥名，因為對中醫師而言，它也叫做「虎骨」。在中醫應用上，虎骨其實分為包括虎、豹、獅骨的「正虎骨」與包括了牛、馬、豬、狗骨頭的「雜骨」兩大系，價錢也有高低之別。

臺灣虎骨市場裡真正賣的就以羊骨最多，「想想看，過去虎骨一斤一萬六千元，和羊骨價錢差一百倍，要關節炎、風濕有起色，必須吃好幾斤，多少人吃得起？」張賢哲說。

不是假藥的禁藥

藥名只是代號的另一個原因，和傳統藥材含有部分精神療法相關，比如四神湯包括一味稱為白虎的藥材，當然不是真白老虎；「龍骨」當然也不只有恐龍的化石，包括有許多哺乳類動物的化石，但「龍骨」聽起來絕對比豬骨、狗骨有「心理療效」多了。

兩年前，衛生署考慮禁用虎骨前，曾希望澄清沖貨觀念，不願因此殃及池魚，把羊骨、水牛角一併都給禁了，對中藥店傷害太大。「但當時考慮到對一般人而言，太複雜了，因此並未有任何措施，就禁掉了，」張賢哲說，於是也造成外人「看到粉都是犀粉、看到骨都是虎骨」，誤以為犀角粉、虎骨滿臺灣。因此中醫師普遍都認為，只要因應今天環境，讓這些藥材「正名」即可。

現在許多藥材在還沒來得及正名之前就被禁了，這種作法留下不少爭議，「不論對中醫、藥是否有實質、或心理影響，要禁掉任何一種藥，最重要的還是要有充分的理由，」黃明德說，衛生單位不應禁用對人體沒有傷害性的藥材。

他以為，即使衛生署有苦衷，但中醫、藥界也不想被禁得糊裡糊塗，政府一定要能明白清楚說服老百姓，不能只為了應付國際保育團體就急著禁用動物藥材。「賣了幾千年的藥，你不准他賣，總要理由充分。」

你賣的是哪一種烏龜的殼？

就有中醫師針對衛生署將禁用麝香表示

「為什麼牠的角比我們的貴？」由於數量、來源少，犀角被中醫視為貴重藥材，自古即以水牛角作為代用品。

"Why are their horns dearer than ours?" Because of the scarce supply, rhino horn is viewed as a valuable ingredient in Chinese medicine, for which buffalo horn has long been used as a substitute.

the doctors and peddlers of Chinese medicine have taken different paths. And when the people choose Chinese medicines for themselves, they don't restrict themselves to just what the doctors recommend. The consumers are apt to believe such concepts as "one gets what one eats" (such as gaining virility by eating tiger's penis). This belief about traditional medicines exists in other cultures as well.

And so people still use—albeit in decreasing quantities—some products taken from endan-

gered animal species (such as banded krait, tiger's penis and bear gall) that doctors never or rarely prescribe or regard as not being suitable for just anyone.

Pharmacies, after all, are in business to sell medicine. Because animal-based medicinal ingredients are expensive, they may overplay the curative powers of rare and expensive medicines for the sake of higher profit margins.

And then there's the problem that Chinese medicine is often the medical avenue of last re-

中醫師指出，由十三種藥材製成的木瓜虎骨酒，即使少了虎骨，若再經過重新調配，療效還是一樣。圖為大陸出產的木瓜虎骨酒。（張良綱攝）

Papaya Tiger Brew from the mainland. Tiger bone is one of the 13 ingredients traditionally used in Papaya Tiger Brew. But doctors say that even if it is removed, the formula can be tinkered with to make the brew just as potent as ever. (photo by Vincent Chang)

異議。麝香是麝肚臍分泌物，在藥材裡，它扮演重要的「佐使」角色，協助藥劑在身體行走、擴散，所謂的「行氣」，許多藥欲發揮藥效，必須靠麝香，因此目前用量還不小。

但問題不在用量多寡，張賢哲說，自己對禁犀角、虎骨無異議，因為動物確實已快滅絕，但目前大陸已發展麝的養殖，而且取麝香時，並不需要殺害麝，沒有禁的道理。

他再以另一被禁的龜板為例，目前屬於保育類的烏龜只有三種，都是海龜，但中藥商用的種類有四十多種，大部分是陸龜，許多陸龜可以養殖，南美洲一些地區也有吃龜肉的飲食習慣，「除非也禁止吃龜肉，」張賢哲提出不同於衛生署的看法。

在中醫師看來，禁用保育類動物相關藥材，還有許多灰色地帶；但在保育人士眼中，卻另有顧慮，「中藥商對藥材的分類觀念很薄弱，」綠色消費者基金會秘書長方儉指出，大部分中藥商對自己藥材來自什麼樣的產地、什麼種類，根本提不出證明。大陸雖然正進行麝的養殖，但數量不多，誰能證明你的麝香不是來自野外的麝？犀角被禁了，不一樣還有人走私，有人盜獵？

別擠壞了豬！

至於養殖的族群，以傳聞將被西方保育團體視為下一波攻擊對象的熊膽為例，雖

220

sort. Teng Fang-nan, the director of the Chinese Medicine Association of Taipei, says that patients often turn to Chinese medicine only after Western medicine has failed them. To attract patients, Chinese drug stores hype precious medicines to treat terminal illnesses.

For instance, "the five treasure powders" (musk, bear gall secretion, ox bezoar, amber and pearls) have been used to treat cancer. Since these medicines are expensive, prohibiting musk and bear gall will naturally have an effect on these stores' gross sales. Chang Hong-jen, a specialist for the Department of Health, holds that the most urgent part of the department's work is to change the thinking of a minority of people that the rarer something is, the better it is for you.

Tiger bones or goat bones?

But many doctors of Chinese medicine point out that 90 percent of the so-called precious ingredients displayed in Chinese medicine pharmacies—especially the rare medicinal ingredients—are actually impostors.

Chang Hsien-che, a professor at China Medical College, says that before there was a prohibition on tiger bones, DNA analysis would have revealed that less than five percent of what was being marketed as tiger bones in the cities was the real McCoy, and virtually none of it in the countryside was. As for bear gall, some 80 percent of it is cow or pig gall, and when the rhino horn incident was at full boil, most of the "rhino horn powder" may well have been ground from the horns of water buffalo.

While it's true that many people believe that Chinese medical pharmacies "hang out gnats' heads to sell dog meat," Chang Hsien-che points out that "fake goods" have a long history in Chinese medicine, because when there are supply shortages, it is very easy for other ingredients to be fobbed off in their place. Indeed the effectiveness of many of these phonies has been clinically proven.

For example, before Western medicine entered China, water buffalo horn was often used as a replacement for costly rhino horn to reduce fever. Chemical analysis and clinical records have been made about water buffalo on the mainland, where it is listed in reference books of Chinese medicine.

Chang Hsien-che explains that the names in Chinese medicine often shouldn't be taken absolutely literally, though they may describe something similar. For example, the Department of Health considered banning "leopard bones." But there is no medicine named "leopard bone" because in Chinese medicine leopard bones are called "tiger bones." And so the tiger bones sold on the black market can be divided into the "real" tiger bones—including tiger, leopard and lion bones—and miscellaneous fakes such as cow, horse, pig and dog bones.

In Taiwan goat bones are the favorite stand-in. "Think about it. In the past a Chinese pound of tiger bone cost NT$16,000, a hundred times that of goat bone. To relieve arthritis and rheumatism, you've got to eat several pounds of it. How many people could afford such treatment?" Chang asks.

No ban on the fakes

Yet the names can have a powerful psychological effect. "Four spirits soup," for instance, includes an ingredient called white tiger, but of course it isn't really white tiger. "Dragon bone" may be made from the fossils of dinosaurs, but more likely from the fossilized bones of some mammal. Still, psychologically "dragon bone" sounds more effective than "pig bone" or "dog bone."

Two years ago, before the Department of Health considered a ban on tiger bones, it thought of trying to clarify that many of these goods weren't really what they were claiming to be, so that the sale of innocent impostors—goat bones and water buffalo horn—wouldn't be affected and the pharmacies would be spared a double whammy.

"But at the time, they thought that this would be too complicated for most people to under-

然目前大陸已經由養殖的熊身上採取膽汁，不需再像過去利用整個熊膽。但看過大陸熊養殖場的師大生物系教授呂光洋就表示，為了以引流管將膽汁導出，熊身上經年累月被開個洞，此外，為防止這些大型動物掙扎，必須將之關在狹小、不得動彈的籠子中。「這種作法過於殘忍、不人道，」他說。

衛生署技監張鴻仁舉瑞典為例，瑞典法令規定一輛卡車運送豬到屠宰場，不得超過一定數量，因為有科學根據證實，若過於擁擠，豬的腦部會分泌出一種物質，造成緊張、不愉快。

在動物福利被高舉的今天，除非能改善養殖品質，「否則衛生署也只能暫時禁用熊膽，」張鴻仁說。

呂光洋表示，雖然麝香、龜板、蛤蚧都有部分種類屬於保育類動物，但國內動物藥材若能仔細清查，確定來源，而中醫、藥公會能自我管理，國貿局統一進口，藥材上蓋有合法印章，避免走私，有一套完整的「遊戲規則」，他並不反對非保育類動物在良好監督下被有限度地作為藥材。

但在目前缺乏一套完善的管理下，保育人士也贊成衛生署階段性禁用部份動物藥材，否則可能會造成合法掩護非法。若仔細探究造成今天中藥市場混亂的原因，不可否認與國內對中藥缺乏管理有關。

撥開中藥雲霧

三年前，國外保育人士結合國內動物學者做犀角存量調查，指出臺灣地區存有十噸犀角。由於調查者對中藥文化並不熟悉，因此結論遭中醫界質疑。但當時衛生署、農委會雖然否定了此一調查結果，卻提不出自己的數據，事後做的調查，已得不到國際信任。

以衛生署的想法，取自自然的傳統藥材，不像西藥，因為擔心有人做假藥、傷害

stand," says Chang. "And so a total ban was called for without any attempt to distinguish." As a result, "when outsiders saw any powder, they immediately assumed it was rhino horn powder, and when they saw bones, they were certain they were tiger bones." And so in light of the situation, most doctors of Chinese medicine believe they should call ingredients by their true names.

Now there is great debate over the fate of many medicines for which bans were implemented before they were called by their true names. "Whether a ban will have a real or just psychological impact on the Chinese medical community, there must be ample reason for banning a medicine," Huang Ming-teh says. Health agancies should not ban drugs that cause people no harm.

He acknowledges that the Department of Health has its reasons, but the Chinese medical community doesn't wish to have bans imposed in a haphazard, illogical fashion. The government has got to make a clear case to convince the public; it cannot simply ban the use of all animal ingredients to appease international conservation groups. "If you are banning them from selling a drug they've been selling for thousands of years, you've got to give sufficient cause."

What kind of tortoiseshell!?

Some doctors of Chinese medicine cite musk to show their differences of opinion with the Department of Health's ban. Musk is a secretion in the musk deer's navel. In Chinese medicine, it plays an important role as an "assistant," helping the medicine spread throughout the body, as a *xing qi* or promoter of circulation. Many medicines rely on musk to come fully into play, and so it is currently used in considerable amounts.

But the problem isn't in the amounts used, says Chang Hsien-cheh, who has no complaints with the ban against rhino horn and tiger bones because these animals are really threatened with extinction. As for musk, which is used in great quantities in Chinese medicine, he points out

「我們的骨頭都叫『虎骨』！」中藥藥名通常是一組藥的代號，在中藥店裡，羊骨、牛骨等都叫做「虎骨」，但價格遠低於虎骨。

"All our bones are called tiger bones!" Specific-sounding names are often used to describe a more general group of ingredients in Chinese medicine. In pharmacies the bones of goats and cows and other animals are often also called "tiger bones" —even if the price may differ dramatically.

that there are currently musk deer raised in captivity, and obtaining musk doesn't hurt the animals, so he feels there is no logic behind the prohibition.

He shifts to another prohibited substance, tortoiseshell. Currently there are only three species of turtles that are the objects of conservation efforts, and all of these are sea turtles. But there are some 40 kinds of turtles used in Chinese medicine and most of them are land turtles. Many land turtles can also be raised in captivity. In some South American countries they eat turtle meat. So he opposes a ban—"Unless there's also a prohibition against eating turtle meat."

From the perspective of doctors of Chinese medicine, there are a lot of gray areas in animal medicine bans, but in the view of conservationists, there is another worry: "The people in the Chinese medicine business have a very weak conception of categories of medicines," says Jay Fang, the secretary-general of the Green Consumer Foundation. Most pharmacies of Chinese medicine have no proof of what their medicines are and where they were produced. And while the mainland may be proceeding with raising musk deer, the numbers aren't great. Who can prove if the musk a pharmacy has on offer was taken from wild or domesticated deer?

Don't crowd the pigs!

It is rumored that Western environmental groups are going to start a campaign against the use of bear gall. Chinese medicine traders point

中醫傳統並不喜歡使用有靈性的動物藥材，即使廢物利用「蟬蛻」(蟬褪下的殼)這樣的藥材，也被大醫所排拒。(張良綱攝)
Ancient Chinese doctors were against using animal-based medicines, because animals were believed to possess spirits. Thus some great doctors even refused to use discarded cicada shells. (photo by Vincent Chang)

人體，才須加以登記管理、控制成分。但臺大藥理學研究所所長鄧哲民指出，即使不由生態保育的觀點來檢視中藥材，站在藥品品質管理上，除了提煉、粹取的科學中藥藥粉，也應該針對天然藥材做清查，藥商才不會賣得糊裡糊塗、病人吃得不明不白。為中醫藥長遠發展著想，一定得走這一步路，沒有捷徑，否則全部禁掉也不是辦法。

事實上，即使犀角、虎骨所有動物藥材都有替代品，卻不表示這些藥沒有存在的價值。在今天，成分、療效非常單純、精確的西藥雖然成為醫藥的主流，但西藥再

科學，仍無法解決所有的疾病，而且副作用多，傳統藥材因此重新被重視，聯合國衛生組織就在全世界設有三十幾個傳統藥材研究中心。

讓它更可靠

雖然要將傳統藥材的有效成分提煉出來，像西藥加以合成，以減少對天然藥材的消耗，目前還很困難。但最起碼的工作，「包括分析成分、記錄臨床效果、替代品的成分差異，哪一些成分在發生作用，都應該進行，」鄧哲民說。

由於過去國內對中醫藥研究投入資源有

out that the mainland has already adopted the method of raising bears where constant gall secretion can be taken from the living bear without killing it. It is no longer necessary to kill a bear to get its gall. But Lu Kuang-yang, a professor of biology at Taiwan Normal University who has observed the raising of bears on the mainland, says that in order to take the gall secretion, holes are cut into bears for months and years. And to prevent these large animals from putting up a struggle, the captive bears must be kept in narrow cages where they have no room to move and stretch out. "This way of doing things is barbaric," he says. "It's immoral."

Chang Hong-jen cites Sweden as an example. Swedish law stipulates that a truck bringing pigs to the slaughterhouse cannot bring more than a certain number of pigs, because research has shown that if the truck is over packed, the pigs' brains will release an enzyme which makes them nervous and unhappy.

In the West today, where animals "enjoy excellent social benefits," if the standard of care of captive animals is not up to snuff, Chang Hong-jen points out, "departments of health can temporarily shut breeders down."

Lu Kuang-yang says that although musk deer, certain tortoises and horned toads are protected animals, if there is clear documentation about the sources of domestically sold medicinal ingredients and a ban on the use of threatened species, then associations of doctors and pharmacists can control themselves. With the Board of Foreign Trade handling all imports, medicinal ingredients can be stamped to show that they are legal and thus prevent smuggling. With "complete rules of the game," he would then not object to unthreatened animals being used in limited quantities.

But with the present lack of an overall system of control, conservationists agree with the Department of Health's extreme step of a temporary complete ban on medicinal ingredients taken from protected animals. Otherwise the situation will arise where legal behavior will obscure illegal behavior. If you look in detail at the mess in the Chinese medicine market today, the lack of domestic control over Chinese medicine is definitely a major factor.

The value of Chinese medicine

Three years ago foreign conservationists and domestic zoologists conducted a survey about rhino horns, which said that the Taiwan area had reserves of ten tons. Because those compiling the information were not familiar with Chinese medicine, people in the field doubted the accuracy of the survey conclusions. But although the Department of Health and the Council of Agriculture disputed the results, they could not present figures of their own.

The Department of Health holds that fake medicines may endanger people's health, so there's a need to register and control the ingredients. Teng Che-ming, chairman of the Department of Pharmacology of the College of Medicine at Taiwan University, says the need for controls goes beyond ecological concerns; they should be implemented to ensure quality as well. Besides those Chinese medicines that are extracted scientifically, there ought to be clear inspections of natural medicinal ingredients. Otherwise traders of Chinese medicine will simply do as they please, and patients will be uncertain as to what they're taking. For the sake of long-term development of Chinese medicine, such steps must be taken. Otherwise, a complete ban won't provide a solution either.

The truth is that even if rhino horn, tiger bone and all of the animal ingredients have substitutes, this doesn't mean that these medicines are of no value. Today, Western medicines, which have pure, effective and precise ingredients, have taken over the medical mainstream. But Western medicine and science still can't cure all illnesses, and Western medicines frequently cause side effects. As a result, greater attention is being paid to traditional medicine, and the UN World Health Organization has established 30

限，特別是動物藥材的研究更少，也因此造成人們對中藥藥效的質疑。一位動物學者就質疑：「犀角、熊膽眞的有效嗎？」實際上，近年來大陸、香港對犀角做過許多臨床實驗，證實它有減輕中風、腦膜炎症狀的功能。但台灣不僅缺乏研究，中醫藥界本身甚至對別人做的研究也不清楚。如果無法提出更科學的中藥療效紀錄，在動物數量急遽銳減下，別人要求禁用，中藥可以反駁的機會就更少了。

危機也許是轉機？近來中醫界有人自行研究水牛角的藥效；中藥商也提出，希望衛生署或農委會能提供禁用龜板所屬的三種保育類海龜照片，中藥行願意遵守規定，絕不進口這三種海龜製品。

殺生求生，去生更遠

一椿犀角、虎骨公案，讓許多人忙得不可開交。但回頭想想，很多中醫師自己也忘了，其實傳統中藥一直有著比今天保育觀層次更高的醫療哲學。

「中藥傳統上，並不喜歡使用具有靈性的動物做藥材，」李仲亮說，這是動物藥材在中藥材裡數量極少的理由。而在食指繁浩的中國各代藥典中，更不時傳遞「好生」的觀念。

漢朝醫師張仲景在《千金要方》書中就針對想要習醫的人，遵守「……夫殺生求生，去生更遠 ……市有先死者，則市而用之，不在此例，能不用者，斯爲大哲」的原則。意思就是爲了救一條生命，卻犧牲另一個生命，就離眞正的愛惜生命更遠了，但如果用其他原因死亡的生命來救人，則不在此列。然而眞正的大醫，卻不論動物是生、是死，都不會將之當成藥材。

這樣的想法，是否也是許多中醫師認爲衛生署若眞禁掉十幾種動物藥材，對他們無傷大雅的原因呢？　□

（原載民國83年6月光華雜誌）

centers for traditional medicine throughout the world.

Making it more reliable

Although people are trying to extract the active ingredients from traditional medicines and then make them synthetically as in Western medicine (thus reducing the consumption of natural medicinal ingredients), right now such work is difficult. But at least some steps can be taken, says Teng Che-ming, including "carrying out component analysis and keeping clinical test results about the differences between the original medicines and the substitutes and about the effects of each component."

Historically very little money has been allotted to Chinese medical research—especially into animal-based medicines—and this has resulted in people having doubts about the effectiveness of Chinese medicines. One zoologist wonders, "Are rhino horn and bear's gall really effective medicines?" The fact is that in recent years the mainland and Hong Kong have done many clinical experiments on rhino horn, which have proved that it reduces the threat of stroke and the symptoms of meningitis. But in Taiwan we not only lack research; the Chinese medical community here isn't even clear about the research done in Hong Kong and on the mainland. If there is no way to present more scientific records attesting to the efficacy of Chinese medicine, when animal numbers are sharply declining and others request bans, Chinese medicine will find it hard to make its case.

Perhaps this crisis represents a turning point. The Chinese medical community also has doctors pursuing their own research about medicine related to buffalo horns. And recently dealers in Chinese medicine have proposed that the Department of Health or the Council of Agriculture provide photographs of the shells of the three protected species of sea turtles. The dealers claim they are willing to follow the regulations and not import any products using these three species.

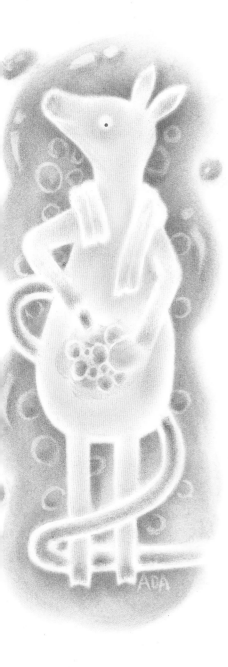

A true reverence for life

Once this public dispute over rhino horn and tiger bones broke, people got very caught up in it. But many practitioners of Chinese medicine themselves seem to have forgotten that Chinese medicine has traditionally revered wildlife to a degree even higher than that seen in the conservation movement of today.

"Traditional Chinese medicine shies away from making medicines out of bird and beast, which are thought to have spirits," says Li Chung-liang, explaining why animals are rarely used in Chinese medicine. And throughout the history of Chinese medicine, reference books have generally discouraged the eating of animals.

The Han Dynasty doctor Chang Chung-ching in the work *Qianjin Yaofang* offers this general principle for those wishing to study medicine: "If you kill for the sake of life, then you're far removed from the true spirit of life. . . . If you buy meat in the market, it is excusable. But it would be best not to use that either." So the truly great doctors will not make medicines from animals dead or alive.

Is this why many doctors of traditional Chinese medicine think that the Department of Health's ban on the use of some dozen animal ingredients does no real harm? ☐

(Chang Chin-ju/drawings by Kuo Hui-fang/tr. by Jonathan Barnard/first published in June 1994)

「採麝香就像清洗肚臍？」中醫藥界認為，如果動物藥材可以像植物藥材，以人工培養，沒有道理不准使用。

"Is extracting musk just like cleaning belly buttons?" The Chinese medical community believes that if the animal-based medical ingredients can be taken from domesticated animals, then there isn't any reason for prohibiting them.

國家圖書館出版品預行編目資料

台灣保育動物新傳 = A new age for wildlife
conservation in Taiwan ／張靜茹等著. --
初版. -- 臺北市 ： 光華雜誌， 民87
　　面 ； 公分. --（光華畫報雜誌叢書；25
）（生態保育系列；3）

　　ISBN 957-9188-39-4（精裝）. --ISBN 957-
9188-40-8（平裝）

1. 動物保護

548.38　　　　　　　　　　　　　87009694

《光華畫報雜誌叢書25》

台灣保育動物新傳

作者／張靜茹等
發行人／程建人
總編輯／王瑩
副總編輯／陳雅玲
叢書編輯／李珊
美術編輯／廖慈文
攝影／張良綱、薛繼光、鄭元慶
英文編輯／ Jonathan Barnard, Phill Newell,
　　　　　　　Robert Taylor, Scott Williams, 彭玲嫻
業務總監／薛少奇
電腦組長／卓宏基
訂戶服務組／陳麗珠、李淑慧
出版者／光華畫報雜誌社
地址／中華民國台灣省台北市中正區100忠孝東路一段54號5樓
信箱／台北郵政8-398信箱
電話／（02）23922256
傳真／（02）23970655
郵撥帳號／0128106-5
印刷／裕華彩藝股份有限公司
　　　　台北縣新店市寶中路95號之8
總經銷／台灣英文雜誌社
初版／中華民國87年8月
　　　　精裝3000本
　　　　平裝3000本
定價／平裝新台幣250元、美金8元
　　　　精裝新台幣300元、美金10元